S0-AAI-749

KEYS TO READING

Cinnamon Peaks

Theodore L. Harris
Mildred Creekmore
Louise Matteoni
Harold B. Allen, *Linguistic Consultant*

THE ECONOMY COMPANY Oklahoma City Atlanta Indianapolis

ISBN 0-87892-450-7

For permission to adapt and reprint copyrighted materials, grateful acknowledgment is made to the following publishers, authors, and other copyright holders:

Atheneum Publishers, for "Construction" by Lilian Moore, text copyright © 1969 by Lilian Moore, reprinted from *I Thought I Heard the City*, for "How to Eat a Poem" and "Metaphor" by Eve Merriam, copyright © 1964 by Eve Merriam, reprinted from *It Doesn't Always Have to Rhyme*, and for "The Measure of Man" by Eve Merriam, copyright © 1970 by Eve Merriam, reprinted from *Finding a Poem*.

Brandt & Brandt, for "U.S.A." by Stephen Vincent Benét, reprinted from *A Book of Americans* by Rosemary and Stephen Vincent Benét; Holt, Rinehart and Winston, Inc. Copyright 1933 by Rosemary and Stephen Vincent Benét; copyright renewed © 1961 by Rosemary Carr Benét.

Polly Burroughs, author, for *The Honey Boat*, text copyright © 1968 by Polly Burroughs. Published by Little, Brown and Company.

Coward, McCann & Geoghegan, Inc., for "Food from the Past," reprinted from *Plants, Food and People* by Winifred G. Hammond, copyright © 1964 by Winifred G. Hammond, and for "When Carlos Closed the Street," reprinted by permission of Coward, McCann & Geoghegan, Inc., from *When Carlos Closed the Street* by Peggy Mann, copyright © 1969 by Peggy Mann.

Thomas Y. Crowell Company, Inc., for "The Big Spring" by Jean Craighead George, from *Spring Comes to the Ocean* by Jean Craighead George, copyright © 1965 by Jean Craighead George; reprinted with permission of Thomas Y. Crowell Co., Inc., publishers.

The Dial Press, for "Song of the Pop-Bottlers" by Morris Bishop, reprinted from *A Bowl of Bishop* by Morris Bishop, copyright 1954 by Morris Bishop. The poem originally appeared in *The New Yorker*.

Doubleday & Company, Inc., for "The Fun They Had" by Isaac Asimov, reprinted from *Earth Is Room Enough* by Isaac Asimov, copyright © 1957 by Isaac Asimov, and for "I Hear America Singing," reprinted from *Leaves of Grass* by Walt Whitman.

E. P. Dutton & Company, Inc., for "The Pioneer" by Arthur Guiterman, from *I Sing the Pioneer*, published by E. P. Dutton & Co., Inc., © renewed 1954 by Vida Lindo Guiterman and reprinted with her permission, and for a stanza from "America the Beautiful" by Katharine Lee Bates, from the book *The Retinue & Other Poems* by Katharine Lee Bates, copyright 1918 by E. P. Dutton & Co., Inc.

Farrar, Straus & Giroux, Inc., for "The Monster We Live On" and the reproduction of illustrations on pages 42, 44, 45, and 46, reprinted with the permission of Farrar, Straus & Giroux, Inc., from *The Serpent and the Sun* by Cal Roy, copyright © 1972 by Calvin L. Roy.

Follett Publishing Company, division of Follett Corporation, for "And Then What?" by Shirley L. Arora, from *What Then, Raman?* by Shirley L. Arora, copyright © 1960 by Shirley L. Arora.

Free To Be Foundation, Inc., for "Free to Be . . . You and Me" by Stephen Lawrence and Bruce Hart, copyright © 1974 Free To Be Foundation, Inc., all rights reserved, and for "The Southpaw" by Judith Viorst, copyright © 1974 Free To Be Foundation, Inc., all rights reserved.

Harcourt Brace Jovanovich, Inc., for "Cycle," copyright © 1962 by John Moffitt, and "To Look at Any Thing," copyright © 1961 by John Moffitt, reprinted from his volume *The Living Seed;* for "Fog" by Carl Sandburg, from *Chicago Poems* by Carl Sandburg, copyright 1916 by Holt, Rinehart and Winston, Inc., copyright 1944 by Carl Sandburg, reprinted by permission of Harcourt Brace Jovanovich, Inc., and two lines reprinted from "Proverbs" by Carl Sandburg, from *The People, Yes* by Carl Sandburg, copyright 1936 by Harcourt Brace Jovanovich, Inc., renewed 1964 by Carl Sandburg; and for "The Rescue" by William O. Steele, reprinted from *Wilderness Journey,* copyright 1953 by William O. Steele.

Harper & Row, Publishers, for "The Coast of a New World" by Katherine B. Shippen, an approved adaptation from pp. 102–115 from *Leif Eriksson—First Voyager to America,* copyright 1951 by Katherine B. Shippen, reprinted by permission; for excerpts from *Harriet the Spy* by Louise Fitzhugh, copyright © 1964 by Louise Fitzhugh, reprinted by permission; and for "Bahama Adventure," abridged from pp. 199–204 in *The Lady and the Sharks* by Eugenie Clark, copyright © 1969 by Eugenie Clark, by permission of Harper & Row, Publishers, Inc.

Hawthorn Books, Inc., for "Balloonomania," by permission of Hawthorn Books, Inc., from *Ladybirds: Women in Aviation* by Edward Jablonski, copyright © 1968 by Edward Jablonski, all rights reserved.

Holt, Rinehart and Winston, Inc., for "Men Work Together," two lines reprinted from "The Tuft of Flowers" from *You Come Too* by Robert Frost, copyright 1934 by Holt, Rinehart and Winston, Inc., copyright © 1962 by Robert Frost, and for "A Minor Bird" by Robert Frost, reprinted from *The Poetry of Robert Frost* edited by Edward Connery Lathem, copyright 1928, © 1969 by Holt, Rinehart and Winston, Inc., copyright © 1956 by Robert Frost.

Houghton Mifflin Company, for "Child of the Silent Night," chapters 7 and 8 of *Child of the Silent Night* by Edith Fisher Hunter, copyright © 1963 by Edith Fisher Hunter, reprinted by permission of the publisher, Houghton Mifflin Co.

Alfred A. Knopf, Inc., for "Water-Front Streets" by Langston Hughes, copyright 1926 by Alfred A. Knopf, Inc., renewed 1954 by Langston Hughes; reprinted from *Don't You Turn Back* by Langston Hughes.

Maxine Kumin, author, and The Atlantic Monthly Company, for "The Microscope" by Maxine Kumin, copyright © 1963 by The Atlantic Monthly Company, Boston, Mass.

George Laycock, author, and *Boys' Life,* for "Their Time Is Running Out" by George Laycock; reprinted by permission of the author and *Boys' Life,* published by the Boy Scouts of America.

Ruth Lechlitner, author, for "Kansas Boy" by Ruth Lechlitner, which first appeared in *Poetry,* November 1931, copyright 1931 by The Modern Poetry Association; reprinted by permission of the Editor of *Poetry.*

J. B. Lippincott Company, for "Four Years in Paradise," adapted from *Four Years in Paradise* by Osa Johnson, copyright 1941 by Osa Johnson. Copyright © renewed 1969 by Mrs. Bell Leighty, executrix. Reprinted by permission of J. B. Lippincott Company.

The Literary Trustees of Walter de la Mare, and The Society of Authors as their representative, for the extract "Wild Are the Waves" by Walter de la Mare.

Little, Brown and Company, for "The Toaster" by William Jay Smith, copyright © 1955 by William Jay Smith, from *Laughing Time* by William Jay Smith, by permission of Little, Brown and Co. in association with The Atlantic Monthly Press.

McGraw-Hill, Inc., for "Marassa and Midnight" from *Marassa and Midnight* by Morna Stuart, text © by Morna Stuart 1966, illustrations © 1967 by McGraw-Hill, Inc.; used by permission of McGraw-Hill Book Company.

David McKay Company, Inc., for "The Loner" by Ester Wier, reprinted from the book *The Loner*, copyright © 1963 by Ester Wier.

The Macmillan Company, for "Crafts Are a Family Thing" by Bruce and Nancy Roberts, reprinted from *Where Time Stood Still* by Bruce Roberts and Nancy Roberts, copyright © 1970 by Bruce Roberts and Nancy Roberts, and for "Stupidity Street" by Ralph Hodgson, reprinted from *Poems* by Ralph Hodgson, copyright 1917 by The Macmillan Company, renewed 1945 by Ralph Hodgson.

Macmillan London & Basingstoke, The Macmillan Company of Canada, Ltd., and Mrs. Hodgson, for "Stupidity Street" by Ralph Hodgson, from *Collected Poems* by Ralph Hodgson.

Julian Messner, A Division of Simon & Schuster, Inc., for "The Great Water" by Frances Joyce Farnsworth, reprinted from *Winged Moccasins: The Story of Sacajawea* by Frances Joyce Farnsworth, copyright 1954 by Frances Joyce Farnsworth.

William Morrow and Company, Inc., for "Underwater Harvest" by Charles Coombs, abridged by permission from the book *Deep-Sea World* by Charles Coombs, copyright © 1966 by Charles Coombs.

New Directions Publishing Corporation, for "You Can See," two lines reprinted from "Written on the Wall at Chang's Hermitage" by Tu Fu, from Kenneth Rexroth, *One Hundred Poems from the Chinese*, copyright © 1971 by Kenneth Rexroth, all rights reserved. Reprinted by permission of New Directions Publishing Corporation.

Peter Pauper Press, Inc., for "We Rowed into Fog" by Shiki, reprinted from *Haiku Harvest*, Japanese Haiku Series IV, translation by Peter Beilenson and Harry Behn, copyright © 1962 by Peter Pauper Press, Inc.

Rand McNally & Company, for "Limerick," reprinted from *My American Heritage* by Ralph Henry and Lucille Pannell, copyright 1949 by Rand McNally & Co.

Random House, Inc., for "The Little Animals of Anton van Leeuwenhoek" by Seymour Simon, reprinted from *Exploring with a Microscope* by Seymour Simon, copyright © 1969 by Seymour Simon, and for "Sea Meadows" by Ferdinand C. Lane, reprinted from *All About the Sea* by Ferdinand C. Lane, copyright 1953 by Ferdinand C. Lane.

The Saturday Evening Post Company, for "Operation Bird Wash" by Percelle Leidy Coryell, adapted from *Young World* Magazine, copyright 1973, The Saturday Evening Post Co.

The Viking Press, Inc., for "Fox at Midnight" by Betsy Byars, reprinted from *The Midnight Fox* by Betsy Byars, copyright © 1968 by Betsy Byars, all rights reserved.

Franklin Watts, Inc., for "City Hall" by Nellie Burchardt, from *Project Cat* by Nellie Burchardt, copyright 1966 by Franklin Watts, Inc.; for "Sea Creatures" by Sam and Beryl Epstein, from *The First Book of the Ocean* by Sam and Beryl Epstein, copyright 1961 by Franklin Watts, Inc.; for "Star Island" by Louise Dickinson Rich, from *Star Island Boy* by Louise Dickinson Rich, copyright 1968 by Louise Dickinson Rich; and for "The Work of Insects" by F. C. Smith, from *The First Book of Conservation* by F. C. Smith, copyright 1954 by Franklin Watts, Inc.

The World Publishing Company for "Cabin Number Seven," reprinted by permission from *Roosevelt Grady* by Louisa R. Shotwell, copyright © 1963 by Louisa R. Shotwell.

The photograph on page 73 is used by courtesy of David Kerr; the photographs on pages 120, 122, 124, and 126 are reproduced by permission of the Martin and Osa Johnson Safari Museum, Chanute, Kansas; the color micrographs on pages 105, 106, 107, and 285 are used by permission of Bert Pullinger/Meyers Photo-Art; and the photographs on pages 266 and 267 are reproduced by arrangement with Connie Hwang, Meyers Photo-Art, H. Armstrong Roberts, and Philip Sapper.

ILLUSTRATORS

Louis Cary, Gus Colichidas, Jim Cummins, Katherine Frame, Jon Goodell, Roger Heubner, David Kerr, Earnie Kollar, Rebecca Lusk, William Mathison, Murray McKeehan, Lyle Miller, Carol Newsom, Tom Newsom, Bill Shires, Philip Smith, Curtis Spitler, Darrell Wiskur, and David Young

Contents

Aura of Gold

Distant Horizon

To Silence Any Song

Remember Tomorrow

Call of the Sea

Americans at Work

A Selection for Independent Reading

Aura of Gold

You can see the aura of gold
And silver ore all around you.

Tu Fu

Harriet the Spy

Louise Fitzhugh

Harriet, who lives in Manhattan, is determined to become a famous writer. What better way, then, than to keep secret notebooks filled with comments about all the people she knows? But disaster strikes. Harriet's schoolmates rebel when the fifteenth notebook falls into their hands. Can you imagine Harriet's feeling of tension when her schoolmates plot against her? Perhaps these two scenes from *Harriet the Spy* will help you understand Harriet's feelings.

That day, after school, everyone felt in a good mood because the weather was suddenly gay and soft like spring. They hung around outside, the whole class together, which was something they never did. Sport said suddenly, "Hey, why don't we go to the park and play tag?"

Harriet was late for her spying, but she thought she would just play one game and then leave. They all seemed to think this was a smashing idea, so everyone filed across the street.

The kind of tag they played wasn't very complicated; in fact Harriet thought it was rather silly. The object seemed to be to run around in circles and get very tired, then whoever was "it" tried to knock everyone else's books out of their arms. They played and played. Beth Ellen was eliminated at once, having no strength. Sport was the best. He managed to knock down everyone's books except Rachel Hennessey's and Harriet's.

He ran round and round then, very fast. Suddenly he knocked a few of Harriet's things off her arms, then Rachel tried to tease him away, and Harriet started to run like crazy. Soon she was running and running as fast as she could in the direction of the mayor's house. Rachel was right after her and Sport was close behind.

They ran and ran along the river. Then they were on the grass and Sport fell down. It wasn't any fun with him not chasing, so Rachel and Harriet waited until he got up. Then he was very quick and got them.

All of Rachel's books were on the ground, and some of Harriet's. They began to pick them up to go back and join the others.

Suddenly Harriet screeched in horror, "Where is my notebook?" They all began looking around, but they couldn't find it anywhere. Harriet suddenly remembered that some things had been knocked down before they ran away from the others. She began to run back toward them. She ran and ran, yelling like a banshee the whole way.

When she got back to where they had started, she saw the whole class—Beth Ellen, Pinky Whitehead, Carrie Andrews, Marion Hawthorne, Laura Peters, and The Boy with the Purple Socks—all sitting around a bench while Janie Gibbs read to them from the notebook.

Harriet descended upon them with a scream that was supposed to frighten Janie so much she would drop the book. But Janie didn't frighten easily. She just stopped reading and looked up calmly. The others looked up too. She looked at all their eyes and suddenly Harriet M. Welsch was afraid.

They just looked and looked, and their eyes were the

meanest eyes she had ever seen. They formed a little knot and wouldn't let her near them. Rachel and Sport came up then. Marion Hawthorne said fiercely, "Rachel, come over here." Rachel walked over to her, and after Marion had whispered in her ear, got the same mean look.

Janie said, "Sport, come over here."

"Whadaya mean?" said Sport.

"I have something to tell you," Janie said in a very pointed way.

Sport walked over and Harriet's heart went into her sneakers. "FINKS!" Harriet felt rather hysterical. She didn't know what that word meant, but since her father said it all the time, she knew it was bad.

Janie passed the notebook to Sport and Rachel, never taking her eyes off Harriet as she did so. "Sport, you're on page thirty-four; Rachel, you're on fifteen," she said quietly.

Sport read his and burst into tears. "Read it aloud, Sport," said Janie harshly.

"I can't." Sport hid his face.

The book was passed back to Janie. Janie read the passage in a solemn voice.

SOMETIMES I CAN'T STAND SPORT. WITH HIS WORRYING ALL THE TIME AND FUSSING OVER HIS FATHER, SOMETIMES HE'S LIKE A LITTLE OLD WOMAN.

Sport turned his back on Harriet, but even from his back Harriet could see that he was crying.

"That's not *fair*," she screamed. "There're some nice things about Sport in there."

Everyone got very still. Janie spoke very quietly. "Harriet, go over there on that bench until we decide what we're going to do to you."

Harriet went over and sat down. She couldn't hear them. They began to discuss something rapidly with many gestures. Sport kept his back turned and Janie never took her eyes off Harriet, no matter who was talking.

Harriet thought suddenly, I don't have to sit here. And she got up and marched off in as dignified a way as possible under the circumstances. They were so busy they didn't even seem to notice her.

At home, eating her cake and milk, Harriet reviewed her position. It was terrible. She decided that she had never been in a worse position. She then decided she wasn't going to think about it any more. She went to bed in the middle of the afternoon and didn't get up until the next morning.

Her mother thought she was sick and said to her father, "Maybe we ought to call the doctor."

"Finks, all of them," said her father. Then they went away and Harriet went to sleep.

In the park all the children sat around and read things aloud. These are some of the things they read:

NOTES ON WHAT CARRIE ANDREWS THINKS OF MARION HAWTHORNE

THINKS: IS MEAN
IS ROTTEN IN MATH
HAS FUNNY KNEES
IS A PIG

Then:

IF MARION HAWTHORNE DOESN'T WATCH OUT SHE'S GOING TO GROW UP INTO A LADY HITLER.

Janie Gibbs smothered a laugh at that one but not at the next one:

WHO DOES JANIE GIBBS THINK SHE'S KIDDING? DOES SHE REALLY THINK SHE COULD EVER BE A SCIENTIST?

Janie looked as though she had been struck. Sport looked at her sympathetically. They looked at each other, in fact, in a long, meaningful way.

. . . .

Harriet looked around and, seeing no one, climbed over the iron railing in front of this alley. A cat with one eye stared at her. She landed with a thump and the cat with one eye hissed, backing away.

She ran to the back of the alley, her tools jangling. She climbed the fence and from there could see the whole stretch of the block of gardens. Rachel's was the fourth one over. Hoping that no one in the buildings would see her, or if they did they would keep their mouths shut, she began to climb fences and run through gardens until she came to the fence right next to Rachel's garden. Through a crack she could see and hear almost everything. She heard their voices, excited and screeching at each other, and saw a big piece of lumber rise up.

"Listen, Pinky, you're just stupid. This piece should go here, not over there." This was clearly Carrie Andrews talking.

Then Harriet saw the flagpole. It was a rather short flag-pole, but it was a real one. At the top of it, fluttering against the blue sky, was a pair of purple socks.

Harriet stared at the socks. A dim feeling began to pene-trate her. She didn't know what the feeling was until her heart began to beat fast, then she knew it was fear. Those socks made her afraid. If she could see what they were doing, maybe she wouldn't be afraid anymore.

"YOU'RE AN IDIOT!" Carrie Andrews said to Pinky Whitehead.

"How can I build anything without a level?" Sport said to everyone in general.

Then Harriet found a hole and looked through. They were building a *house!* Incredible. But there they were. Everyone was rushing around with tools and wood and there was the semblance of a house emerging right in front of her. It leaned, of course. In fact the two back walls were the corner of the fence and it appeared to be pulling the fence down; but, never mind, it was a house.

Sport was in charge. He was telling everyone what to do in a very irritated way. Carrie Andrews seemed to be the second in command. Except for about three pieces of new wood, the rest was old rotten wood from a chest they had broken up. The three new pieces didn't seem to bear any relation to each other. There were a couple of chairs being chopped up by Pinky right at that moment. Harriet scrunched closer to the fence to see better.

It was a funny scene. Carrie Andrews stood over Sport, yelling at the top of her lungs even though her mouth was right next to his ear. Sport was hammering a floor together. Laura Peters, Marion Hawthorne, and Rachel Hennessey were running around like fools. They had no idea how to do anything. Rachel tried to hammer and smashed her finger. After a while they got bored with trying and got into a conversation near Harriet's post. Janie joined them after an upright fell on her head.

"She's going to die when she finds out."

"Serves her right, mean thing."

"Boy, will she be jealous."

"She has delusions of grandeur anyway," said Janie, rubbing her head.

Harriet was puzzled. Who? Who were they talking about? She looked over and saw Beth Ellen in a corner by herself. What was she doing? She appeared to be drawing something on an old piece of wood. That was the one thing Beth Ellen could do, draw. But then Harriet looked more closely and saw that she wasn't exactly drawing, she was making letters on a sign in a very painstaking way.

Just at that moment the back door opened and Mrs. Hennessey called out, "Okay, kids, the cake is ready. Come and get it."

Homemade cake. Of course. That's why they had chosen Rachel's garden. Not everyone had a garden, but Janie did, and Beth Ellen did. Beth Ellen probably wouldn't even give you an olive to eat over there. Once Harriet had spent the afternoon there and just to pass the time had looked in the refrigerator. There hadn't been anything but a jar of mayonnaise, a jar of artichoke hearts in olive oil, and some skimmed milk. Beth Ellen had agreed with her that it wasn't enough and had added that she felt hungry all the time because her nurse was on a diet and her grandmother was always out to dinner.

There was a mad scramble on the other side of the fence as they all ran to the back door and piled inside. Harriet felt lonely and rather hungry. She stood a minute thinking, then she went back through the gardens the way she had come.

Marassa and Midnight

Morna Stuart

The setting for historical fiction is, of course, always in the past. This story can help you find out what it might have been like to live in France at a time when wealthy people ruled without much concern about the poor. You can also find out what it might have been like to be a slave.

A Negro slave boy stood alone in the great entrance hall of his master's Paris house. It was late afternoon in January of the year 1791, and snow had fallen all day. Since noon, the boy had stood there waiting. He had nothing to do till the bell should sound which summoned him to attend the noble Marquis, his master. In spite of the weather, crowds had been out in the Paris streets, shouting as usual, angry and violent.

The boy, listening, was cold and frightened. He stood tall and upright, so still he might have been not a living boy but a dark, polished statue, the only ornament in this huge, echoing hall. He wore an elegant page's uniform of black satin with silver buttons. There were silver buckles on his shoes.

He did not like his fine clothes, especially the shoes.

They made his feet unhappy, those long, dark feet with long toes that used to be as clever as his fingers. He had never worn shoes till he came from the West Indies to France. He hated France, where the sun was pale and had no warmth, where the full moon came small and cold like a silver button. This big, gray city of Paris was a prison to him. Even its air was dirty. And, now that it was winter, terrible things had come overhead and underfoot, things they called snow and ice, such as he had never seen before.

Nobody cared enough about him to know his age or his name. They thought he was thirteen or fourteen. They called him Boy when they spoke to him at all. He was not cruelly treated or starved. Many, many slaves were worse off than he was. He had seen them in the French colony of San Domingo from which he had been taken away just thirteen moons ago. Thirteen full moons! The boy had counted them.

He did what he was told and gave no trouble, so he was ignored—except when he coughed. He had developed a cough which annoyed the noble Marquis; it came bursting out and he could not stop it. Page boys have no business to cough; they are supposed to be silent.

In fact, this boy was only eleven years old. His name was Marassa. Someone, he did not know who it was, had given him his name at the coffee plantation in San Domingo where he was born. The name Marassa means "twins." Anyone who spoke Creole, the Negro language of the West Indies, would have known that a boy with the name Marassa must be a twin. He was a twin, yes, so like his brother that nobody had ever been able to tell them apart. Until thirteen months ago, they had never been apart. Marassa's brother was called Midnight because that was the hour at which they were born.

Dusk was falling over Paris and the crowd noises were quieter. The boy could hear more plainly now the voice of his master the Marquis, giving orders and scolding behind those double doors which opened into his library. Of late, the Marquis scolded more than usual and he seemed anxious. He had already sent away his family to live in a place called England. All the big furniture and most of the servants had gone. That was why the hall was empty and full of echoes. The snow light made it all more ghostly.

They seemed to have forgotten the slave boy standing there alone in the hall while dusk fell. He had been hungry earlier; now he was just tired and cold. Since he had been parted from his twin, Marassa had felt only half alive. Midnight was the younger, but he had always been the clever twin who took the lead. Midnight would have known and told Marassa what all these things meant, why the Paris crowds were angry, why the Marquis was troubled, why they were going to England. Midnight, if he had been here, would have managed already to find out something about England as well as everything about France.

Even to himself, Marassa never thought to complain of the parting with his brother, nor of being taken from the land he loved. He was born a slave boy, the master's property, bought or sold as the master wished, taken where the master liked, doing what the master told him. Slaves had no minds or wishes or wills, no home, no family of their own. In San Domingo, all his life, Marassa had heard wailing and grief when a Negro woman was taken from her husband, or her children were taken from her. He had heard cries of pain; he had heard strong men crying out, "Ogoun, Ogoun!" when they suffered unbearably. Ogoun was the name of the African god of fire and war upon whom they called to help or avenge their pain. They were sure the god had not abandoned them when they were taken from Africa as slaves. No, he was here also in San Domingo and

walked in his own secret places. And Marassa, when torn away from his brother Midnight, had called silently on Ogoun to help him show nothing, no grief, no fear.

The life in Paris was not so hard that it exhausted a strong boy. It was dreadful only because it was deadly boring after the color and movement of a coffee plantation. Marassa had to endure hours of standing still, alone, waiting, like this. Then would follow hours of standing still behind his master's chair at fashionable parties. He had to be ready to hand hat, cane, or gloves to the noble Marquis—and carry about a basket full of pet miniature spaniels. That was all a page boy had to do. It wasted Marassa's spirits because it was so useless. He was just an ornament in satin and silver, with shoes that made his feet unhappy. The tall, strong boy was gentle and obedient. Midnight, the clever twin, was more forward and fierce. Nobody had ever suggested making a page boy of *him!* So

Midnight had been left where he was, on the plantation in San Domingo. Was he doing field work or stable work? Marassa did not know and maybe he never would know what had happened to his twin.

One thing Midnight would have enjoyed in Paris was going out with the carriage and pair. Marassa had liked that too, till recently. After handing in the basket of spaniels, he had to jump up to a step behind the carriage and hold on tight by a little rail. The Marquis's fast-trotting, matched bays went at a splendid pace through the streets. The crowds of poor people, on foot, were obliged to jump out of the way. Noblemen in San Domingo treated crowds just the same. The only difference was that here, in Paris, the masses of poor people were white and not black—men, women, and children. Amazing! Marassa had never seen white women and children working till he came to France. All labor in San Domingo was slave labor. He was startled to see the white working people of Paris in tattered clothes, with pinched hungry faces. They cursed and shook their fists at the noble carriage. Since the snow came, they had taken to throwing snowballs after it. Most of the snowballs hit Marassa and sometimes there were stones in them. So he did not enjoy going out with the carriage anymore. Even the sound of the crowds made him shrink inside himself. It seemed they hated him and he did not know why. He did not understand, and nobody thought to tell him that there was revolution in France. The poor people, little better off than slaves, were rising against the rich masters. Marassa, understanding nothing, was just frightened. But fierce Midnight would have found an answer to it all.

Marassa was miserably homesick for the brilliant skies of the West Indies, for a peacock-blue sea, clear over the coral reefs, for the full moon, glowing low like a golden lamp, for rose-colored mountains and the darker mountains beyond. Suddenly now, standing in an empty, shadow-filled hall, he seemed to see clearly the beloved twin mountain peaks called Dove and Diamond, which the boy twins had pretended were their own. Diamond, they said, belonged to Midnight and Dove to Marassa. There was a bird haunting these heights; it had a strange and lovely cry; its name was the Magic Dove. Midnight said the bird was his too, because they had heard it first on his mountain, the Diamond.

Sundays were free days on the plantation and the boys were allowed to go scrambling then, up into the hills. They could stay away all night if they were back for work at dawn the next day. They went alone, for none of the other slaves dared to go where they did—not even the oldest, tallest, or strongest of the men. The slaves were afraid of these beautiful mountains, Diamond and Dove. Ogoun had been seen walking through their jungle paths. Most of all, they were afraid of a great bare lonely summit which towered over the fertile twin peaks. It was there they believed the Warrior God, Ogoun, had his real dwelling. He lived in cloud at the summit of blue bare rock. Sometimes, men said, they had seen him, dancing in the moonlight and flourishing his brilliant steel blade. Some said this blade was sickle-shaped, like a machete or pruning knife. Some said it was a straight blade, like the swords carried by the white masters. During the stormy hot season of the year, Ogoun could be seen, terrible in the lightning flashes.

The little boy twins had never been in the least afraid of the peak towering above their own twin peaks. As for Ogoun, they refused to believe he lived up there. They were sure it was the spirit of their own father that walked on that height. From his home, up among the skies, he looked down on Diamond and Dove, which he had given as homes to his sons, where no gods or ghosts troubled the jungle and forest. The boys knew nothing about their father except that he had been a king of Dahomey in Africa, or so people said. When they were older, they meant to climb up his lonely mountain and find him. It was farther than ten-year-old boys could go in their free time.

And there, too, they would find the nest of the Magic Dove. They had searched and searched all forest ways, all jungle ways in their own mountains, Diamond and Dove, but no nest was there. "Later," they had said to one another, "when we are full grown!" They had never thought they could be separated. Twins cannot be separated! Yet it had happened.

Perhaps, Marassa thought, Midnight is old enough now to

have gone up to the King's Mountain. Perhaps he has found the nest! But maybe he has been sold away, like me, to some place where he cannot see our mountains nor hear the call of the Magic Dove any longer. Oh, if there were one day, just one day more to be with Midnight, in the green jungle ways and the deep forest! Just once more to come back together and look down over slave huts set in the warm earth of the plantation like a little African village. To smell the coffee flowers and orange trees! And a Negro supper of boiled plantains, yams, and sweet potatoes! Then, in the mango season, to share a great mango between them.

Like an echo in his head the sound of drums haunted Marassa, bare feet moving in a Negro dance and the wild, glorious Negro singing. Every Saturday night, the masters allowed their slaves to dance, and the boys had joined in since they were old enough to stand. But, of course, their best dances were the ones special to Marassa and Midnight, which they danced alone. Each mirrored what the other did, but Midnight led every movement. Anything they found together which pleased or impressed them came to have its own dance. Their Magic Dove dance was the one they liked best. They would look up to the King's Mountain and smile, as if their father saw and was satisfied with his sons. Marassa's long toes curled in the hateful shoes as he thought of these things. Ah, the drums of San Domingo, the Negro drums! In all gray France, there was no sound so stirring. It was like a secret, brave language that had called from end to end of that magic island which the French masters called San Domingo. They did not know the Creole name for it, used by every Negro slave. Marassa spoke its true name silently now in his own mind. Haiti! It means "the land of high places."

Suddenly, Marassa's cough began and he could not control it. It hurt him dreadfully, tearing his chest. He had never known pain like this. "Ogoun, Ogoun!" he cried in his mind, trying to bear the pain, trying to stifle the cough. The double doors were thrown open and he heard the angry voice of the Marquis saying, "I had forgotten that boy! Tell him to be quiet!"

The library was lighted by lamps, and a huge fire blazed in the hearth. The dancing of flames is beautiful, especially when you look through from cold shadows. Marassa, coughing and shivering, saw his master sitting warm by the hearth. He was dressed in plain traveling clothes; his fur-lined cloak lay over the back of a chair. He was tearing up papers and throwing them into the fire, but he stopped to stroke one of his little spaniels, whining from the basket at his side. He said peevishly, "Shut that door and turn the boy out!"

A manservant came out of the library, shut the door behind him, and said, not unkindly, "Get out into the courtyard, Boy, till you are told to come in again. Look sharp!"

Marassa took himself and his cough into the icy courtyard. A northeast wind cut like a blade through his thin satin coat. A flurry of snow blinded him, so that he did not see the Marquis's carriage drawing up from the stables. He stumbled away just in time from the big wheels that were wound around with chains. The horses slipped in the snow as they pulled up with steaming breath. The coachman on his box was wrapped in a heavy overcoat with three capes. He shouted to Marassa to open the iron gates between courtyard and street. Struggling with the pain of cold and the pain in his chest, Marassa obeyed, dragging back the heavy gates, kicking away the drifts of snow. He did not know this would be the last service he would perform in the employment of the noble Marquis.

He had been told not to go back into the house till he was sent for, so he tried to shelter from the wind. Huddled against a stone wall, he thrust his frozen hands into his armpits. Then everything began to happen and it happened so quickly he was taken by surprise. First the house door opened and out came the Marquis, heavily cloaked, hurrying into his carriage. Two menservants followed, handing in fur rugs and the basket of spaniels. They did not call to Marassa to do anything, so he stayed where he was, watching them. He saw them bring some heavy leather cases from the house and pack them into the carriage. After that, they shut the carriage doors, one of them jumped up beside the coachman, and the other jumped to the step behind the carriage where Marassa used to travel. The carriage moved across the courtyard and swung out of the gate.

They were gone! The great house was empty now, nobody left! They had gone to England; they had forgotten the Negro boy or they did not want him. They did not care for him, nor could Marassa love them, but there was nobody else he knew in all gray France. As the carriage swung past him, he gave a wretched cry, "Master!"

There was a gleam of light from the cold, rising moon, that thirteenth full moon of loneliness. Through the carriage window, moonlight, mingled with snow light, shone on a pale, handsome face. But the noble Marquis did not notice Marassa; he was petting one of his little spaniels.

Marassa ran out of the courtyard and down the street after the carriage, crying out, "Master! Master!"

None of them heard him, not even the servant clinging to the rail outside the carriage. Faster and faster it went, smaller and smaller in the distance; then it glided round a corner and was gone altogether. In the cruel snow stood the Negro slave boy, alone and wretched.

Then he turned quickly where he stood, for he heard the scuffle of hurrying feet. From two sides they surrounded and fell on him, a crowd of savage street boys that sprang from nowhere. They mocked him, squeaking out, "Master! Master!" and tumbled him into the snow. Marassa was up in an instant, fighting like a tiger, fighting for his life.

"Ogoun," he shouted. The call went up clear and brave. It was as if Midnight, the fierce twin, uttered this warrior's call, "Ogoun!" which the street boys tried to imitate but could not. How many of them? Ten or twelve. Marassa did not know, only that their leader went head over heels backward from a ringing punch under his chin. Marassa's dark hands closed on

another boy's throat; he kicked at a third and heard a yelp as the kick went home. "Ogoun!" he yelled, and rammed his head into the mass of them. But there was one who carried a club. He stood clear and swung at Marassa's skull. They were at him like a pack of animals as he went down senseless, fighting one another for his silver buttons and buckles, tearing off his coat and shoes. In less than a minute, he was stripped to his shirt; then one of them shouted loudly, "Watch out!"

A man's voice sounded down the street; the cry was strange and savage, as Marassa's had been. A man came running, running furiously. His heavy cloak streamed out behind him and there was the shiver of steel as his sword was whirled out of its sheath. And the crowd of street boys melted and ran, vanishing into alleys and courtyards, so that in another minute there was no boy to be seen, only a Negro boy lying still in the bloodstained, trampled snow.

The stranger sheathed his sword and kneeled down by Marassa. He stripped off his cloak and put it over him before he listened to hear if the heart were alive in this dark, still body. Having listened, he stood up and then lifted Marassa, cloak and all, in his arms. He was a strong young man, and Marassa, though tall, was very light. So the young man carried him easily for a quarter of a mile, and he whistled all the way when he was not singing. He came to a quiet little street where there was an apothecary's shop; it was shuttered now for the night. This was where he lodged, in a back room above the shop. He knocked on the door by kicking it. The bolts were unfastened from inside and an old man's face looked out.

"Captain!" the apothecary said. "Is there something wrong?"

"This boy is hurt, my friend. It may be he is badly hurt. Will you help me?"

"Surely!"

The old man brought them in, bolted the street door again, then bustled ahead up the stairs to a small, neat room where a neat little fire was burning. Here Marassa was laid on the Captain's own bed.

"Why, it is a black boy!" said the old apothecary. "And, dear, dear! His head is cut!"

He listened to Marassa's heartbeats and then to his breathing. He said again, "Dear, dear! The poor boy was ill before he was hurt. His lungs, his chest! This is bad! It is cruelty to bring a Negro boy to this northern climate and not look after him. But that is what rich men do, Captain, I am sorry to say."

All the time, he was feeling the boy's head with gentle and clever hands.

"First, we get him warm," he said. "His eyes are opening! Look! That is good!"

"He is trying to say something," said the Captain, and he leaned down to hear what it was. When he heard it, he looked puzzled.

"Midnight," he repeated. "Midnight?"

"Not yet, not yet," the old man said kindly to Marassa. He could not have known that the boy was calling for his brother; he thought perhaps he was frightened because he was out late and might get into trouble. So he said again, hoping to comfort him, "Not yet midnight, not yet."

"Midnight! Not yet!" Marassa repeated, and his dark, hurt head weaved on the pillow, and tears burst from his closed eyes. Midnight would reproach him if he cried, he knew that. Midnight was brave and Marassa must be brave. Only so could they grow to be strong men like the great father they did not remember, who was King of Dahomey in Africa.

Marassa, though he was very ill now and very badly hurt, fought back his tears and he said, as grandly and clearly as he could, "Later! When we are full grown. But not yet, Midnight! Not yet!"

The Fun They Had

Isaac Asimov

Fantasies set in the future are often called science fiction. In the next story Margie lives far in the future. And she wonders what it was like to live in the past, the time in which you are living.

Margie even wrote about it that night in her diary. On the page headed May 17, 2157, she wrote, "Today Tommy found a real book!"

It was a very old book. Margie's grandfather once said that when he was a little boy *his* grandfather told him that there was a time when all stories were printed on paper.

They turned the pages, which were yellow and crinkly, and it was awfully funny to read words that stood still instead of moving the way they were supposed to—on a screen, you know. And then, when they turned back to the page before, it had the same words on it that it had had when they read it the first time.

"Gee," said Tommy, "what a waste. When you're through with the book, you just throw it away, I guess. Our television screen must have had a million books on it and it's good for plenty more. I wouldn't throw *it* away."

"Same with mine," said Margie. She was eleven and hadn't seen as many telebooks as Tommy had. He was thirteen.

She said, "Where did you find it?"

"In my house." He pointed without looking, because he was busy reading. "In the attic."

"What's it about?"

"School."

Margie was scornful. "School? What's there to write about school? I hate school."

Margie always hated school, but now she hated it more than ever. The mechanical teacher had been giving her test after test in geography and she had been doing worse and worse until her mother had shaken her head sorrowfully and sent for the County Inspector.

He was a round little man with a red face and a whole box of tools with dials and wires. He smiled at Margie and gave her an apple, then took the teacher apart. Margie had hoped he wouldn't know how to put it together again, but he knew all right, and, after an hour or so, there it was again, large and black and ugly, with a big screen on which all the lessons were shown and the questions were asked. That wasn't so bad. The part Margie hated most was the slot where she had to put homework and test papers. She always had to write them out in a punch code they made her learn when she was six years old, and the mechanical teacher calculated the mark in no time.

The Inspector had smiled after he was finished, and patted Margie's head. He said to her mother, "It's not the little girl's fault, Mrs. Jones. I think the geography sector was geared a little too quick. Those things happen sometimes. I've slowed it up to an average ten-year level. Actually, the overall pattern of her progress is quite satisfactory." And he patted Margie's head again.

Margie was disappointed. She had been hoping they would take the teacher away altogether. They had once taken Tommy's teacher away for nearly a month because the history sector had blanked out completely.

So she said to Tommy, "Why would anyone write about school?"

Tommy looked at her with very superior eyes. "Because it's not our kind of school, stupid. This is the old kind of school that they had hundreds and hundreds of years ago." He added loftily, pronouncing the word carefully, "*Centuries* ago."

Margie was hurt. "Well, I don't know what kind of school

they had all that time ago." She read the book over his shoulder for a while, then said, "Anyway, they had a teacher."

"Sure they had a teacher, but it wasn't a *regular* teacher. It was a man."

"A man? How could a man be a teacher?"

"Well, he just told the boys and girls things and gave them homework and asked them questions."

"A man isn't smart enough."

"Sure he is. My father knows as much as my teacher."

"He can't. A man can't know as much as a teacher."

"He knows almost as much, I betcha."

Margie wasn't prepared to dispute that. She said, "I wouldn't want a strange man in my house to teach me."

Tommy screamed with laughter. "You don't know much, Margie. The teachers didn't live in the house. They had a special building and all the kids went there."

"And all the kids learned the same thing?"

"Sure, if they were the same age."

"But my mother says a teacher has to be adjusted to fit the mind of each boy and girl it teaches and that each kid has to be taught differently."

"Just the same they didn't do it that way then. If you don't like it, you don't have to read the book."

"I didn't say I didn't like it," Margie said quickly. She wanted to read about those funny schools.

They weren't even half-finished when Margie's mother called, "Margie! School!"

Margie looked up. "Not yet, Mamma."

"Now!" said Mrs. Jones. "And it's probably time for Tommy, too."

Margie said to Tommy, "Can I read the book some more with you after school?"

"Maybe," he said nonchalantly. He walked away whistling, the dusty old book tucked beneath his arm.

Margie went into the schoolroom. It was right next to her bedroom, and the mechanical teacher was on and waiting for her. It was always on at the same time every day except Saturday and Sunday, because her mother said little girls learned better if they learned at regular hours.

The screen was lit up, and it said: "Today's arithmetic lesson is on the addition of proper fractions. Please insert yesterday's homework in the proper slot."

Margie did so with a sigh. She was thinking about the old schools they had when her grandfather's grandfather was a little boy. All the kids from the whole neighborhood came, laughing and shouting in the schoolyard, sitting together in the schoolroom, going home together at the end of the day. They learned the same things, so they could help one another on the homework and talk about it.

And the teachers were people. . . .

The mechanical teacher was flashing on the screen: "When we add the fractions ½ and ¼—"

Margie was thinking about how the kids must have loved it in the old days. She was thinking about the fun they had.

Afterthought

1. Do you prefer your own school or Margie's? Why?
2. What is the theme of the story?

The Monster We Live On

Cal Roy

This myth comes from far in the past. It can help you understand how the ancient Aztecs of Mexico explained some of the mysteries in their lives.

Before there was anything else, there was darkness—darkness and the hollow roar of the sea stretching from nowhere to nowhere. There was no land to be called by any name.

The only living thing in the black sea was a monster. She was there before anything else. Only the gods and the sea itself were older than she was. Some say she was a giant shark or a crocodile almost as big as the ocean she swam in or a mountainous toad. She had thousands of eyes and noses and mouths.

In the dark heavens above the sea lived two gods with a single thought, to create the earth and man. One of the gods was called Plumed Serpent. His splendor shone in the heavens like chiseled sparks of water-green jade. On his head he wore a tall hat trimmed with ocelot fur and flowing feathers of red, green, and gold. The feathers made a faint sound, as of future birds singing. The earrings of the god were fiery turquoise and around his throat lay a golden collar hung with many seashells. His sandals were white, trimmed with pearls. About his legs were tied many bells. On one arm Plumed Serpent carried a shield adorned with a sign called the wind jewel, and over his face he wore a mask that looked like the beak of a large bird. This was the wind mask, for Plumed Serpent was the morning star who swept the road to the gates of dawn.

The second god was black as night, but he had a band of yellow painted across his eyes and another across his mouth.

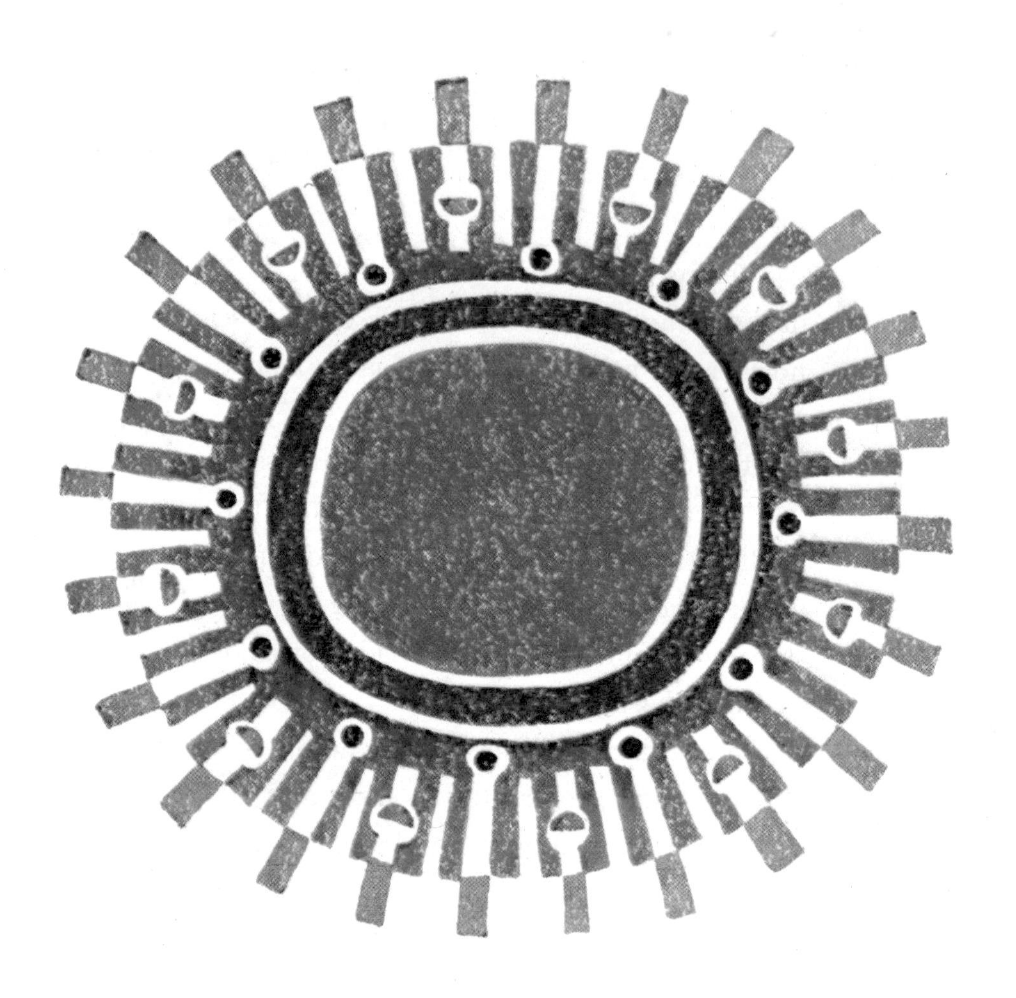

Young and handsome, he wore gold earrings, black sandals, and rattlesnake rattles on his legs. The hair on one side of his head hung down. On the other side it was combed upward. Future warriors would wear their hair this way in his honor. But this god was more than a warrior; he was a sorcerer too. He could change himself into a jaguar, a star, a human skeleton, a turkey. He could drop from the sky by a spider's thread. He could make himself invisible. About him floated an icy air. Was it the chill of northern ice and snow in the region of the heavens from which he came, or was it the shivering breath of eerie things, of death and witchcraft? White heron feathers floated from his rattling headdress.

Donning his wind mask, Plumed Serpent blew upon the dark waters below. The waters separated and showed the gods where the sea monster lay. Together they descended from one heaven to another until they had passed through nine in all. But before they reached the water they turned themselves into serpents.

Then, working together, they attacked.

Mountains of foam spiraled from the churning waters. Torrents poured down as the tail of the infuriated monster flung wave after wave aloft. Between them, god and god locked her in gigantic, crushing coils, squeezing her, stretching her, and finally parting her in two. The struggle lasted longer than any struggle since. But in the end the monster was divided.

Her upper half sank to the bottom of the sea, the highest points of her craggy surface rising out of the waves to become

what we call land. Shored continents, cliff-skirted peninsulas, and islands ringed with ruffled beaches were formed. The heavens felt something new pressing up from below—mountains, hills, and plains. The monster had been converted into earth.

Not yet finished with their task, Plumed Serpent and the other god stood on the land risen from the sea to raise the monster's lower half. One at one end of the world and one at the other, they planted themselves like trees and slowly raised their arms. Seawater poured through their fingers and down their sides as they pushed up the underside of the monster higher than the mountaintops. They hung it in space above the stars, to become the distant, all-encircling sky.

Meanwhile, the monster's sunken half was still changing its appearance. From her hair sprouted grass, from her scaly skin flowers of many colors. From her thousands of eyes gushed inland seas, lakes, rivers, springs. Some flowed clear, reflecting the stars. Others lay in murky pools. Her mouths hardened to form deep caves. And her noses froze into the rocks of tall mountains.

This is how the gods created the earth. But one of the gods paid for the harm done to the sea monster. During the fight, Plumed Serpent's partner lost one foot. The hot blood smoked as it poured from the wound. It glittered like glass. He could see his face reflected in it—his face, which is the night-sky itself. That one-footed god is called Smoking Mirror.

Cabezon

In this realistic story, Francisca discovers that being in the wrong place at the wrong time can demand all the courage a young girl can muster.

Mrs. Guterman, the fifth-grade teacher, stood by the classroom door as her students poured out into the hall. Francisca Garcia was the last to leave. "*Felices Pascuas,* Francisca," Mrs. Guterman said with a big smile. Francisca's dark eyes sparkled.

"Happy holiday to you, too, Mrs. Guterman," Francisca answered as she zipped her coat against the cold December wind.

"Are you leaving town?" Mrs. Guterman asked.

"Yes, Mamá and I are flying to Albuquerque to visit my grandparents, Papá and Mamá Garcia."

"It's a long way from Dallas to Albuquerque. But the airline pilots know the way. I'm sure you'll have a good trip."

Francisca laughed. "I know my pilot knows the way. Mamá rented a plane for the holidays, and she's the best pilot in the world."

"I'm sure she is. Have a nice trip. I'll see you in two weeks."

"*Felices Pascuas,*" Francisca shouted again as she skipped down the hall, out the front door, and up the street toward her home.

In her excitement, Francisca almost flew up the street. Her shiny black hair blew behind her as she ran. "Flying to Albuquerque . . . flying to Albuquerque," she hummed in time to her feet on the sidewalk. She hardly slowed as she leaped up her front steps straight into the arms of her mother. "*Alto ahí,*" her mother laughed. "Stop! You're not flying yet." Her mother was a small pretty woman only a few inches taller than Francisca. Her hair was as dark as Francisca's, but shorter.

"Oh, excuse me, Mamá. I was afraid I'd be late."

"You're not late. You're right on time. The suitcases and packages are in the car. Are you ready?"

"Ready? Am I!" Francisca shouted as she climbed into the car and fastened her seat belt.

It was a thirty-minute drive to the airport. Francisca had been this way so many times that she usually closed her eyes for a short nap on the way. But not this time. Holiday lights brightened the houses and stores along the streets. "Flying to Albuquerque . . . flying to Albuquerque," went round and round in her head.

"Here we are," her mother said as she parked the car next to a bright red and green airplane.

"Mamá, look at the plane. It's a holiday airplane!"

"What?" Francisca's mother replied. "Why, you're right. It is. I didn't think of that when I rented it yesterday. But it is, isn't it?" Francisca's mother smiled at Francisca. "Let's load the plane, and we'll be on our way."

Francisca and her mother quickly loaded the Christmas packages and the luggage. "In you go," Francisca's mother said. Francisca climbed into the airplane. Her mother closed the door securely after her and climbed in on her side. "Is your seat belt tight?" Francisca's mother asked as she pushed the starter button.

"Yes, Mamá."

The starter whined. The cold engine sputtered for a moment and then started. The propeller became a blur as it turned faster and faster.

Soon they were cleared for take-off. Slowly at first, then more and more rapidly the little red and green plane rolled down the runway. The engine roared. The ground rushed by Francisca's window. The airplane gave a little bump, and Francisca knew they were in the air. Francisca and her mother were alone in the clear, blue winter sky. Far below, the trees were brown spots against the ground.

"What are you looking at, Francisca?"

"Oh, I'm just looking at the cars below on the highway. They look like tiny bugs," Francisca answered. Then she added with a grin, "But I guess our airplane looks tiny to the people in the cars."

"Yes," Francisca's mother said, "that is true. But you will have something more interesting to look at soon. I've been saving it as a surprise."

"A surprise? What is it Mamá?"

"Do you remember where I was born? I've told you the story before—but not for a long time."

"In New Mexico?" Francisca answered.

"That's right. But where in New Mexico?"

Francisca thought for a moment as the plane flew through the air toward New Mexico.

"Oh, I remember now. You were born on a *rancho* near the mountain called Big Head. And you lived there until Papá and Mamá Garcia moved to Albuquerque."

"Good! But no one called it Big Head. Everyone used the Spanish name, *Cabezon*. And the mountain does look like a giant's head. It frightened me when I was a little girl. The *rancho* where I was born is gone now. And the town of Cabezon, at the foot of the mountain, is just a ghost town on the Rio Puerco."

"Mamá, *rio* is river in Spanish. But I don't remember *puerco*. What does it mean?"

"It means *muddy*. Rio, *river*—Puerco, *muddy*. Rio Puerco, Muddy River."

Francisca's eyes glittered with excitement. "That's my surprise! We are going to Cabezon, where you were born!"

Francisca's mother chuckled. "I'm afraid ghost towns have no airports. But we are going to fly over the giant's head, Cabezon. And you will be able to see the ghost town and the Rio Puerco."

On and on the little airplane flew. For a while Francisca stayed awake. But halfway across Texas, the smooth purr of the motor and the warm air inside the plane made her eyelids heavy. Soon she was asleep. Her mother leaned over, smoothed her hair, and smiled. "You are a good daughter, Francisca, even if you are asleep and cannot hear me tell you so."

Francisca's mother hummed happily to herself as she piloted the little plane into New Mexico. Finally she gave Francisca's arm a gentle tug to awaken her. "Francisca, look below."

Francisca rubbed her eyes, yawned, and peered out the window. Beneath the plane a huge city was spread like a brightly colored patchwork quilt. The holiday lights below glittered. "What city is that?"

"That is Albuquerque, the home of your grandparents."

Francisca groaned with disappointment. "Oh, no! We are here, and I missed Cabezon. Why didn't you wake me sooner?"

"You didn't miss Cabezon. Cabezon is on the other side of Albuquerque. We will fly over to Cabezon and then fly back to Albuquerque."

"Oh," Francisca said quietly, a little ashamed of her outburst. "I think I'll stay awake now."

"Look out the window, Francisca. Do you see that highway? It looks like a silver ribbon."

"Yes," Francisca answered.

"We will follow that highway for a short distance, and then we will turn west. Then you see if you can find Cabezon, the giant's head."

In a moment Francisca felt the plane bank sharply to the left. She peered through the window at the ground below. There were few trees, only scrubby brush. The brown land was cut with *arroyos*. And from her seat in the airplane Francisca could see that they all finally ran into a dry riverbed. "Is that the Rio Puerco, Mamá?"

"Yes, and before long you should see Cabezon."

"It should be called dry river, not muddy river," Francisca said half to herself.

"I have seen a cloudburst fill the *arroyos* with rushing water and the river almost out of its banks," Francisca's mother said.

"Look!" Francisca shouted. "Look over there! Cabezon! And it looks just like. . . ."

Before she could finish, the airplane shuddered as if a giant hand were shaking it.

"Mamá, what? . . ."

Francisca's mother worked at the controls of the airplane. But the motor coughed once and died. For a moment the only sound was the ghostly whistling of the wind outside the plane. "This is Zebra, X-ray, Niner! This is Zebra. . . ." With a grim look, she stopped. The radio was as dead as the engine. Francisca's mother spoke calmly as she struggled to hold the plane level. "Francisca, tighten your seat belt as much as you can, and cover your face with your arms. We must land the plane."

Francisca's eyes grew wide with fear. "But there is no place to! . . ."

"Relax, my daughter," Francisca's mother said quietly. "We will be safely on the ground in a moment. Now do as I say."

For a second Francisca stared at the rough ground below. It was bare and unfriendly and frightening. The last thing Francisca saw before she covered her face was Cabezon, the giant's head, standing in the distance like an ugly watchman.

Time seemed to stop for Francisca. She could hear only the wind. Then with a hard jolt they were on the ground. Brush whipped against the bottom of the plane as it bounced across the rough, rocky earth. Suddenly Francisca felt as if the ground had been jerked from beneath the plane. And

N18970

almost at once there was a terrible, grinding crash as the plane nosed into the side of an *arroyo*. Francisca was thrown hard against her seat belt. She felt as if she would never breathe again.

The plane rested on its nose deep in the brushy *arroyo*. One wing hung down like the wing of an injured bird.

"Francisca . . . Francisca, can you hear me? Are you hurt?" Francisca's mother's voice trembled slightly.

Francisca fought for breath. Finally she was able to speak. "I . . . I think I'm okay," she said weakly.

Her mother sighed with relief and then groaned softly. Francisca turned quickly in her seat. "You're hurt, Mamá!" She could see the pain in her mother's eyes. "Where are you hurt?"

"My leg, Francisca. I think my leg is broken."

"But, Mamá, what can we do? We must be miles from town." Francisca could feel tears in her eyes. Her throat felt as if a large stone were stuck in it. She swallowed. "How can we call for help?"

"The radio is out. We will just have to wait for someone to find us."

Francisca felt a tear run down her cheek. *No*, she thought, *I must be brave. I am not hurt. I must be brave.* She felt another tear and turned toward the window.

She could not see beyond the edge of the deep, wide *arroyo* that the plane had crashed into. But around the plane, twisted bushes grew in scattered bunches in the dry, brown soil.

"Francisca, . . ." her mother called softly.

Francisca quickly rubbed her eyes and turned to face her mother.

"Francisca, never be ashamed of tears. It is what we do after the tears that is important. Listen carefully. My leg is broken. I must depend on you." Her mother's voice was calm, but her face was pale. "I am sure we will not be missed before morning. So we must spend the night here."

"Can't we stay in the plane?" Francisca asked.

"No," her mother replied, "you should never stay in an *arroyo*. It is dry now, but if it should rain, the *arroyo* would fill with water rushing down to the Rio Puerco. We must get out of the plane."

"How can you move with a broken leg?"

"We will have to make a splint to hold my leg. That is why I must depend on you. Climb out of the plane and find two straight branches. While you are gone, I will get out of the airplane."

Francisca turned the handle on the door and pushed. She could not budge it. It was jammed tight from the crash. She unfastened her seat belt and turned half around in her seat. Placing both feet against the door, she pushed hard. Still the door did not move. She gritted her teeth, pulled her legs back, and kicked as hard as she could. With a crack, the door popped open. Francisca dropped to the ground.

The sides of the *arroyo* were steep. At first Francisca leaned against the side of the plane to keep from tumbling to the bottom. Quickly she glanced around. There was nothing for a splint near the plane. "I must get out of this *arroyo*," she said to herself.

The uneven ground made climbing difficult. And three times she tripped and fell to her hands and knees to keep from falling backwards. Using the scrubby brush to pull herself along, she neared the top of the *arroyo*. Here the sides were even steeper than before. Finally she grabbed a bush growing just at the edge. And by throwing one leg over the top, she was able to pull herself out.

She lay on the cold, hard ground at the top of the *arroyo*. Her chest and stomach ached from the climb. Her breath came in painful gasps. Again she felt tears in her eyes.

In the *arroyo* she had been protected from the wind. But here in the open the north wind was bitter and cold. She got to her feet and stuck her hands in her coat pockets. Slowly she looked around.

In front of her loomed the dark face of Cabezon, the giant's head. From the air it had been interesting. From the ground it was dark and frightening. She shivered and turned to look in the other direction. She gave a little yelp of surprise, for in the distance she saw a group of buildings dimly outlined against the darkening evening sky. *People*, she thought. *There must be someone there*. Then she remembered—*Cabezon, the ghost town of Cabezon*.

She began to search for sticks for her mother's splint. But the sticks near the *arroyo* were small and brittle. Finally she turned toward the ghost town of Cabezon.

Walking was hard. Rocks tripped Francisca at every step. And the rough ground made her stumble again and again. Once she fell, and a dry bush scratched her face. With every breath needles seemed to poke into her chest. But she walked on.

At last she reached the empty town. The old wooden buildings seemed to lean with the cold north wind. Loose shutters creaked and banged. Doors hung at odd angles. Quickly Francisca picked up two boards from a broken fence.

As she huddled out of the wind by one of the ruined buildings, she thought for a moment. *Here there is wood for a fire. Here there is shelter from the wind. I must get Mamá here. But how? How?*

Then something caught her eye. A large wagon left behind by a child years before rested upside down in the dirt. Quickly she ran over to it. "Perhaps it will work," she muttered. "Perhaps . . . just perhaps." She turned the wagon over and tossed the boards in. Then she started back toward the plane and her mother.

The wagon squeaked and rattled as she pulled it over the rough ground. Her face and hands ached from the wind. In the west the sun was slowly setting. Dark clouds were moving toward Cabezon from the north.

At last she reached the edge of the *arroyo*. "Mamá!" she called. "Mamá!" But there was only the whistling of the cold wind. Francisca scrambled down into the *arroyo*. She ignored the brush that tore at her face and body. Her mother lay on the ground next to the plane. "Mamá!" she repeated as she knelt next to her mother.

"Francisca . . . Francisca, I must have fainted. Did you find some sticks?"

"Yes, Mamá. But are you all right?"

"I will be, I am sure. But we must get out of the *arroyo*."

Francisca fought her way up out of the *arroyo* again. Grabbing the boards, she climbed back down to her mother.

Her mother placed a board on each side of her injured leg. Then she ripped wide bands of cloth from the lining of her coat. "Francisca, you will have to help me. Wrap the cloth tightly around the boards. My leg must be held firmly between them. It cannot move."

Francisca began at her mother's ankle. Once her mother groaned softly. "Is that too tight, Mamá?" she asked.

"No . . . no, the leg is just tender. Go on. It must be tight."

At last Francisca finished. "But you still cannot walk on it," Francisca said. "How can you climb up the side of the *arroyo?*"

"I am afraid I must depend on you again, my daughter. You must take the place of my bad leg. Do you think you can?"

Before Francisca could answer, thunder rumbled from the direction of Cabezon. "I must, Mamá. I must," Francisca answered.

"Can you do one more thing, Francisca? We must have something to eat and something to drink. And we must have a fire to keep us warm. In the plane is the fruitcake we were taking to your grandparents and a Thermos of cocoa. And there should be some matches in the first-aid kit under the seat. Get all of those and carry them to the top of the *arroyo*."

Again Francisca slowly struggled to the top of the *arroyo*. Climbing was even harder with her load of food, cocoa, and the first-aid kit. And when she again reached the bottom, her legs were shaking. She collapsed on the ground next to her mother. "Mamá, do you think someone will find us?"

"Of course," Francisca's mother replied. But she frowned when she looked at the dark clouds and listened to the wind. "Come, help me stand. We will climb to the top and find a place to spend the night."

Francisca forced herself to her feet.

"Just stand still," her mother said. "Let me get up and I will lean on you." Slowly, slowly she pulled herself to her feet. Her face grew pale from the pain in her leg. Twice she fell back against the airplane. At last she was up, her weight resting on her good leg.

"How can I help?" Francisca asked.

"I will lean on your shoulder as we climb." She smiled at Francisca. "I will try to be as light as I can."

Carefully Francisca and her mother began to climb the steep side of the *arroyo*. Once Francisca's mother tripped over a rock, and they both fell forward. But little by little they climbed to the top. At the top, Francisca and her mother lay quietly on the ground, unable to move after the climb. Despite the cold wind, they were both sweating.

"Francisca, we must move. It is growing dark. And we must find a place to stay warm. We will die in the open."

Francisca pulled herself to her feet. "We can stay in the ghost town. That is where I found the boards for your splint."

"I'm sorry, Francisca. I don't think I can walk that far. My leg is already beginning to swell."

"But, Mamá, you won't have to walk. I found a wagon. Look. Look behind you." Francisca's mother turned her head toward the wagon.

"We can try, Francisca. We can try. I don't think you can pull me all the way. But I can sit in the wagon and push with my good leg. Together we can do it."

Francisca helped her mother into the wagon. Then she placed the fruitcake, Thermos, and first-aid kit in with her.

Slowly Francisca and her mother moved across the cold land. Before they were halfway to the old, deserted town, darkness fell. It was not the darkness of the city. It was like no darkness Francisca had ever experienced. Even the stars were hidden by clouds. In the distance a high-pitched howl broke the silence.

"Mamá, what was that?"

"Only a coyote, Francisca. When I was a little girl, they sang me to sleep each night." Her mother spoke calmly, but Francisca shivered.

Suddenly the moon broke through the clouds. It was almost as if someone had turned on a light. Francisca hardly noticed. She walked with her head down, using the last of her strength to pull the wagon. Her breath wheezed from her lungs.

"Francisca, look! I can see an old house! We are in the town."

Francisca lifted her head to look. But instead of stopping, she pulled the wagon through the open door. Once inside she stopped. "Mamá, I didn't think we could. . . . I was afraid to stop. I was afraid I couldn't start again."

"I know," her mother answered. "But together we did it." The weakness and pain in her mother's voice gave Francisca strength. She lifted her head and looked at their home for the night.

Moonlight flooded the small room. Francisca could make out an old fireplace at one end and a stack of wood next to it. In the first-aid kit she found some matches. In a moment she had built a fire in the old fireplace. "Mamá, how is your leg?"

"Help . . . help me out of the wagon," her mother answered weakly. Gently Francisca helped her mother to the floor. Then she lay down beside her. Three times during the night Francisca was awakened by the cold and tossed wood on the fire.

She awoke the next morning while it was still dark. The fire had died and she was chilled to the bone. Every muscle ached when she pulled herself to her feet. Quickly she rebuilt the fire. Then she sat next to the fireplace with her back against the wall.

"Francisca. . . ."

"Mamá, I didn't know you were awake."

"I was just thinking, Francisca. This is not what I had planned for our holiday treat. But even so, let's have some fruitcake and cocoa for our breakfast." She pulled herself up and leaned against the wall next to her daughter. "Francisca, I was very proud of you last night. Had it not been for your strength, we might have frozen. But we are warm, and we have food and something to drink. I am sure we will be found today."

Together Francisca and her mother watched the gray of morning turn to bright sunlight. Francisca got up and walked to the door. "Mamá, I can see Cabezon, and . . . Mamá, I see an airplane over Cabezon!"

Francisca ran out into the deserted street and waved her arms. The airplane came closer and closer. For a moment Francisca thought it was turning away. But it made a big circle and zoomed back low over the ghost town. Twice the pilot of the plane circled above Francisca. Then the plane was gone.

Francisca dashed into the house. "The plane left, Mamá! I know the pilot saw me, but the plane left!"

Francisca's mother smiled. "Of course, the plane left. But the pilot will send help. No one wants to land in this ghost town."

Francisca looked at her mother and laughed. "You're right, Mamá. No one wants to land in this ghost town."

How to Eat a Poem

Don't be polite.
Bite in.
Pick it up with your fingers and lick the juice that
    may run down your chin.
It is ready and ripe now, whenever you are.

You do not need a knife or fork or spoon
or plate or napkin or tablecloth.

For there is no core
or stem
or rind
or pit
or seed
or skin
to throw away.

Eve Merriam

Fog

The fog comes
on little cat feet.

It sits looking
over harbor and city
on silent haunches
and then moves on.

Carl Sandburg

Catalogue

Rosalie Moore

Cats sleep fat and walk thin.
Cats, when they sleep, slump;
When they wake, stretch and begin
Over, pulling their ribs in.
Cats walk thin.

Cats wait in a lump,
Jump in a streak.
Cats, when they jump, are sleek
As a grape slipping its skin—
They have technique.
Oh, cats don't creak.
They sneak.

Cats sleep fat.
They spread out comfort underneath
 them
Like a good mat,
As if they picked the place
And then sat;
You walk around one
As if he were the city hall
After that.

If male,
A cat is apt to sing on a major scale;
This concert is for everybody, this
Is wholesale.
For a baton, he wields a tail.

(He is also found,
When happy, to resound
With an enclosed and private sound.)

A cat condenses.
He pulls in his tail to go under bridges,
And himself to go under fences.
Cats fit
In any size box or kit,
And if a large pumpkin grew under one,
He could arch over it.

When everyone else is just ready to go
out,
The cat is just ready to come in.
He's not where he's been.
Cats sleep fat and walk thin.

The Toaster

A silver-scaled Dragon with jaws flaming red
Sits at my elbow and toasts my bread.
I hand him fat slices, and then, one by one,
He hands them back when he sees they are done.

William Jay Smith

Limerick

A fly and a flea in a flue
Were imprisoned, so what could they do?
  Said the fly, "Let us flee,"
  Said the flea, "Let us fly,"
So they flew through a flaw in the flue.

Anonymous

Song of the Pop-Bottlers

Pop bottles pop-bottles
  In pop shops;
The pop-bottles Pop bottles
  Poor Pop drops.

When Pop drops pop-bottles,
  Pop-bottles plop!
Pop-bottle-tops topple!
  Pop mops slop!

Stop! Pop'll drop bottle!
  Stop, Pop, stop!
When Pop bottles pop-bottles,
  Pop-bottles pop!

Morris Bishop

The Stone

Paul Blackburn

The stone found me in bright sunlight
around 9th and Stuyvesant Streets and
found, if not a friend, at
least a travelling companion.
Kicking, we crossed
Third Avenue, then Cooper Square, a-
voiding the traffic in our oblique and
random way, a cab almost got him, and I had
to wait a few seconds, crowding
in from the triangular portion edged about
with signs, safety island, crossed
Lafayette, him catching between the cobbles, then
with a judicious blow
from the toes of my foot (right), well, a
soccer kick aiming for height, we cleared
the curb and turned left down Lafayette,
that long block,
with a wide sidewalk and plenty of room to maneuver
in over metal cellar doorways or swinging
out toward the curb edge. The low worn
curb at 4th was a cinch to make, and

at Great Jones Street the driveway into a
gas station promised no impediment. But
then he rolled suddenly to the right
as though following an old gentleman in a long
coat, and at the same time I was addressed
by a painter I know and his girl on their way
to Washington Square, and as I looked up to
answer,
I heard the small sound. He had fallen
in his run, into water gathered in a sunken
plate which they lift to tighten or loosen
something to do with the city water supply I think,
and sank out of sight.
I spoke to Simeon and Dee
about a loft it turned out he hadn't gotten, but
felt so desolate at having lost him they didn't
stay long, I looked at the puddle, explained
we'd come all the way from beyond Cooper Square,
they hurried away.
I suppose I could have used my hands, picked him
out and continued, he'd have been dry by the time
we got home, but just as I decided to abandon him
the sun disappeared.

I continued on down Bleecker finally,
a warm front moving in from the west, the
cirrus clotting into alto-cumulus, sun seeping through
as the front thickened, but not shining, the air turned
cool, and there were pigeons
circling
over the buildings at
West Broadway, and over them a gull, a
young man with a beard and torn army jacket walked
a big mutt on a short leash teaching him to heel.
The mutt was fine, trotting alongside, nuzzling
lightly at his master's chino pants, the young
man smiled, the dog smiled too, and on they went.
They had each other.
I had left him there in the puddle, our game
over, no fair using hands I had told myself.
Not that he could have smiled.
The sun gone in.
He had been shaped like a drunken pyramid, ir-
regularly triangular.
I liked him.

SHAFTWAY
SHAFTWAY
273

Distant Horizon

The Pioneer

Long years ago I blazed a trail
  Through lovely woods unknown till then
And marked with cairns of splintered shale
  A mountain way for other men;

For other men who came and came:
  They trod the path more plain to see,
They gave my trail another's name
  And no one speaks or knows of me.

The trail runs high, the trail runs low
  Where windflowers dance or columbine;
The scars are healed that long ago
  My ax cut deep on birch and pine.

Another's name my trail may bear,
  But still I keep, in waste and wood,
My joy because the trail is there,
  My peace because the trail is good.

Arthur Guiterman

The Coast of a New World

Katherine B. Shippen

Hundreds of years before Columbus sailed, men from northern Europe set out in search of rich new lands. These explorers sailed in open wooden ships with no compass or charts to guide them. In this story Leif Ericson and his men are sailing west from Greenland.

The men grumbled. They had been forty days at sea and now they came to land and could not go ashore. But Leif would not relent, not yet. The land would wait for them. He wanted to know what kind of people were there before any of them landed.

To quiet their restlessness, he had them get out food and prepare a meal. They had salt fish and dark bread and cheese. And there in the bay off an unknown land, they sat and ate with healthy appetites born of salt air and young bodies.

Leif too was hungry, but he ate standing, his eyes on the shore. He could see that it was a land of rocky cliffs that came down sharply into the water. Only here and there he saw a gnarled tree rooted in some crevice in the rocks. It was an inhospitable land, and a deserted one apparently. If any people lived here they must be fishermen, for there was no grass for feeding cattle, no forest where deer or even rabbits might be hunted. But if the people were fishermen, they were not on the shore. There were no traces of them: no boat was pulled up on the rocks, no nets were drying. . . .

The men of the crew finished eating at last. The scraps were tossed into the water, and the sea gulls circled down and took them.

Then Leif said, "Take whatever weapons you have with you. The people may have been watching from behind some rock."

And the men took knives and spears, and Leif and the others climbed down into the little boat and rowed to the shore.

They clambered up on the rocks, and keeping close together for safety's sake, began to climb the cliff. When they had reached the top, they looked around. There was the bay, their galley anchored in the harbor, and along the shore to north and south as far as they could see were rocks. Here and there they saw a wind-twisted tree, here and there a juniper bush—nothing else.

"Even Greenland has some grassy places," one of the men said, looking down along the barren shore.

"True," Leif answered. "This is the bleakest place I ever saw. Let's call it Helluland—the Land of the Flat Rocks."

The men agreed, feeling indignant because they had come so far and found such a bleak place.

"We'll sleep aboard the ship tonight," Leif said. "It will be safer. Tomorrow we'll sail south along the shore. Perhaps the land will be more fertile further south."

Next morning they started early, sailing south along the coast with a strong northeast wind. They concluded this was no island they had found. It was an enormously big land. They sailed two days and two nights past islands, past little bays and inlets, and always along the coast they saw the same rocks, the same barren shore.

But on the third day they sensed that the air was a little warmer, and there was a smell of earth and trees. And the rocks gave way to green forests: the trees came down to the shore. The men stood looking at the trees with hungry eyes.

Soon they had landed on a sandy beach and waded ashore. It was not necessary to lower a boat; they sailed up close and jumped down into the water, and it was easy to beach the galley on the sand. Soon leafy branches were waving over their heads, ferns brushed against their knees as they passed, and small white flowers were blooming. They put their hands down on green moss, and felt it moist and cool.

"A land of forests!" Leif kept saying, walking under the tall swaying trees. "A land of beautiful forests! Let's call it Markland—the Land of Forests!" No one could think of a better name.

Again that night they lay in the galley, but most of them did not sleep. For in their minds they kept seeing the forests and the earth green with its ferns and mosses. They were like hungry men satisfied, after their long tossing at sea.

At daylight they were up again, ready to go on. It was a bright clear day, and they sailed across a wide bay under a gentle wind. That night they did not land, but sailed on in moonlight, talking of the land that they had found.

Next day they rounded a little promontory and found a place where a stream of fresh water poured down into a bay. Here they beached the galley again and stood silent on the shore, looking around them. The air was warm and sweet, for a gentle offshore breeze was blowing. "Look!" one of them said, and near them the bushes parted and a brown deer, not heeding them at all, came down to the edge of the stream and put its head down to the water to drink.

Leif said, "We'll make a camp here. We'll stay here awhile and explore this land." And soon the men were cutting trees to build a shelter big enough for them all, and carrying their gear from the galley, and pulling the galley up on the beach where it would be safe until they wanted it again.

And all the time no human being came near them: they saw no trace of any habitation, no footprint, no ashes of a burned-out fire.

That night they remained for the first time on the land. And at evening the air was filled with bird music, and in a pool at the edge of the river they heard the high-pitched voices of a

hundred frogs. After the darkness came, there was an owl hooting from a branch in a far-off tree. But there were no other sounds.

Leif said in the morning, "It's spring now. We can stay all summer. Judging by the looks of these trees, we can take a good cargo of logs back to Greenland in the autumn."

The men were eager to explore. They wanted to start at once, to see what they could find. But Leif was still cautious. It seemed impossible to him that there could be a place like this without inhabitants. And whether the inhabitants would prove friendly or hostile, he had no way of knowing.

"Form into two groups," he said. "It will be safer that way. Let the men in each group stay close together: don't separate on any account. We cannot tell who may attack us. I will stay at the camp and wait for you. Come back at sunset, and tell me what you have found."

So the men set off. Soon they had disappeared into the forest.

By sunset they came back again.

"What did you find?" Leif asked when he saw them approaching. And again. "What did you find?"

"We found salmon leaping in the stream," they answered. "Big plump salmon—bigger than any we have ever seen. There

were so many we could almost catch them with our hands. We shall have no want of fresh fish," they said.

"What else did you see?" Leif asked.

"We saw rabbits running through the woods, and deer, and game birds aplenty—there will be no dearth of food," another said.

"And there were lovely flowers," Thyrker was speaking now. "There were mayflowers like those that grow in Germany. And some flowers whose names I do not know."

"Did you see any men?" Leif asked. "Or any footprints, or the ashes of any fires?"

"No, we saw none of these," they said.

So it was on the second day, and on the third day, and on the fourth day. Every day the men came back at sunset, and every day they told of the rich treasures of this country, the great trees of the virgin forest, enough to send endless cargoes of timber back to Greenland. They told of the animals that would be so easy to trap—they would get rich with the furs alone, they said. One day they came back telling of a field of grain.

"What kind of grain?" Leif asked. "What kind of men have planted it?"

"We do not think that it was planted," they said. "It seems

to grow wild—so much of it that it covers a whole valley. The heads of it are heavy, ready to be cut. It is something like wild wheat. We could harvest it and put it into sacks," they said. And some of them remembered the smell of baking bread their wives had made.

But one day when the men came back, Leif saw that Thyrker was missing.

"Where is Thyrker?" Leif asked, casting a quick look over the company.

"We do not know," they answered. "He kept stopping to look at some flower, or some special kind of tree. He kept exclaiming that this one had a certain Latin name, and that one grew in Germany. We told him to come on: he was so slow. And then we noticed that he was not there. We went to look for him. We called and called. And we could not find him anywhere. . . ."

"Thyrker," Leif said. And in his mind, fear for his foster father filled him with anguish. What had become of him?

They threw fresh logs on the fire, thinking that the light might help to guide Thyrker back. They shouted till his name echoed and reechoed through the forest. There were only shadows and quietness. Thyrker did not come.

In the morning they set out to search for him again. Through all the woods they went, shouting his name. But they could not find him. And Leif was full of sadness for the little German who had taught him so much, of whom he was so fond. Could some animal have fallen on him and torn him to pieces, he wondered. Had he fallen from some cliff or met with hostile people whom none of the rest of them had seen?

They searched and searched, until the evening shadows filled the forest, and the birds were making their evening songs.

One after another then, they came back to the shelter: they could not find the little man.

They were seated around the fire in silence. What could they do? The forest was endless, and darkness was coming down again. They had called until they were hoarse. They had searched and searched. If Thyrker was dead, they could not even find his body. The stillness was heavy around them.

Then from far off they thought they heard a cry. They sprang to their feet and listened. The cry came again. The voice undoubtedly was Thyrker's. They knew it well.

Leif ran toward the woods in the direction from which the voice seemed to come. Was Thyrker hurt? Where had he been?

Then in the firelight the men saw him coming. He was running, and in his arms he held a bundle wrapped in the old cape that he always wore.

"Thyrker!" Leif cried.

And Thyrker ran toward him, holding out the bundle in his arms.

But Thyrker was not hurt. His old face was wrinkled with smiles. And he was talking, a great stream of German that none of them could understand.

He ran into the circle of the firelight and put down his bundle on the ground. And then, as if he had found all the treasure of the Indies, he drew aside his cape. The men gathered around him in a circle to see what he had found. And on the ground they saw a heap of purple fruit.

"They're grapes!" Thyrker cried. "They are grapes, like the ones that grew on the hillsides in Germany. I could not believe it when I saw them. They are growing wild there. Just like the ones in Germany that we had to plant." He was speaking their own language again now.

None of Leif's crew had ever seen grapes. They looked at Thyrker as if they thought him insane. But he was not abashed.

"Look at them," he cried. "All through my boyhood I saw them like this in the vineyards in Germany. Look at them!" He held a purple cluster up for them to see. "Smell them," he said. "How sweet!"

And then he took a bunch between his hands and pressed his palms together, and the juice flowed down over his wrists. "They're full of juice," he said. "Full of the delicious purple juice, just like in Germany."

"Where have you been?" Leif asked. "We have searched everywhere for you. We thought some harm had come to you."

"No harm," Thyrker said. "Good fortune. I was examining the plants and the trees, and the others went on faster. And I walked on through the forest by myself—such *rare* plants I found. *Wunderbar*—wonderful. And then I came to a hillside, and there the grapes were growing—lots of them, all over the hillside. I stopped, and I ate them—the taste was so good, *wirklich*, truly—it was like being home in Germany again. So I sat down on a stone and the smell of them was so good. I think I must have fallen asleep.

"It was dark when I woke, but I could still smell the grapes. And it was not cold. I pulled my cape around me, and I slept there with that good smell in my nostrils.

"When it was morning, I started to pick them. I picked and I picked till I had a great mound of them. I thought I would bring them back here. But how could I carry them? I filled my cape with them, and my hat, and I took off my shirt to carry some in that—but I couldn't carry them—they kept rolling out. So I just brought these.

"If you will come back, I will show you. We can each carry some."

Leif had been annoyed with Thyrker at first. But when he listened to this long recital, he could not help smiling. Thyrker was so excited that he could hardly talk, and every now and then he lapsed back into German.

"Let's go and see them," Leif said. "Do you think you can find them again?"

"*Aber natürlich*, of course," Thyrker said, pulling Leif by the arm.

But it was not until morning that they followed Thyrker to the place where the grapes grew. There on the ground they saw the heap that Thyrker had picked. And up over the hill-side, tangled among the branches of the trees they saw the curling tendrils of the vines, the rusty green leaves, the fragrant fruit. They tasted the fruit, and then they began to pick in earnest, and every man carried some of them back to the camp as best he could.

In the days that followed, the place was full of activity. For they discovered that the vines that Thyrker had found were not the only ones. There were grapes in many nearby places. They scoured out the casks that had held salt fish and ale and set them in the sun to air, and they carried them to the hillsides and began to pick. And Thyrker showed them how to squeeze the juice.

So the days of the late summer passed. And still there were grapes on the vines.

"Let's pick a load of the grapes and take them back to Greenland," the men said. "If we fill the hold of the galley with timber, we can put the grapes into the little boat. We'll be the first ever to bring such a cargo to Greenland!"

That was what they did. All day their axes rang in the forest. Tree after tree was felled and stripped of its branches and loaded into the hold of the galley. They brought timber of many different kinds, but the wood they valued most they called *mosur* wood, a kind of maple.

When the timber had all been loaded, they collected the grapes, and heaped the little boat with them, and tied it to the stern of the galley. And at last all was ready, and they hoisted the yellow sail. The light wind filled it. They were under way.

They crossed the bay, and rounded the promontory, and stood on the deck, watching the green shores dropping away behind them. And they reckoned Greenland lay ahead of them, and home. They wanted to go home: they had been away so long. But they were sorry to leave those green shores they had found.

"We'll come back next year," they said. "Back to this

lovely land. We'll come back for another load of timber and another load of grapes."

"We'll come back to the land of the grapes," Thyrker said.

And Leif said, "We'll come back to Vinland the Good."

So they sailed on across the ocean toward the east. And they left behind them the green forests, the fields where the grain was growing, and the hillsides with their fragrant grapes.

"The strange thing is that we never saw a single person there," one of the sailors said. "How could there be a land so beautiful, and not a single man was there until we came."

Afterthought

1. What sort of man was Leif Ericson in the story?
2. Where do you think he and his men were?
3. In what way were they mistaken about the land?

The Boy Dreamer

Helen M. Roberts

People often laugh at dreamers. But a boy's dreams may not be as idle as they seem. He may have qualities that will make those dreams come true.

Characters

CHRISTOPHER COLUMBUS, *14 years old*
BARTHOLOMEW COLUMBUS, *his 10-year-old brother*
PIERO, *a 12-year-old neighbor*
BIANCHETTA COLUMBUS, *sister of Christopher*
SUSANNA COLUMBUS, *mother of Christopher*
ALONZO, *Captain of the* Santa Clara
MIGUEL, *19-year-old sailor*
FRANCISCO, *an old sailor*

SETTING: *The beach at Genoa, Italy, middle of the fifteenth century.*

AT RISE: CHRIS, *a boy of about 14, and* PIERO, *his friend of 12, are lying under a tree near the edge of the water.* CHRIS *is propped against the tree, drawing charcoal maps on a roll of paper, while* PIERO *wriggles around like a young puppy. The other boys and sailors carry in filled sacks.*

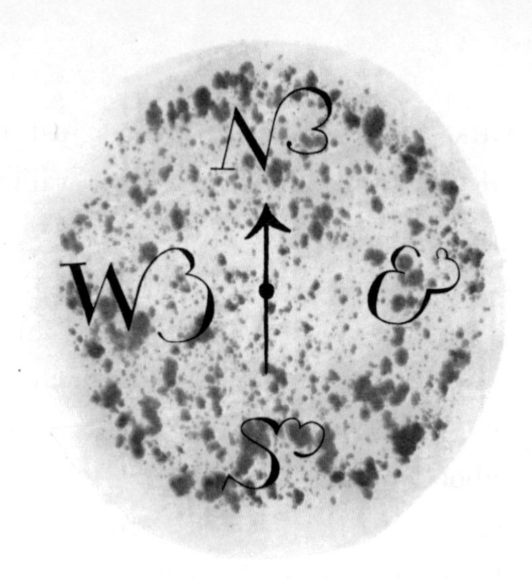

PIERO: What are you always drawing maps for, Chris? Why don't you work like Bart and me?

CHRIS (*Importantly*): Work! What do you think I'm doing? This is real work . . . and mighty important work too, if you want to know. It's a lot better than getting a penny a load the way you do loading boats like that old tub of a *Santa Clara*.

PIERO: So the *Santa Clara*'s an old tub now, is it? Good thing Captain Alonzo didn't hear that.

CHRIS: Hmph! What do I care?

BARTHOLOMEW (*Enters with a load, tired and querulous*): Say, Chris! I wish you'd never run away and gone to sea. Ever since you sailed way out in the Atlantic that time you've done nothing but draw maps, while *I've* had to carry all the loads for you.

PIERO (*Laughing*): Cheer up, Bart! That's what little brothers are for. I'm glad *I'm* not his brother. Chris is an important man these days with his everlasting maps.

CHRIS (*Very superior*): That just proves that you children don't know anything about sailing yet. Any good sailor knows how important maps are.

BARTHOLOMEW: Sure! But I don't have to be a sailor to see how those silly maps get you out of all the hard work!

CHRIS: Aw, forget about it, Bart. Why, I've studied and studied about maps. Besides, I've read all the books in town about maps and travel.

BARTHOLOMEW: You'd better work more and read less then.

PIERO: You're tired, Bart. Sit down and rest here beside us a moment. (*To* CHRIS) What kind of map do you call that?

CHRIS (*Holding out his map*): See! Here's where *we* are, right in Genoa, Italy.

BARTHOLOMEW (*Grumbling*): You don't need to tell us *that!* We may not be as old as you, Mr. Christopher Columbus, but at least we know where we live.

CHRIS (*Pointing*): Here are Spain and Portugal . . . and here are the Canary Islands . . . and here are the Azores far out in the Atlantic. And beyond that . . .

PIERO: What, Chris? Just tell me that, and you'll really be saying something.

CHRIS (*Seriously*): Nobody knows for sure. Maybe India, maybe some country no one's ever heard of yet.

PIERO: Now, you're talking just plain foolishness, Chris. Everyone knows India and China are east of here, not west. And besides, how do you know there's anything way out where ships have never been? It's most likely the end of the earth.

MIGUEL (*Entering; he is a teasing sort of bully*): Well, well, Chris! At your old trick of map making, eh? Where are you sailing this time? Out on the horizon with the sea serpents and monsters?

CHRIS (*Frowning*): Who wants to know?

MIGUEL (*Teasing*): Why, no one. But you'd best stop that drawing and help load the ship before Captain Alonzo catches you here. Go along, all of you.

CHRIS: You're not the boss. The tide doesn't turn for two hours yet. What's the big hurry?

MIGUEL: Smarty, aren't you? Guess that's why you don't have to work to help your mother out. It's lots easier to let Bart here support you while you just dream of being a master mariner.

CHRIS: I don't intend to be a common sailor.

MIGUEL: Oh, no? Well, just listen to him brag!

CHRIS: I'm going to sail away and discover new lands. That's why I'm working so hard on these maps now. Someday I'll be . . . why I'll be a famous explorer. (*Positively.*) And I *won't* take any load to that boat until I'm good and ready. So there!

SUSANNA COLUMBUS (*Offstage, very clear and commanding*): Chris! Chris! Chris—to—pher Columbus! Where are you?

CHRIS (*Jumping up with alacrity and starting off after* PIERO *and* BART *with a load, while* MIGUEL *laughs scornfully*): Such luck! Why did she have to come when I'm right in the middle of an important map? (CHRIS, PIERO, *and* BART *exit left, as* SUSANNA *enters right.*)

SUSANNA (*Seeing* MIGUEL): Miguel, where's Chris?

MIGUEL (*Obviously in awe of* SUSANNA, *points offstage*): He . . . he left in a hurry. (*Exits.*)

SUSANNA (*Calling*): Chris Columbus! You come right back

here! I need some money for my marketing. You don't want to go hungry, do you? (CHRIS *reenters from left.*)

CHRIS (*His self-assurance gone, handing her the coins*): Here's all I have.

SUSANNA (*Sharply*): But Chris! This is only for two trips. There's some mistake! Didn't they pay you for the rest?

CHRIS: That's all the trips I made.

SUSANNA (*Hands on hips, lecturing angrily*): Only two trips! Why, you're a disgrace to the name of Columbus! To think that hardworking people like Domenico and Susanna Columbus could have such a lazy son! Why, Bartholomew is worth twice as much as you any day. (BARTHOLOMEW *and* PIERO *enter timidly.*) Christopher Columbus! You're a shiftless, good-for-nothing dreamer . . . and you deserve to have no supper . . . or breakfast either.

BARTHOLOMEW (*Approaching his mother to defend his brother*): But Mother! Chris really has been working hard. Just look at all the maps he's made this morning. (*Gives her his money.*) Someday, Chris is going to be a great sailor. He told me so himself. And someday . . . he'll even discover new lands, maybe, and . . . and . . .

SUSANNA (*Interrupting*): And in the meantime we'll all starve most likely. (*Holds out hand, looking at the money.*) Look at

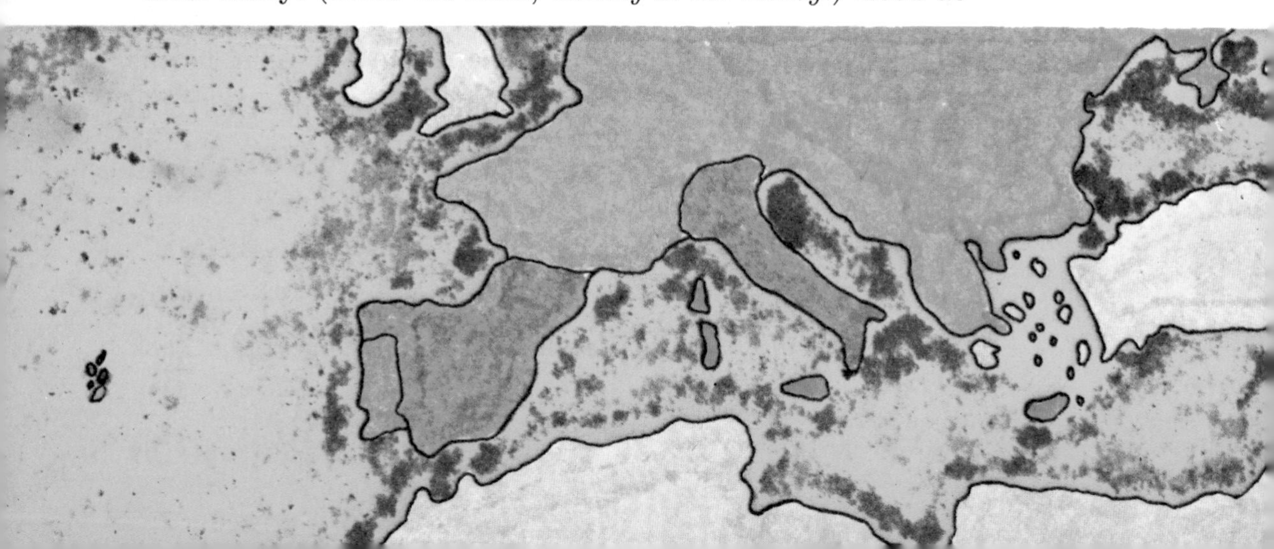

that! Ten pennies! As if that would feed two great big hulking boys, to say nothing of your sister, Bianchetta. Now, get busy, and carry as many loads of grain as you can! (*Exits.*)

BARTHOLOMEW: Come on, Chris! You heard what Mother said.

CHRIS (*Grumbling*): How could I help it? I wish I didn't have to load ships for someone else. I don't like it one single bit.

PIERO (*Coaxingly*): It's not so bad when we all work together. We could even sing or whistle and make a game of our work. (*Whistles encouragingly.*)

CHRIS (*Disgustedly*): Game? Nothing! (*Examines maps longingly as he rolls them up.*) Well . . . I guess all great men were most likely misunderstood by their families.

PIERO (*Laughing*): Sure thing! My mother never thinks I do enough either. Always scolding! (*They go out.*)

MIGUEL (*Enters singing a sea chanty; his empty sack is slung over his shoulder*): Coast is clear now. Looks as if Signora Columbus meant business this time. She must have laid down the law to that smart son of hers. (*Sees the maps, picks them up, and looks at them.*) Never knew him to go off and leave his precious maps before! (*Turns them first one way, then another; examines the backs, then upside down, greatly puzzled.*) Wonder what they're all about, anyway! Might be something to 'em, I suppose.

FRANCISCO (*Enters, unobserved, carrying a load*): Don't tell me *you're* in the map business, Miguel!

MIGUEL: Not I! Not with these hands! They're good for climbing rigging or carrying cargo, (*Laughs.*) but not for handling little pieces of charcoal like this. (*They examine maps.*) What do you know about maps? Are these any good?

FRANCISCO: I can't rightly tell. Chris has spent a lot of time poring over old maps and studying navigation.

MIGUEL: To hear him tell it, you'd think he was most as good as a sea captain.

FRANCISCO: He's done considerable sailing for a boy his age, to say nothing of the schooling he's had.

MIGUEL: He doesn't need to boast as if he really were going to be somebody. He's got a way with him, though. You know, sometimes, I almost believe him myself.

FRANCISCO (*Laughing*): Then he *must* have a way with him. (*Seriously.*) 'Twouldn't surprise me any if he turned out to be a great man. He does a lot of dreaming, and thinking, and planning. Who knows? Maybe he'll make some of his dreams come true.

MIGUEL (*Paying no attention to* FRANCISCO, *turns back to maps*): I get it now. Look here, Francisco! Look what the boy has done here! This is meant to be Spain and the Atlantic Ocean. Bless me if he hasn't put China and India across the Atlantic . . . west of here, instead of over east, (*Points to opposite side of map.*) where everyone knows it belongs. (*Laughs uproariously as* CHRIS *comes in, unnoticed by* MIGUEL, *hurt by what he hears.*)

FRANCISCO (*Noticing* CHRIS): You'd best put those maps down, Miguel. They're not so foolish as you might think.

CHRIS (*Elated, joins the others*): Francisco! Do you mean it?

FRANCISCO (*Soothingly*): Sure I mean it! Why, I'll be glad to pay you—(*Takes coins from pocket and looks at them.*) the same that Captain Alonzo would pay for five loads to the *Santa Clara*.

CHRIS (*Overjoyed*): That's wonderful. No one has ever paid me

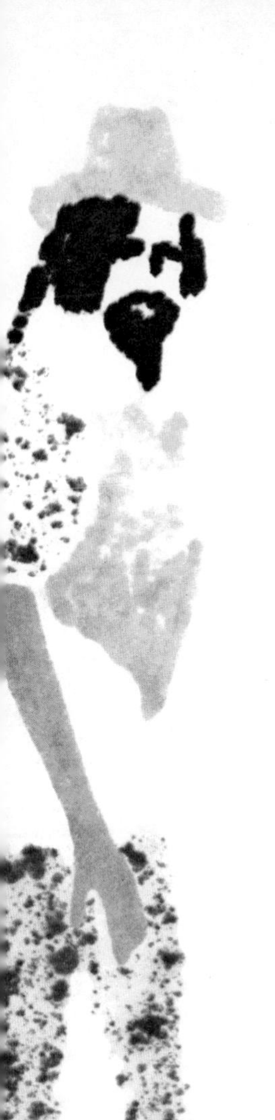

for a map before, Francisco. You're not just saying that to tease me, are you?

FRANCISCO (*Giving him coins*): Not on your life! Why, I'll hang that map somewhere aboard ship where I can see it every day. Maybe you can make more money on maps than in sailoring or loading ships. (*Puts his bag on shoulder, tucks map under his arm.*) Next time the *Santa Clara* puts into port here, we'll talk some more about maps. (*Exits.*)

MIGUEL: He's certainly an easy mark! Wish I could make money like that without working.

CHRIS: You still think I'm just playing, don't you, Miguel? Well, I'm not!

MIGUEL: Oh, no? Sounds mighty odd to me. Why do you think China's west, when we know it's east? You know good and well you can't sail west to find the east.

CHRIS (*Mysteriously*): But you can!

MIGUEL: You can't make me believe that east is west and west is east.

CHRIS: Of course not. That wouldn't be true, and no one wants you to believe what's not true.

MIGUEL (*Puzzled, half-convinced*): But you just *can't* sail west (*Points.*) and find east. (*Points in opposite direction.*) It just can't be done. It doesn't make good sense!

CHRIS (*Looking around*): Maybe I can explain it to you. I've thought about it such a lot, Miguel, that it seems simple enough to me. I'll try to make you understand. I wake up nights thinking about it. (*Picks up maps to show* MIGUEL.) I can't seem to get it off my mind.

BIANCHETTA (*Entering*): Well, Chris! I didn't expect to find you just fooling around here. Mother said you were working.

She'll surely make a fuss when I go back and tell her there isn't any more money after all.

CHRIS: But there is! Here! Will this help? (*Gives her map money.*)

BIANCHETTA: But Chris! You haven't had time to carry five loads yet. I just saw Bart, and he had money for only two loads. Where'd you get this money?

CHRIS (*Casually*): I sold a map, Bianca. That's how I got it.

BIANCHETTA: A map! You make them without even batting an eye! Surely they can't be worth this much money!

CHRIS (*Bursting with pride and importance*): Why not? Francisco says maybe they'll be worth much more. He says cartographers—that's the name they call people who make maps—are in great demand by good sea captains these days.

PIERO (*Entering with* BART *during last speech*): Are you going to be a cart—whatever it was you called it—instead of a sailor?

CHRIS: I should say not! Drawing maps is only the beginning. I'm going to learn all that the best sea captains around here know, and more, too. Then I'm going to be a great explorer, the discoverer of a new route to China and India.

MIGUEL: That's just a dream, Chris, and you know it. You'd best stick to your maps.

CHRIS: I'll show you. . . .

MIGUEL: People have been trying to find a short route to India for years and years. So far nobody's found one. That's why all the goods from there cost so much money, and are so hard to get.

CHRIS: I'm going to change all that, when I grow up.

MIGUEL (*Laughing*): Chris, your yarns get wilder and funnier all the time. Next thing we know, you'll be telling us about mountains of gold and rivers of diamonds. . . .

BIANCHETTA: Miguel's right. People will think you're crazy, Chris, and will lock you up if you tell stories like that.

CHRIS: Don't you believe in anything, Miguel?

MIGUEL (*Laughs, teasingly*): Why, of course! I believe that east is west . . . and west is east.

CHRIS (*Doggedly, almost in tears*): I'll find that mountain of gold someday, and when I'm rich and famous you'll wish you *had* believed in me.

PIERO (*Looking at map, trying to console* CHRIS): You promised to show us how you were going to get to India by a short route.

CHRIS (*Encouraged*): Well . . . you know the earth is round. . . .

MIGUEL (*Arguing*): Who says so?

CHRIS: Why, lots of people say so, and I'll prove it! You know how the tip of a ship's mast is the last thing you see in the distance, and how it's the first thing you see when a boat's coming in.

BARTHOLOMEW: Of course! I've seen that lots of times.

PIERO: So have I! There's one way out there at sea now. And if you climb a cliff you can see it even longer.

CHRIS: So . . . the earth must be round.

MIGUEL (*Unwillingly, tracing imaginary figures in the air*): Maybe it does curve a little.

CHRIS: Look! Let's pretend this big sack is the earth. (*Sets it up. Takes charcoal and draws rough map big enough for audience to see, while the others walk around sack wondering what he is going to do.*)

MIGUEL: What a funny-looking earth that is!

CHRIS (*Pointing*): Here are Spain and Portugal. (*Moving finger.*) And here are China and India.

PIERO: Sure! That's right, Chris! We all know that!

MIGUEL: Aha! That's where I caught you! You said it was the other way round!

CHRIS: So it is!

BARTHOLOMEW (*Running around bag, suddenly understands*): It's both ways at once! I see it now. (*Walks around bag.*) We can get there *this way*, or—(*Walks around other way.*) or else we can get there this way.

MIGUEL (*Scratches his head, still puzzled*): Why, I can't believe it. . . . (*Walks around, first one way, then another, shaking his head.*)

FRANCISCO (*Entering with* CAPTAIN ALONZO *during demonstration*): Do it again, Chris, so Captain Alonzo can see.

ALONZO (*Blustering*): What's the idea of all this monkey business when there's work to be done?

FRANCISCO (*Soothingly*): It'll only take a minute, Captain.

ALONZO: I'm in no mood for such nonsense.

FRANCISCO: It's not nonsense! The boy has a good head on him.

CHRIS (*A little timidly, but with growing assurance*): This is the way you usually sail the *Santa Clara* when you're getting a load from India, isn't it, Captain Alonzo? (*Traces routes on sack with a long stick he picks up.*) Way down here through the Mediterranean, and then a long trip overland to India. Then back to your ship with what's left of the load.

ALONZO (*Fascinated, in spite of himself*): Of course! There's no other way to go.

CHRIS (*Retracing it*): It's a long journey, isn't it, and a dangerous one, too, with pirates all along the coast of Africa here? It takes time and money to bring the supplies across the land and then load them aboard the *Santa Clara*.

ALONZO (*Losing interest*): Yes, yes. But what's that got to do with it all? You're just wasting my time, now.

CHRIS: No, Captain. *I'm saving it!* See how much better this route is. (*Traces his new route on the map.*)

PIERO (*Pleased and excited*): There'd be less danger from

pirates, too, as they'd never know which way you were going to take.

MIGUEL (*Mildly enthusiastic*): There'd be no way for pirates to find you . . . way out in the ocean. (*Dismayed.*) But, you could never cross it, could you?

CHRIS: I don't see why not.

MIGUEL: No one's ever done it.

FRANCISCO: There always has to be a first time!

MIGUEL (*Dubiously*): It's so far! Why, it must be hundreds of miles.

ALONZO: You're all talking nonsense. You don't know the first thing about it. It's one thing to sail along the coast of northern Africa, where you know there's land somewhere near, but it's something else again to go straight out into the unknown sea.

CHRIS (*Persuasively*): But with a fleet of ships, you could make it.

MIGUEL (*Laughing boisterously*): Ho, ho! That's a good one! A fleet of ships he says! (*Pulls out empty pockets.*) I suppose you think Captain Alonzo would let you sail the *Santa Clara* out over the edge of the sea.

CHRIS (*Belligerently*): Who said I'd want to sail the *Santa Clara?* (*Steps up to* MIGUEL *threateningly.*) So you don't think I could get ships, eh? I suppose you think so too, Captain Alonzo?

ALONZO: I'm not even thinking about it. This nonsense has gone to your head. You're not only wasting *my* time, but you're keeping the others from loading my ship. Come on, Francisco. It's near sailing time and there's still a lot to do. (ALONZO, FRANCISCO, *and* MIGUEL *start out.*) But just remember this, boy! Captain Alonzo's taking the *old* route to India. The *old* route, mind you! (*He laughs at his joke;* MIGUEL *joins him, but* FRANCISCO *shakes his head unhappily. The others look crestfallen.* ALONZO, FRANCISCO, *and* MIGUEL *exit.*)

BIANCHETTA: You surely made a mess of everything that time, Chris. Maybe you and Bart won't get any more work from Captain Alonzo next time he's in port. *Then* what'll we do?

CHRIS (*Defiantly*): *I don't care!* Someday seafarers will be glad to have me show them this new route. (*Boasting to cover his hurt pride.*) Why, I'll bet even kings and queens will *beg* me to tell them my secret.

BIANCHETTA: Come on, Chris! Let's go home! You're just putting on a show now. What's the use of getting so excited about it?

CHRIS: Excited, am I? Not half as excited as they'll be to hear my plan. Bianca, you sit down there. (*Pushes her down under the tree where he had been.*) Now, you're a queen on her throne. Bart, you're the king of . . . well, it doesn't matter much where. You two are king and queen.

BARTHOLOMEW: I'm too tired to play such silly games. Besides, we've got to finish loading the *Santa Clara*.

CHRIS (*With powerful appeal*): Don't you understand, Bart? *This* isn't a game!

PIERO: *I* understand, Chris. You're showing us how you'll really do it someday. I'll be chancellor or royal secretary or something like that. (*Stands proudly at the side of others.*)

CHRIS (*Bowing deeply and seriously, others lost in his spell*): Your Majesties! You are very great and noble, but great as you are, I wish to make you even greater. All the world knows of your great wealth and power, and *I* will show you how you can increase these and become the greatest monarchs in the world.

BIANCHETTA (*Playing up and loving her role*): My dear Christopher Columbus. I have heard of your great—(*Falters.*) great skill and—and learning. How would you suggest we gain this added fame?

BARTHOLOMEW: You two almost make me believe you.

PIERO (*Whispering*): Your Majesty! A king mustn't act that way.

BARTHOLOMEW (*Impressed*): I'm sorry.

CHRIS (*Bowing again*): Your Majesty! Through my studies I've learned of a new route to the wealth of India and China. I have read of a mountain of gold, and I ask the privilege of bringing it to lay at your feet.

BIANCHETTA: Bring a mountain of gold to my feet? (*Bursts out laughing.*) *Oh*, Chris! You can't expect me to be serious when you say such silly things. I just can't help laughing. Why, any queen with half an ounce of sense would have you thrown out and put in chains as a lunatic.

PIERO: And that'd finish you and your crazy schemes.

CHRIS (*Unheeding, absorbed in his role*): I am overjoyed that you approve of my plan. I promise you will never regret it.

BIANCHETTA (*Thrilled*): Chris! You're wonderful.

CHRIS (*Gesturing elegantly*): So you want me to take your splendid fleet of new ships and bring back all this gold? (*Strokes his imaginary beard.*) On second thought, I believe it would be better to take only a few ships on the first trip. You see, Your Majesties, if there were too many ships, they might get separated during the voyage.

PIERO (*Nodding*): So they might, and that would be such a pity.

CHRIS: Now, in order to make this voyage for you, I must ask that you grant me certain terms.

BIANCHETTA (*Laughing to* PIERO): The young man is bold. He demands terms of the king and queen.

CHRIS (*Grandly*): It is really little I ask as reward for my services.

BARTHOLOMEW (*Aside*): Here it comes! Same old Chris!

CHRIS: First, I wish the title of Admiral of this fleet. That's right. *Admiral Christopher Columbus!* How fine it sounds!

BARTHOLOMEW: It does sound grand—for a *poor* boy!

CHRIS: And second, I would ask to be knighted, so that my family may keep the title of nobility forever. (*Bows to* BARTHOLOMEW *and* BIANCHETTA.) That would be enough for this time. Admiral Sir Christopher Columbus. (*Bows.*) The obedient servant of your august Majesties. (*Bows deeply again.*)

BIANCHETTA: A mere trifle to demand from your king and queen. (*Curtain falls.*)

The Little Animals of Anton van Leeuwenhoek

Seymour Simon

Not all explorers go on dangerous journeys. Curiosity led a shopkeeper to discover a strange new world in a drop of water.

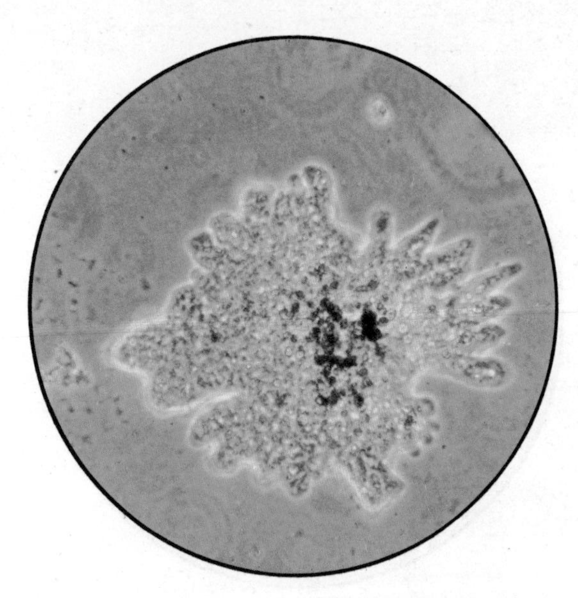

Three hundred years ago there lived in Holland a great explorer named Anton van Leeuwenhoek. Leeuwenhoek was not the usual kind of explorer. He seldom journeyed far from home. In fact, most of his trips were taken in his own home. Leeuwenhoek found a hidden world by looking through a microscope.

"In the year 1675, I discovered living creatures in rainwater, which stood for a few days in a new pot." So begins one of the many letters that Leeuwenhoek wrote to the scientists of the Royal Society of London.

The learned men of the Royal Society read these letters with great surprise. They had never heard of such things. They found them hard to believe. They even had one of their members make a microscope to check Leeuwenhoek's findings. They marveled when he was proved right.

Anton van Leeuwenhoek was born in 1632 in Delft, Holland. His family were businessmen and merchants. He left school at an early age to learn a trade in a dry goods shop, selling cloth. When Leeuwenhoek was 21 years old, he set up a store of his own in Delft. Hardly the beginnings for a scientist, you might think.

But Leeuwenhoek became interested in making lenses. A lens is a curved piece of glass (or any other clear material). One kind of lens makes objects look larger than they are. It is said to magnify objects. People may have first discovered magnifying lenses by noticing that

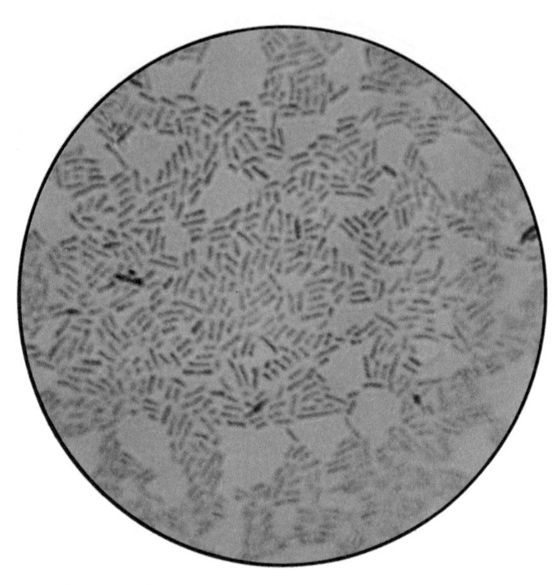

things looked larger when seen through glass beads. A glass bead acts as a lens. By Leeuwenhoek's time, a few people knew how to carefully grind down a piece of glass into a smoothly curved lens.

Leeuwenhoek was the greatest lens maker of his time. Perhaps he made his first magnifying lens simply to examine the linens in his dry goods store. But his curiosity was such that he soon used the lens to enlarge other objects that could not be seen in detail with his eyes alone. He looked at the head and wings of a fly; he looked at the hairs of animals; he looked at bits of dust, parts of plants, human skin, and the eye of an ox.

Soon Leeuwenhoek was spending hour after hour making more lenses and peering through them. The lenses were small but excellent. Some magnified up to 300 times. Leeuwenhoek made hundreds of simple one-lens microscopes. With them, he made discovery after discovery. He kept notes and made drawings of all that he saw.

In his notes, Leeuwenhoek wrote of tiny animals that he saw in rainwater, in seawater, in vinegar, and in mixtures of spices and water. He wrote of the way the animals moved and how they were shaped. He told of some that wriggled like tiny eels and others that moved through water "with very thin little legs."

Scraping a bit of white stuff from his teeth, Leeuwenhoek looked at it through a microscope and saw

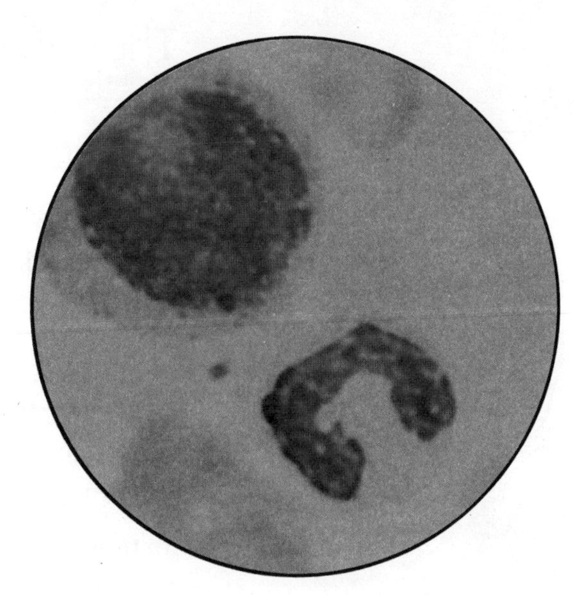

"many very little animals, very prettily moving." Some of the little animals "shot through water like a pike." Others "spun round like a top." Still others seemed to make "not the least motion." Today we call some of the "little animals" that Leeuwenhoek saw protozoa. The ones that made "not the least motion" we call bacteria.

Leeuwenhoek was curious about everything. He examined a drop of blood and discovered red blood cells. He looked at the tail of a fish and discovered tiny blood vessels. He studied each object many times. He observed carefully and accurately.

Many important visitors came to look through Leeuwenhoek's microscopes. The King and Queen of England, the Emperor of Germany, Peter the Great of Russia, and scientists from the Royal Society all paid visits to the simple Dutch storekeeper. Other people asked to come and were put off. Leeuwenhoek was just too busy.

When Leeuwenhoek died, he and his microscopes were famous throughout the world. In the several hundred years since then, microscopes have been much improved. And nowadays, microscopes are readily available. You no longer have to grind your own lenses. Many department and hobby stores sell microscopes. With a microscope, you can rediscover the "little animals" of Anton van Leeuwenhoek. You can become an explorer in the hidden world of the very small.

The Microscope

Anton Leeuwenhoek was Dutch.
He sold pincushions, cloth, and such.
The waiting townsfolk fumed and fussed
As Anton's dry goods gathered dust.
He worked, instead of tending store,
At grinding special lenses for
A microscope. Some of the things
He looked at were:
mosquitoes' wings,
the hairs of sheep, the legs of lice,
the skin of people, dogs, and mice;
ox eyes, spiders' spinning gear,
fishes' scales, a little smear
of his own blood,
and best of all,
the unknown, busy, very small
bugs that swim and bump and hop
inside a simple water drop.
Impossible! Most Dutchmen said.
This Anton's crazy in the head.
We ought to ship him off to Spain.
He says he's seen a housefly's brain.
He says the water that we drink
Is full of bugs. He's mad, we think!
They called him dummkopf which means dope.
That's how we got the microscope.

Maxine Kumin

The Great Water

Frances Joyce Farnsworth

In 1803 President Jefferson asked Meriwether Lewis and William Clark to find and map a route to the northern coast of the Pacific Ocean. Without the help of Sacajawea, an Indian woman, they and their men might have failed.

Janey, as Captain Clark called her, and her baby Pomp were with the explorers when they reached the coast. The following story begins with Christmas at the fort the men had built.

One morning, Sacajawea was greeted by the words "Merry Christmas, Merry Christmas." Everyone was saying it to everyone, and the few who found it hard to feel merry found little support in their companions.

"Nothing to be merry about? Why, man, we're here, and now all we'll have to do is to go home in the springtime."

"Yes, just think where we were last Christmas. Ought to be mighty thankful we're here. We've done it, boy. We've done it! If Jefferson could know, I'll wager it would be his best Christmas present. Come on, Cruzatte, where's your fiddle? What in the name of all that's holy did we bring you along for?"

"Cook's fixing Christmas fixings! Going to have a real Christmas feast 'way out here sitting on the banks of the Pacific. Everywhere Christmas, even here. Folks back home are shouting 'Merry Christmas' to everyone they see. 'Merry Christmas,' folks back home. We're a-saying it to you even though you can't hear us!" A shout went up, "Merry Christmas, folks at home."

"Merry Christmas," repeated Sacajawea softly. "The birthday of God's son when a star came and stood over the manger bed where he lay. A day to be happy and to make others happy."

She had a secret, a wonderful secret. Captains Lewis and Clark had small gifts for the men, and they had made gifts for one another. Sacajawea, who had never heard of "Merry Christmas" until a year ago, had a gift too. It was a nice one and she was very proud.

When she placed her bundle in the hands of Captain Clark, she said the two words that were such good medicine on this wonderful day: "Merry Christmas."

Captain Clark was surprised. He had not thought that she would remember the gift-giving from the previous year. The package contained two dozen white weasel tails—a fine gift indeed. Weasel tails, such as these, were one of the most prized forms of decoration among the Indian tribes, for in winter the weasels turn white with black at the very tips of their tails. Indians prized them for decorating their ceremonial robes. She had given him what she thought was fitting for a captain or a chieftain. He could trim his jacket with them. He thanked her warmly, knowing the hours she must have spent in trapping the little creatures. Of course there had been a small gift for her today from him as well as from the men. Pomp had received many gifts from the men too. Now the youngster was playing with a set of blocks one of the men

had given him made from bits of wood that had been smoothly cut and sanded.

Then Cruzatte tuned up his fiddle and began to play a tune. Soon the men were singing, and their voices filled the room with Christmas music.

As the weeks passed and the food supply began to grow low, everyone seemed to know it; but no one talked about it. The men ate less now, hoping to stretch out their supplies until they were able to replenish them.

It was amazing how much food it took to feed thirty people. There was only a very little flour left. "We had no idea it would take us so long," said Captain Lewis. "If we had, I wonder if we would have had the courage to attempt it. Sometimes it is well that we do not know what lies ahead."

"Janey certainly knows how to make the most of things," said Captain Clark. "I found her breaking up the bones that the men usually throw away. She boiled them, and it was amazing the quantity of fat and good food she extracted. When she is through with a thing, there really isn't too much left for good old dog Scannon. The men are fine about getting out after food. They all realize our predicament. It is a good thing we have been able to get some fish too. It all helps our bill of fare."

That evening the men came in very excited. Sacajawea knew from their voices that something unusual had happened. She tried to understand. There were some words that she knew and many that she could say. But when the white men became excited, their words seemed to flow together. There was one word that she heard over and over. "Whale." But what was whale? She could not recall hearing the word before.

Her French trapper husband was not good at giving details, and it was difficult to learn all the things she wished so very much to know. A whale, she discovered, was a monster that lived in the ocean. Whales were the largest animals in the world. The one the men had found was a small whale not yet full-grown that had been washed up on the shore. But still it was a very large animal. It was something like a fish. It lived in the water but, unlike fish, had to come to the surface for air. Some of the meat was good to eat. The fat would be useful in many ways, and even its bones were useful, for they were strong and supple.

In her corner by the fire Sacajawea pondered over all she had heard. To think that one of the greatest animals in the world lay not far away! Perhaps none of her people had ever seen a whale. Perhaps no Mandan had ever seen one, and certainly no Minataree. But she, Sacajawea, was going to see it! She would see the whale, and she would see the Great Water too.

Each day when new parties went down, Sacajawea was left behind. Soon she came to understand that Charbonneau was making no effort to have her taken along. Perhaps he did not wish her to go. So she set to work to make Charbonneau understand that she must go and he must help her. At last the Frenchman went to Captain Clark and told him of her desires. He did it reluctantly, and showed no interest in having her request granted.

"She acts very bad," he told the Captain. "She cries and says she is badly treated. She says she has done all she could to help and she wants to see the whale and the great water. There is much to do here—moccasins to make, skins to prepare. There is no need for her to go. You tell her to behave and stay here where she belongs."

"Bring her here," said Captain Clark. "It is a long cold trip, and perhaps I can persuade her to give it up."

But when "Janey" came, he knew she was going to see the whale. If they did not take her, she would go herself. She had not come all this distance to be stopped by a little cold and discomfort when something so fascinating lay so near. In a way he was surprised at her determination and earnestness. For the first time he had a little flash of understanding of this wild young creature—her urge to see what lay beyond the next hilltop, and the next. This was the living thing within her that kept her spirit alive and eager. The whale, the ocean—they, too, were hilltops.

"Tell her," he said, turning to Charbonneau, "that a trip shall be arranged. You and I, Charbonneau, and three or four of the men will go tomorrow. If she wishes so much to see these things, she should not be denied."

It was a dark day when they set out, and the ocean looked cold and gray. The great waves came rolling in, racing high upon the sandy beach and then slowly receding before the next that came plowing in like mighty steeds with white foam upon their crests. White sea gulls fluttered over the waves, sometimes riding out on the receding waves. It was fascinating to the Indian girl. She watched the motion of the water and seemed to forget that she was not alone.

At last she had seen it, the Great Water at the setting sun. It was more than she had ever dreamed of seeing back in the days when she worked with the bone hoe at the bend of the river where the Minataree made his camp. The Great Water! There was water as far as the eye could see and farther, still farther! She had heard of the Great Water, for the knowledge of it had passed from tribe to tribe; but she had never expected to see it.

She was to marvel still more at the monster of the sea. All the men said it was a small whale, but to her it was the largest animal she had ever seen. And it lived in the water! The water must be very deep to have such huge creatures make it their home. She stood and looked and wondered. If the whale came from the water, then what other great creatures must be in its depths? It must hold wonders beyond anyone's dreams. She studied the whale carefully so that she might be able to describe it to her people when she returned, and tell Pomp about it when he was old enough to understand. It would make much food for them, that she could see. How glad she was that she had been able to come and see it! Captain Clark had been kind to make the trip. Now she had seen the Great Water and the whale. She had made a mental picture of them, deep in her mind, that she would not forget. She had seen so much, so much! She thought of the squash vine and smiled. She had not taken root. She would never take root! And for one startled instant, she remembered she was returning to that life when springtime came. But she shook away the thought. No, she would never take root. She would always be free. She stumbled a little as she turned reluctantly when the men called, at last, that they must be back at the fort before dark. She was thinking of the long trail she had followed, and she knew there would be other hilltops!

Darkness was drawing the curtains of the day when they reached the fort. They could smell the good warm food before they reached the doorway, and hear Pomp's shrill cry of glee as he saw them coming. He shouted and danced, and Captain Clark scooped him up in his strong arms and perched him on his shoulder.

"We couldn't take you, young man," he said. "Your mother will have to tell you about the whale and the Pacific Ocean."

Sacajawea smiled. Here were warmth and comfort. Here was her child well and happy. The men were in a good mood, and Cruzatte's fiddle sang a merry tune.

Afterthought

1. How did Sacajawea's gift to Captain Clark mix Indian ways with those of the white man?
2. How did Sacajawea's desire to see the ocean and the whale help Captain Clark understand her?
3. What qualities did Sacajawea have in common with other explorers you have read about?

Four Years in Paradise

Osa Johnson

Osa Johnson and her husband, Martin, were among the first explorers to record the mystery and beauty of Africa on film. In this selection you can see East Africa through the eyes of Osa Johnson, one of the pioneers in photographic exploration.

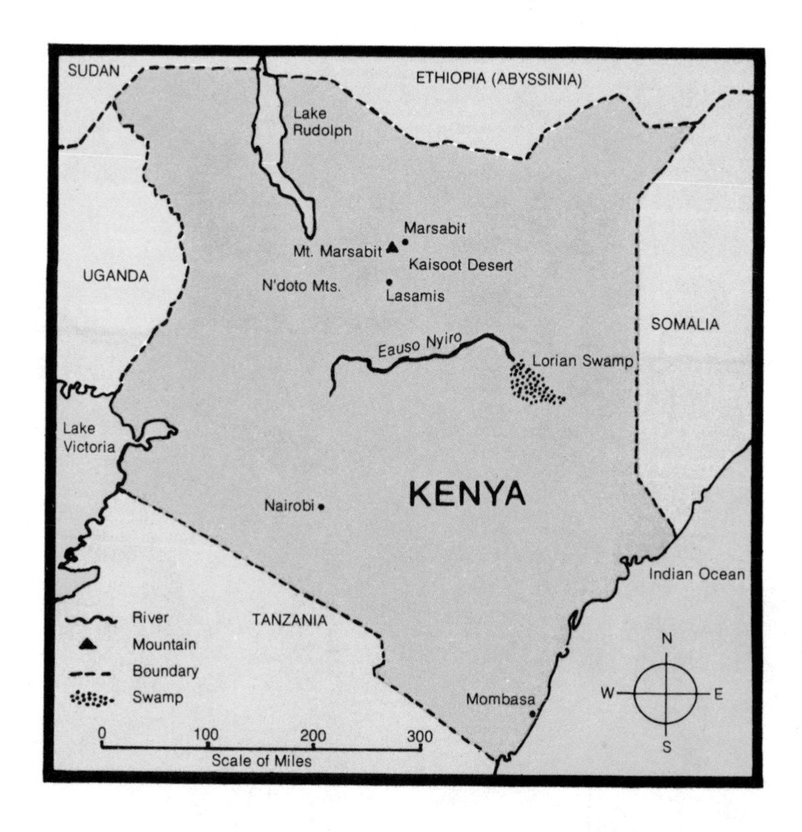

The following excerpts from my diary at Lake Paradise are presented with the thought that they may impart a picture of our day-to-day life.

Lake Paradise, December 21, 1924

It is so beautiful everywhere we go, even outside the immediate Lake area for one hundred and fifty miles in any direction, that we have decided it is all Paradise! Every safari we make out into the plains is full of beauty and interesting experiences.

If anyone had told me a few years ago that I would be making a home in the jungle, hundreds of miles from anywhere, and would be as happy as we are here, I could not have believed him. And it will probably be impossible to make our friends at home understand.

The rains have washed the air and brought up the flowers and a thousand fragrances. I walked around the volcanic crater as far as I could go and still get back for dinner—about fifteen miles in all. The rim of the crater is thirty miles around, and today I would have walked it all had there been time.

The trees are bright green, and the silvery Spanish moss everywhere gives the forest a brightness and movement that is more than ever animating. It is always full of life, however. Today we saw elephants, some of the few that have not yet gone to the plains; and several rhino and buffalo. And a little Abyssinian bushbuck and her fawn, both in bright reddish-brown coats with white polka dots. The bushbuck looked at me, trembling all over, and then scampered away, their bushy white tails spreading out like fans behind them.

The trails around the rim are very irregular and give you a good workout. In and out of the forest, through dongas and up their steep sides where elephant trails and footprints are often a great help, and over logs and boulders these trails wind. And just often enough—to keep you from forgetting that you are tired—you have a brush with game or catch a clear view of the Lake or of the Kaisoot Desert for a rest and reward.

Lake Paradise, January 9, 1925

Martin jollies me a great deal about "having a way with animals," and I think he believes it. But no one can ever be sure about any animal, let alone a wild one, and there is no "way with them," except to be always on the alert and to molest them as little as possible.

Animals are curious—and some much more so than others. If they are in a friendly mood, they like to look you over at as close a range as is safe. Elephants, rhino, buffalo, lions, giraffe, the plains animals, will often steal up to within a few yards without charging, especially if you are in a car, so that they get the scent of rubber and gasoline and do not make you out. But a little movement and they will charge or be gone in a flash. If advances are going to be made, they want to make them; and that is just as true of pets as of animals in the wilderness.

If a wild animal has been wounded by some person, he is much more likely to charge the next human being he sees. And even if he has been gored by one of his own kind, he is more likely to be bad-tempered than pleasant. Long memories in this respect are no monopoly of the elephants.

Heat, humidity, and weather conditions generally affect animals just as they do human beings, or at least similarly. Many times I don't blame animals for being mean-tempered, for I feel the same way myself. All I ask is that they don't take it out on me, for I want to be left alone just as much as they do.

When an animal gets to be so mean that his bad disposition is chronic, the rest of the family or the herd throws him out. This is a pretty sad state for an elephant or almost any animal, for he has a much harder time getting his food and he is in much more danger having to shift for himself. When he grows old and his tusks or his teeth are bad, or he becomes crippled in some way, he has a really bad time of it. But once he has become marked as a "rogue," no animal will take him in. He is then a real outcast. I think some of these lonely animals really go insane and that, no doubt, is why they do the things they do to native villages; for sometimes they go berserk and tear into a group of huts and wreck everything they can reach, for no apparent reason whatever.

On Safari, Logga, February 8th

These safaris take much more planning than an ordinary hunting trip, where food and ammunition and clothes are the only stores to carry. The cameras weigh a great deal and have to be handled with extreme care, and we also have to carry duplicate equipment to guard against loss and accident, including extra springs, crank handles, magazines, clamps, and parts.

On Safari, Logga, February 11th

Last night we slept out in the blind. Nothing but a leopard came down. He fooled around for half an hour and then went away without giving us a good picture. But crickets came in billions. I have never heard such a din. Beginning shortly after dark and continuing until long past midnight, there was such a racket that Martin and I could scarcely hear each other talk. The sound was so continuous that I began to wonder if there were not something wrong with my ears and whether they might go on ringing like this the rest of my life. I began to long for a moment's silence. Then it came. The silence lasted for about an hour, when suddenly the tree frogs started up just as bad a racket. When morning finally dawned, our nerves were on edge. We were so jumpy that we were ready to bite each other's head off. But after a good walk back to camp, some hot coffee, and a good breakfast, we were ready for work again.

For days we have been seeing big game, but they have remained in the forest through the day and our night pictures have been nothing to boast about. But we have made up for this in gorgeous safari material, and Martin has made beautiful bird and butterfly pictures.

The rains are so unseasonal and disappointing for pictures that we are going back to the Lake.

Lake Paradise, March 3rd

After dinner, we take a walk to the forest or over to the cliff, or if we are very tired we sit on the veranda and watch night fall over the Lake. There is always life at the Lake, whatever the hour, and in the evening birds in great numbers are usually leaving the water to go to

roost. They give the air a constant movement and color. Night comes swiftly and the animal calls increase until we have a tremendous symphony of jungle sound all about us. It throbs through us and we seem to become a part of it. I can feel my heart keeping the beat of it, and its rhythm lulls us to sleep.

Below our veranda is a natural clearing with great trees standing about. We have named this Paradise Park. Practically all the trees have had their bark rubbed off by elephants. And since they are bare for as high as fifty feet, I suppose that elephants have scratched their backs here for fifty to a hundred years.

Lake Paradise, August 15th

So many animals sleep during the day, or remain in the deep forest where photography is impossible, coming to the waterholes only at night, that we are forced to use a flash to get pictures. This means that we have to sit all night in a brush pile or perched in a treetop where we are not only pretty cold and uncomfortable, but exposed to leopards. And it is hard to stay awake, for our days are full of work and we are often exhausted. Then the animals often get our scent and shy away from the waterhole, and we spend the night without getting a single picture.

Here at the Lake we can at least sleep in bed. But when the flash goes with a boom, we are too excited to wait and usually get up and take a gun and rush down to get the plates and reset the cameras. Then we go into the laboratory and develop and if the picture comes out well, we forget that we are sleepy.

Last night we sat in a treetop blind across the Lake with a flash set up on the trail. At the foot of the tree we set up a small tent where we could rush the cameras in case of rain. About midnight a rhino came down from our rear, touched the tent, sniffed at it, and backed away. He got a whiff of us but could not make out where it came from and circled around us for nearly an hour, then went away. Bright moonlight and we could see him perfectly. About two, a couple of hundred buffalo came noisily along the trail and went down to the Lake but missed the flash apparatus. Nothing else came, because of a hundred or more baboons in the trees near us, who sensed us and kept up a continuous racket. By morning, I could have wrung every one of their necks.

On Safari, Lasamis, October 1st

Today we saw a lion sitting right on top of an ant hill. The light was bad, but we tried a picture. What a shot it will make if it comes out well!

They dote on fresh pork and often hang around the ant hills looking for an easy dinner. Wart hogs use the abandoned ant hills for refuges and they are good safe ones, but Mr. Lion waits around, hoping that in the evening the old razorback will come out to prowl for his food. Then the lion has only to make an easy spring and he has nice juicy chops for himself and his family.

Leopards also like pork, and they frequent the ant hills for the same reason.

But the wart hog can put up a good fight, if he has half a chance. His tusks are keen and he knows how to use them. He is one of the most pugnacious creatures on the plains. He trots along with a comical egotism and self-assurance, as though he were just as big and tough as anything in sight, and as if he dared anything to tackle him. He is so ugly I should think he would scare off almost any but a very hungry adversary.

I saw a little wart hog go after a leopard that attacked him recently and not only fight to the finish but completely wear out the leopard. He left him exhausted and very badly cut up. That leopard won't trouble the little pigs for a long time, I am sure.

On Safari, Eauso Nyiro River, October 7th

I went scouting and found a rock kopje that was alive with hyrax, the little "rock rabbits," but the light was so bad I could get no decent pictures of them. Except that they had dark brown fur, they reminded me of cottontails back home and were just as nimble. The father would come out to look at me, sit up like a chipmunk, with his forepaws in the air; mother would follow him and sit alongside; then the babies would come scurrying out and sit up in line. At my first move to get out a camera, they were gone. Family after family went through this routine and through the glasses I could see them screwing up their noses and faces, trying to sniff me. They shook with nervous excitement. We have tried again and again to photograph them; someday we will succeed.

Balloonomania

Edward Jablonski

If you've ever watched a hawk soaring in the sky or puffed the parachute seeds of a dandelion, you can understand why humans have always wanted to float in the air. In this selection you can read about some men and women who felt just as you may have—and then did something about it.

Floating down from great heights, like flying through the air, has been a human preoccupation going back to antiquity. The idea of a device for this originated in China a couple of hundred years before Christ. Whether or not an actual parachute was ever used, except in legend, is not known. Leonardo da Vinci's famous sketch for a parachute, made around 1500, reveals the artist's interest in flight. But again, his idea remained a theory rather than a practical attempt.

In 1783, no doubt emboldened by the success of the Montgolfier balloon, a French physician, Sebastien Lenormand, safely descended from

the tower of the Montpellier Observatory in a parachute of his own design. It remained for André Garnerin, inspired by Lenormand, to make the first parachute drop from an aircraft. This took place over Paris on October 22, 1797. Garnerin rose about three thousand feet into the air in a balloon with a parachute attached. Then he cut the cord.

Garnerin did not exactly float down, as he might have in a modern parachute. There being no vent in the center of the chute to permit a steadying column of air to escape, Garnerin's parachute descended oscillating, rather nauseatingly, like a clock's pendulum. He arrived on the ground safely, if slightly green in the face, and found himself famous.

André Garnerin's wife, Jeanne-Geneviève, won an even greater accolade when, in 1799, she became the first woman in history to make a solo flight. Women had, of course, already proved that they had no fear of flying, but they had always been the passenger of a male pilot. Madame Garnerin, however, managed the trip alone in one of her husband's balloons. But Madame Garnerin was by no means the only woman balloonist. Another French balloonist, Madeleine-Sophie Blanchard, had made her first ascent in 1804 accompanied by her husband, Jean-Pierre, who had returned from a tour of America. Despite all the money her husband had made from his exploits, when he died in 1809 following a balloon accident in Holland, Blanchard left his wife penniless.

Before he died, Blanchard took a rather dim view of his wife's prospects. "All my wife can do now," he said, "will be to commit suicide or live on public assistance."

Madeleine-Sophie Blanchard chose to do neither. She became, instead, the most famous woman balloonist of her time. On June 24, 1810, she made an ascent at a festive display given by the Imperial Guard before Napoleon and the new Empress Marie Louise. Impressively launched upon a career as an aeronaut, she also took the position left vacant by the discredited Garnerins, *Aéronaute officiel de l'Empire.*

Like her late husband, Madame Blanchard set off on a tour of Europe. She was a tiny person, judging from engravings of her made at the time. She had rather large, brooding eyes and a pointed little face—although that might be attributed to the style of drawing at the time, which "makes all women look like pet mice," according to French writer Herve Lauwick. Another illustration, however, depicts her as small-waisted and quite attractive.

She has also been described as a plain but intrepid little person, with neurotic fear of noise and of riding in carriages. Madeleine-Sophie, instead, preferred the silence of flight and seems to have had a great love for night flights.

There were, of course, hazards in her profession. In 1817 during an exhibition flight at Nantes, she mistook a flooded field for a grassy meadow. She nearly drowned until some of the spectators, who had been following the progress of her flight on

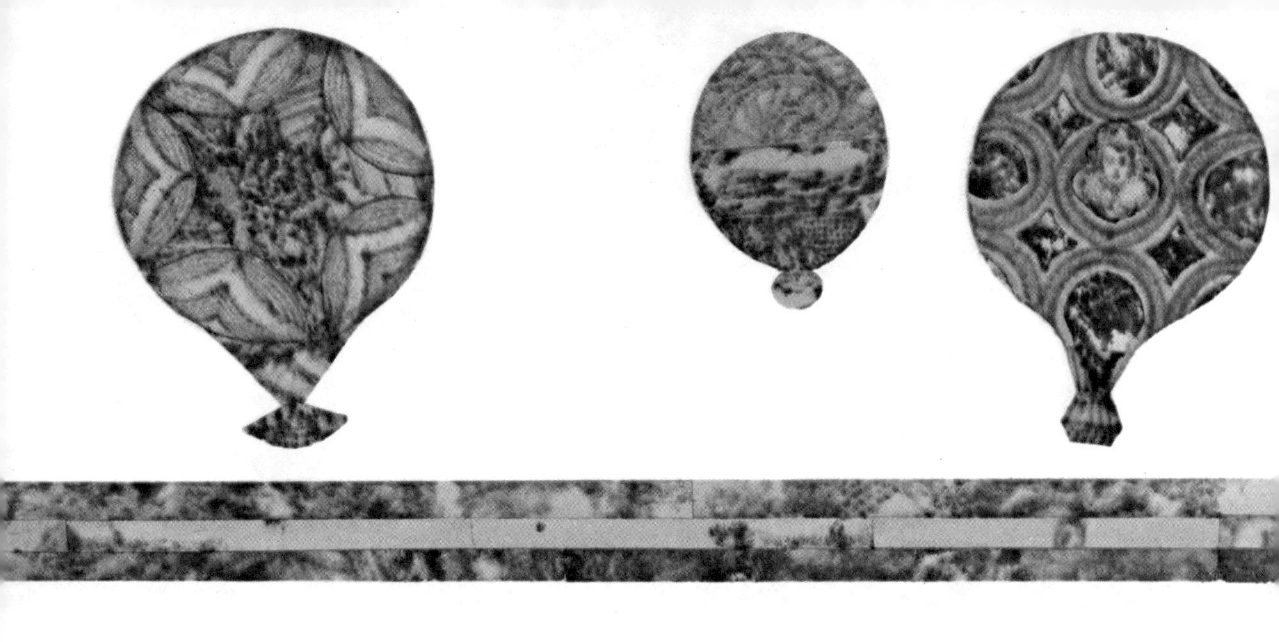

horseback, rushed into the field to rescue Madeleine-Sophie from under the water.

When Napoleon was deposed and France again had a king, Louis XVIII, Madame Blanchard retained her position as official aeronaut to the Crown. Her career came to an end on the evening of July 6, 1819. She was scheduled to make an ascent at the Tivoli Gardens, a famous amusement park in Paris, to give a fireworks display. For days in advance of the event posters appeared all over Paris advertising the forthcoming "extraordinary celebration."

A jubilant, excited crowd gathered at the Tivoli Gardens to see what was promised in the posters to be an "exceptional ascent." Madeleine-Sophie Blanchard was a true celebrity, the most famous in Europe, who never failed to attract large, festive crowds. As she lifted into the calm of her beloved night, it was with some sense of relief, for the mob was noisy and a band accompanied the balloon as it withdrew into the twilight.

As promised, a cascade of golden light sprinkled down from the rising balloon, leaving a beautiful pattern in Madeleine-Sophie's wake. As this breathtaking sight slowly drifted across the sky, the balloonist released a small parachute carrying a device which sparkled with silver particles. To many it seemed that Madeleine-Sophie, a child of the heavens, had found the secret of bringing the stars near to the earth for all to see.

And then there came a sudden, great puff of flame, certainly the most spectacular of all the fireworks up to

that moment. The balloon became suffused with a reddish glow. And it began dropping at a very fast rate. The full horror of the spectacle was soon evident to many of the spectators; the fireworks had ignited the hydrogen and the burning balloon was crashing to the ground.

Aboard the balloon, the fall of which nearly extinguished the flames, Madame Blanchard, no less "cool, intrepid, and determined," than her husband had been during his flight across the English Channel, threw out ballast. She hoped thus to lighten the balloon and check its precipitate fall into the streets of Paris. As she did this, the still burning balloon swept dangerously low over the rooftops. The descent was not as fast, but the balloon swung erratically. As she swept in over the *rue de Provence,* her car struck the corner of a house and Madeleine-Sophie was pitched headlong into the street, where she died instantly of a broken neck. She was the first woman to die in an air accident.

U.S.A.

So we march into the present
And it's always rather pleasant
To speculate on what the years ahead of us will see,
For our words and thoughts and attitudes,
All our novelties and platitudes,
Will be Rather Ancient History in 2033.

Will they find us wise—or silly?
Looking backwards, willy-nilly,
At our queer old-fashioned costumes and our quaint old-fashioned ways?
When our doings face the ages,
Printed down on textbook pages,
Will they cry, "This Savage Era"? Will they sigh, "Those were the days!"?

I don't know—you may be wiser.
Time's a curious capsizer
Of a lot of reputations that seemed certain to endure,
While he'll sometimes make his heroes
Out of people, once thought zeroes,
For the most well-grounded reasons, by the solemnly cocksure.

So, instead of prophesying
(Which is fun, but rather trying)
Who they'll pick to be our great ones when the books are on
the shelves,
Here's the marching panorama
Of our past and present drama
—And we shan't know all the answers till we're history, ourselves.

Stephen Vincent Benét

To Silence Any Song

A Minor Bird

I have wished a bird would fly away,
And not sing by my house all day;

Have clapped my hands at him from the door
When it seemed as if I could bear no more.

The fault must partly have been in me.
The bird was not to blame for his key.

And of course there must be something wrong
In wanting to silence any song.

Robert Frost

Fox at Midnight

Betsy Byars

At first Tom did not like the idea of spending his summer at Aunt Millie's farm. He was sure that he would not like animals and that they would not like him. But one day, while wandering in the woods, he saw a beautiful black fox running through the grass. Tom found where the fox lived, and he spent much of his time secretly watching her play with her baby. The following story begins near the end of Tom's summer.

We went into the house and I said to Uncle Fred, "What are you going to do with the baby fox?"

"That's my bait. Every hunter alive's got some way to get a fox. They got some special trap or something. Mr. Baynes down at the store makes up a special mixture that he says foxes can't resist. My way is to set up a trap, using the baby fox for bait. I'll sit out on the back porch tonight and watch for her."

"Oh."

"It never fails. That is one bait a fox can't resist."

"Are you getting sick?" Aunt Millie asked at supper that night.

"I guess I'm a little tired."

"Well, I should think so! Helping with the pump out in the broiling sun all morning and then tracking that fox all afternoon. It's a wonder you don't have heatstroke. You eat something though, hear? You have to keep up your strength."

"I'm just not hungry."

"It's the heat. But, listen, you drink your tea. You *will* have heatstroke sure enough if you let your body get dried out."

I finished my tea and went up to my room. I did not even look out the window, because I knew I could see the rabbit hutch by the garage, and I never again wanted to see that baby fox cowering against the wall.

Hazeline came out of her room and looked in at me on the bed. "You feeling better?"

I nodded. She was all dressed up now in a blue dress she had made for 4-H. Her face looked good, as if letting it get swollen had been beneficial. I knew she was going downstairs to sit on the porch and wait for Mikey. I knew he would come, too. One time Petie and I had had the worst argument in the world. We were just sitting on the steps one afternoon and Petie had been thinking in silence for a while and then he said, "I wonder what I'll look like when I'm grown."

And I said, "Porky Pig." I don't know why I said that, because I wasn't mad at him or anything. And he said, "Well, that's better than looking like Daffy Duck." And I said, "Meaning *I* look like Daffy Duck?" And he said, "Yes, around the mouth." And then we both got angry and started screaming things and I thought our friendship was over, only two days later it was just like it had never happened.

"Mikey will come over," I said.

"Who cares? I don't care if I never see him again," she said, twisting her fingers in her pearls. He had given her those when she had graduated from high school two months ago.

"I know, but I bet he comes anyway."

"Well, I can't stop him of course. It's a free country."

"Hazeline?"

"What?"

"You know that fox I was telling you about? The black one?"

"Sure."

"Well, your dad has her baby out in the rabbit hutch and he's going to shoot her."

"I know it. I heard. But, listen, don't let it upset you, hear?"

"Hazeline, I don't want anything to happen to that fox."

"Tommy, listen, all wild animals die in some violent way. It's their life. Wild animals just don't die of old age. They get killed by an enemy or by the weather or they have an accident or they get rabies or some other disease or they get shot. That's the way nature is."

"I know that," I said quickly, because I did not want to hear any more.

"You just forget the fox. Tomorrow maybe we can go to the picture show in Clinton or something."

"All right."

She went down the steps then and out onto the porch, and I could hear the swing begin to creak.

I got up and went down the steps and walked to the tree in front of the rabbit hutch. I could not explain why I did this. I didn't want to see the baby fox again, and yet here I was.

He did not see me. He was busy biting the wires of his cage with great fury and determination. I could hear the clicking of his sharp tiny teeth against the wire, but he was making no progress. Then he stopped. He still had not seen me, but he had heard or smelled something, and he raised his head and let out a short cry. He waited; then after a moment he began biting the wires again.

I remained by the tree watching him, listening for the quavering cry that he uttered from time to time.

"Don't get your fingers in the cage," Uncle Fred warned

behind me. "He may not be able to cut wire yet, but he sure could hurt a finger."

"All right."

"In a bit, when it starts getting dark, you can sit up here with me and watch for the fox."

A car came slowly up the drive, and I said to Uncle Fred, "It's Mikey."

Behind him in the doorway Aunt Millie said, "Did you say it's Mikey, Tom?"

I nodded.

"Praise be."

I walked around the front of the house and stood there for a minute. Mikey had not gotten out of the car but was sitting with one arm out the window, looking at Hazeline on the porch.

"What you doing?" he asked.

"Not much of anything," she said. "Just fighting the heat."

"You don't look hot—you look real good and cool."

"Sometimes looks are deceiving."

He ran his fingers over the steering wheel. There was a pause; then he said, "Do you want to ride up to the lake?"

"I don't know."

"When you going to make up your mind?"

"I just don't know whether I feel like looking at boats racing all over creation tonight."

"Do you want to go for a ride?"

"I don't know."

"I'll give you"—he looked at his watch—"one minute to make up your mind."

He started watching the seconds tick off, and I held up my watch too and counted, and only eleven seconds had gone by when Hazeline got up and said, "I'll go," and started laughing. "Tell Mom I'm going off with Mikey," she said over her shoulder and got in the car.

I went into the kitchen where Aunt Millie was standing in front of the electric fan and said, "Hazeline has gone off with Mikey."

I heard the cry of the baby fox again, and I thought I would be hearing that sound forever. One time Petie Burkis fell down and broke his leg on the school playground and he said, "Oh!" in this real terrible, painful way, and I never could forget it. Later I tried to make him say it again that same way, and one whole afternoon Petie did nothing but say the word *Oh* over and over—a thousand times maybe—and in all those thousand tries, he never sounded that same way again. I still remember it though, exactly, like I will always remember the way that baby fox sounded when he cried.

It seemed to get dark quickly that night. Uncle Fred was already out on the back porch. He had brought out a chair and was sitting with his gun beside him, pointing to the floor. I never saw anyone sit any quieter. You wouldn't have noticed him at all he was so still.

I stood behind him inside the screen door. Through the screen I could see the tiny fox lift his black nose and cry again. Now, for the first time, there was an answer—the bark of his mother.

I looked toward the garden, because that's where the sound had come from, but Uncle Fred did not even turn his head. In a frenzy now that he had heard his mother, the baby fox moved about the cage, pulling at the wire and crying again and again.

Just then there was the sound of thunder from the west, a long rolling sound, and Aunt Millie came to the door beside me and said, "Bless me, is that thunder?" She looked out at the sky. "Was that thunder, Fred?"

"Could be," he said without moving.

"Look!" Aunt Millie said. "I swear I see black clouds. You see, Tom?"

"Yes'm."

"And feel that breeze. Honestly, when you think you have reached absolutely the end of your endurance, then the breeze comes. I could not have drawn one more breath of hot air, and now we are going to have a storm."

We stood in the doorway, feeling the breeze, forgetting for a moment the baby fox.

Then I saw Uncle Fred's gun rise ever so slightly in the direction of the fence behind the garage. I could not see any sign of the fox, but I knew that she must be there. Uncle Fred would not be wrong.

The breeze quickened, and abruptly the dishpan which Aunt Millie had left on the porch railing clattered to the

floor. For the first time Uncle Fred turned his head and looked in annoyance at the pan and then at Aunt Millie.

"Did it scare your fox off?" she asked.

He nodded, then shifted in the chair and said, "She'll be back."

In just this short time the sky to the west had gotten black as ink. Low on the horizon, forks of lightning streaked the sky.

"Now, Fred, don't you sit out here while it's thundering and lightning. I mean it. No fox is worth getting struck by lightning for."

He nodded, and she turned to me and said, "You come on and help me shut the windows. Some of those upstairs are stuck wide open. Just hit them with the heel of your hand on the side till you can get them down."

I started up the stairs and she said again, "Fred, come on in when it starts storming. That fox'll be back tomorrow night too."

I went upstairs and started hitting the sides of the windows. I had just gotten one window to jerk down about two inches when I heard the gunshot. I had never heard any worse sound in my life. It was a very final sound, like the most enormous period in the world. Bam. Period. The end.

I ran out of my room and down the steps so fast I could not even tell you how many times my feet touched the stairs, none maybe. I went out the back door, opening it so fast I hit the back of Uncle Fred's chair. I looked toward the rabbit hutch, said, "Where?" then looked at the back fence. Then I looked down at Uncle Fred, who was doing something with his gun.

"Missed," he said.

Suddenly I felt weak. My legs were like two pieces of rope, like that trick that Hindu magicians do when they make rope come straight up out of a basket and then say a magic word and make the rope collapse. My legs felt like they were going to collapse at any second. I managed to force these two pieces of rope to carry me up the stairs and into the room.

I closed two windows, and the third one, in sympathy perhaps, just banged down all by itself. Then I sank to the bed.

I had no intention of going to sleep when I lay down on the bed; I did not think I would ever be able to sleep again, but that is what I did. I fell right asleep and did not even move until four hours later when I awoke. It was one o'clock in the morning.

The storm was in full force, or perhaps it was a second storm, but the house was quiet. I got up and went out into the hall. I could not hear anything but the sound of the rain and Hazeline's transistor radio, which was sputtering with static beside her on the pillow.

I went down the stairs, one by one. I did not make a sound. I stepped on the part of the steps near the wall because Petie

had told me that was how burglars go up stairs unheard. I was just stepping into the hall, when without warning, the hall light went on. Aunt Millie was standing there in her bathrobe, squinting at me.

"What's wrong?" she asked.

"Nothing. I just didn't know what time it was."

"Well"—she looked closely at her watch—"it's just past one o'clock."

"I went to sleep in my clothes."

"Well, you get on your pajamas and get back to bed. This is the first good sleeping night we've had, and you mustn't let it go to waste."

"Sure."

"Well, go on back up the steps." She watched me go up two steps and then she said, "Goodness, we've gotten on so well all summer, I'd hate for anything to happen now right before your parents get home."

"Aunt Millie, did Uncle Fred get the fox?"

"No."

"Is he still out on the porch?"

"In this rain? No, he is fast asleep in his bed like you ought to be."

She waited until I was up the stairs and then she turned out the light. I went into my room and she called, "Are you getting in bed?"

I lay down. "Yes."

"And go to sleep."

I lay in bed for a long time, still in my clothes, and then I got up very carefully. I walked over to the window and looked out at the tree. Bubba and Fred Jr. used to just run up and down all the time like monkeys. I could imagine them climbing up, laughing and brown, racing, going out on all sorts of perilous limbs just to be first at the window. I opened the window, pushed out the screen, reached out into the rain, and felt for the smooth spot Aunt Millie had told me was worn into the bark of the tree.

I took off my shoes and knelt on the windowsill. There was an enormous flash of lightning that turned the whole world white for a moment, and then I climbed out onto the nearest branch and circled the trunk round with my arms.

I thought that I could never get one step farther. I thought that I could never move even one muscle or I would fall. I thought that in the morning when Aunt Millie came up to see why I wasn't at breakfast, she would find me here, pressed into the tree, still frozen with fear.

The rain was hard and slanting directly into my face. Finally I got up just enough courage to turn my face out of the rain. Then the lightning flashed again and I saw the ground about a million miles below. I held the tree so tightly the bark was cutting into my cheek.

I don't know how long I stayed that way. If I had tried

to look at my watch, just that little movement would have thrown me off balance. After a while, though, I began to sort of slip down the tree. I never let go of the main trunk for a second. I just moved my arms downward in very small movements. Then, slowly, when I was practically kneeling on the first limb, I let my foot reach down for the next one.

If there were smooth spots on those branches, my feet never found them. They only touched one rough limb after another as, slowly, I kept inching down the tree, feeling my way, never looking down at the ground until, finally, my foot reached out for another limb and felt the cold wet grass. It shocked me for a moment and then I jumped down, landing on my hands and knees.

I got up and ran to the rabbit hutch. The baby fox was huddled in one corner of the pen where there was some shelter from the rain. The lightning flashed and I saw him watching me.

"I'm going to get you out," I said.

He crouched back farther in the hutch. In the next flash of lightning, I looked on the ground for a rock and I saw at my feet a small dead frog. I knew that the black fox in all this rain had brought that frog here to her baby. She was right now watching me somewhere.

There were bricks stacked in a neat pile under the hutch, and I took one and began to bang it against the lock. I was prepared to do this all night if necessary, but the lock was an old one and it opened right away.

The noise had scared the baby fox, and he was now making a whimpering sound. I unhooked the broken lock, opened the cage, and stepped back against the tree.

The baby fox did not move for a moment. I could barely

see him, a small dark ball in the back of the cage. He waited, alert and suspicious, and then after a moment he moved in a crouch to the door of the cage. He cried sharply. From the bushes there was an answering bark.

He crouched lower. The lightning flashed again, and in that second he jumped and ran in the direction of the bushes. He barked as he ran. There was an immediate answer, and then only the sound of the rain. I waited against the tree, thinking about them, and then I heard the black fox bark one more time as she ran though the orchard with her baby.

And I thought, Someday I will be in a famous museum, walking along on the marble floors, looking at paintings. There will be one called "Blue Flowers" and I will look at that for a while, and the next one will be "Woman on the Beach" and I will look at that for a while, and then I will glance at the name of the next painting and it will be "Fox with Baby at Midnight," and I will look up and my heart will stop beating because there it will be, just the way it was this night, the black fox and her baby running beneath the wet ghostly apple trees toward a patch of light in the distance. And I thought, leaning against that tree in the rain, If there is a picture like that, I hope sometime I will get to see it.

Suddenly the rain began to slacken and I walked around the house. I had never been so wet in my life, and now that it was over, I was cold too. And I was tired. I looked up at the tree, and there didn't seem to be any point in climbing back up when in just a few hours everyone would know what I had done anyway. I went up on the porch and rang the doorbell.

In all my life I have never felt so dumb and foolish as I did barefooted, soaking wet on that slick porch at two o'clock in the morning, waiting for someone to come and answer the door.

It was Aunt Millie in her cotton robe who turned on the porch light and peered out through the side windows at me.

I must have been an awful sight, like the poor little match girl, for she flung open the door at once and drew me in.

"What are you doing out there? What are you doing?"

"Who is it?" Uncle Fred asked as he came into the hall. He was pulling his pants up over his pajamas.

"It's Tom," Aunt Millie said.

"I meant who's at the door."

"Tom," she said again.

"Tom?"

"Yes, he was just standing out there on the porch."

They both turned and looked at me, waiting for an explanation, and I cleared my throat and said, "Uncle Fred and Aunt Millie, I am awfully sorry but I have let the baby fox out of the rabbit hutch." I sounded very stiff and formal, and I thought the voice was a terrible thing to have to depend on, because I really did want them to know that I was sorry, and I didn't sound it the least bit. I knew how much Uncle Fred had looked forward to the hunt and how important getting rid of the fox was to Aunt Millie, and I hated for them to be disappointed now.

There was a moment of silence. Then Aunt Millie said, "Why, that's perfectly all right, isn't it, Fred? Don't you think another thing about that. You just come on to bed. You're going to get pneumonia standing there in that puddle." She started for the linen closet. "I'll get you some towels."

Uncle Fred and I were left in the hall alone and I looked

up at him and he looked like an enormous blue-eyed Indian.

"I'm sorry," I said again.

He looked at me and I knew he was seeing through all the very casual questions I had been asking all summer about foxes, and seeing through the long days I had spent in the woods. He was remembering the sorry way I had tried to keep him from finding the fox's den and the way I had looked when we did find it. I think all those pieces just snapped into place right then in Uncle Fred's mind, and I knew that if there was one person in the world who understood me it was this man who had seemed such a stranger.

He cleared his throat. "I never liked to see wild things in a pen myself," he said.

Aunt Millie came down the hall and threw a towel over my head and started rubbing. "Now get upstairs. I am not going to have you lying in bed with pneumonia when your mother arrives."

We went upstairs, she rubbing my head the whole way, me stumbling over the steps, and Hazeline calling from her room, "Who was that at the door?"

"Tom," Aunt Millie said.

"Who?"

"Me," I said.

"Oh."

We went into my room. "There," Aunt Millie exclaimed at the sight of my open window, "I knew it! I knew you'd be out there on that tree at the first opportunity." She shut the window with a bang. "There is no explaining a boy."

She turned down my bed, went out, and came back with a glass of milk.

"I'm sorry about your turkey and hen," I said.

"Oh, that! I bet you think I'm awful, carrying on the way I did."

"No."

"It was more the heat than anything else, like Fred said. Just don't think about it any more. That fox and her baby are miles away from here now, and they'll never come back to bother my birds. That's one thing about a fox. He learns."

She turned out the light, said, "It is starting to rain again. I declare we are going to be flooded out," and then went downstairs.

Afterthought

1. Reread Hazeline's statement about "the way nature is." In what ways do you agree or disagree with it?
2. Why did Tom free the baby fox?
3. Why were Aunt Millie and Uncle Fred not angry with Tom for freeing the baby fox?

The Balance of Nature

In "Fox at Midnight" a boy saved the life of a wild animal. Perhaps you have heard somebody say he would like to save the lives of all animals that face death. Do you think such a person knows very much about the way nature works? The following article will help you answer this question.

Scientists are aware of a system at work among living things. In this system the number and kinds of plants and animals in a given area remain fairly stable. All animals and plants within the area depend upon each other for the necessities of life. When all goes well, nature remains in balance.

The Food Chain

One very important part of the balance of nature is the food chain. All living things must eat in order to stay alive. Plants and their seeds are the food of many animals. And these animals in turn become the food of other animals.

For example, picture a frog sitting on a stone. He seems to be asleep, but he is really waiting for something to eat. Suddenly he flicks out his long tongue and catches a fly. Again and again his tongue darts out, catching more flies. The frog gulps them down and sits still again, waiting for more food. Then, without warning, a snake glides up behind the frog and swallows him. Later a hawk swoops down, grabs the snake, and eats it. This is the way the food chain works.

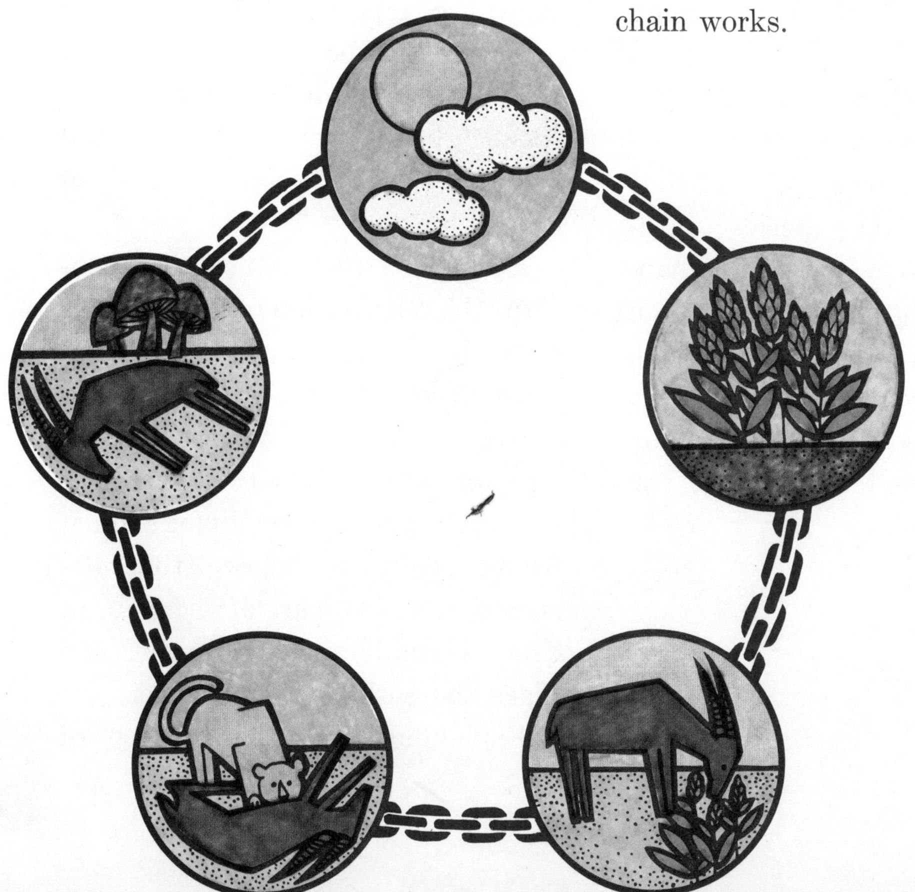

Animals that use other animals for food help to maintain the balance of nature. Natural enemies eat enough wildlife to prevent any species from becoming so numerous as to endanger other groups. Usually, enough creatures of each kind stay alive to prevent the species from becoming extinct. Natural enemies also help prevent some animals from becoming so numerous that they eat all the plants needed for food by other wildlife.

Among other effects upon the balance of nature are water supply, climate, and disease. Such natural disasters as flood, fire, and drought can upset this balance. Sometimes a disaster may kill many animals, thus allowing a surviving species to become too numerous. When this happens, many of the survivors will then die because there will not be enough food for all of them. Once the balance of nature is upset in an area, many years must pass before things can return to normal.

People and Nature

Sometimes nature must have the help of people if it is to regain its balance in a certain area or among certain species of animals. This is usually necessary when we ourselves have destroyed the balance. The people who are most concerned with this problem are conservationists and ecologists.

The meaning of *conserve* is "to protect or keep safe." A conservationist is a person who works to protect our natural resources and to help us make wise use of them. Insects, fish, reptiles, birds, and mammals are all part of our natural resources. Wildlife conservationists spend their lives protecting and helping these different forms of animal life.

Ecology is the science that concerns the relationship of living things to their surroundings, or environment. Ecologists are aware that no creature can exist alone. Each is part of a great web of life that includes every other living thing. Many ecologists believe that destruction of any part of the web, or even a sudden change in it, can place the entire web in danger.

Explaining how the balance of

nature works is one of the most important jobs of conservationists and ecologists. They realize that most of the harm man has done to nature is the result of ignorance. They are convinced that the more information people have about the balance of nature, the less likely they are to upset it.

Cycle

Cats
swallow
barley
corns
hollowed
out
from
within
by
busy
weevil
kin
(bent
on
raising
more
young
weevils
to
devour
more
nice
barley
corns)
chewed
up
without
salt
by
mice
thinking
them
not
empty
shells
but
solid
food
for
building
juicy
sweet
mouse
meat
which
when
all's
done
hungry
cats
may
eat
where
if
and
when
cats
swallow
barley
corns
hollowed
out
from
within
by
busy
weevil
kin
(bent
on
raising
more
young
weevils
to
devour
more
nice
barley
corns)
chewed
up
without
salt
by
mice.

John Moffitt

Lessons in Balance

Ron Krajnovich

This article will show you nature in and out of balance.

The big mountain lion crouched low to the ground. She had suddenly come upon a small herd of mule deer. Her nose wrinkled slowly as she caught the scent of the deer. Except for an occasional twitch of the tip of her tail, not a muscle of the cat's large body moved.

Slowly a broad paw inched forward and settled without a sound on the bed of pine needles. A few more quiet steps brought her to a hiding place behind a large piñon tree. The mighty cat was now in position for her strike.

Occasionally a deer raised its head from where it grazed on the tender spring leaves. Ears alert, it listened for enemies. The wind was blowing toward the mountain lion, and the deer did not smell the cat's scent. The closest deer was a young doe. She continued to eat, unaware of the approach of danger.

Suddenly the cat sprang from her hiding place. In three swift, powerful leaps she covered the distance between herself and the deer. Her sharp teeth and claws killed the doe instantly.

As the drumming hoofbeats of the survivors faded in the distance, the mother cat dragged her heavy load to the edge of some thick underbrush. Here she lay to dine on her fresh meal. She finished quickly and covered her half-eaten prize with leaves and twigs to hide it for a later meal.

The cat then hurried off to a

nearby cave high on the rim of a deep canyon. Upon her arrival three small balls of fur tumbled out to greet her. As she flopped down at the den's entrance, her hungry kittens drank greedily of her warm milk.

This mountain lion family lived in a cave overlooking the famous Grand Canyon of northern Arizona. A century ago, before many white men had come to this part of the Southwest, there were hundreds of mountain lions. They fed on thousands of mule deer in the area and kept the deer from growing too numerous. A balance existed between these predators and their prey. There were about 200 deer (prey) for every mountain lion (predator).

The cats would usually kill only the very young deer or the very old or injured ones because they were the easiest to catch. In this way the strong deer were left to make up healthy herds. On the average a mountain lion would kill a deer every other day, or about 180 deer each year. With the help of other predators, the mountain lions kept the size of the herd stable.

Then man entered the picture. President Theodore Roosevelt, who had hunted mountain lions near the Grand Canyon, decided that the areas surrounding the Canyon should be set aside for the protection of game animals. He wanted to preserve the splendid herd of mule deer that lived there. In 1906 President Roosevelt created the Grand Canyon National Game Preserve. The forest in which the deer thrived is called the Kaibab National Forest.

Shortly after the Kaibab was set aside, men moved into the area, bringing cattle, sheep, and horses with them. The mountain lions sometimes found these animals easier to catch than the swift deer on which they usually fed. The ranchers decided that it would be easier to kill the cats than try to protect their livestock. Because of this and because President Roosevelt wanted to increase the size of the deer herd, the mountain lions were hunted as dangerous, unwanted killers of game and livestock. It did not seem to occur to the hunters that with the lions gone the balance of nature in the forest would be upset.

Before many years had passed, almost all the predators in the Kaibab National Forest were killed by bounty hunters. These men were paid a fee by the government for every mountain lion, bobcat, coyote, or wolf they killed. Within twenty-five years government hunters had shot, poisoned, or trapped 4,849 coyotes, 781 mountain lions, 554 bobcats, and 30 gray wolves.*

With the predators largely gone, the once stable deer herd began to grow. In fewer than ten years the number of deer in the park doubled. In two more years it had doubled again. Between 1907 and 1923—the years in which the greatest number of mountain lions were killed—the deer population grew from about 4,000 to an estimated 100,000. Some sightseers described watching nearly 2,000 deer in one meadow. The visitors enjoyed seeing all these animals, but not many people understood what was happening to the land.

The normal food of deer is browse, the tender leaves of shrubs and trees. The large numbers of deer were eating their food faster than it could grow back. Browse was eaten from every tree and shrub in the forest. The deer killed the small trees and shrubs by completely stripping off all the leaves. The larger trees were cleared of all the branches and leaves the deer could reach. Grass was also grazed to the bare ground. With the undergrowth gone, the forest became a wasteland where nothing but tall trees grew.

Having no browse to eat, the deer became thinner and thinner. They were slowly starving to death. As winter approached, they began to die by the thousands. During the next few years a large percentage of the deer herd was completely eliminated from the forest.

The number of animals that can find adequate food in an area is called the carrying capacity of that area. Today the size of the Kaibab deer herd is kept within the carrying capacity of the forest through regulated sport hunting. Certain kinds of deer can be shot at certain times of the year. The Kaibab herd has remained stable for a number of years under the watchful eyes of the forest rangers. But is it too late to bring back the predators and a natural balance to the area?

Not too many years ago a natural balance developed on Isle Royale, a 210-square-mile island in the northern part of Lake Superior. Here a herd of moose had grown so large that there was not enough food for all of them. Many were sick and

*From *The Kaibab North Deer Herd—Its History, Problems and Management* by John R. Russo, Wildlife Bulletin No. 7, 1970, Phoenix, Arizona.

starving. These great beasts, which can grow nearly eight feet tall at the shoulder and weigh as much as 1800 pounds, had few natural enemies strong enough to keep their numbers stable. With no predators around, the moose herd quickly exceeded the carrying capacity of the island.

Fortunately, a pack of Canadian timber wolves reached Isle Royale. They crossed over to the island in the middle of winter, when ice forms a bridge with the mainland. The wolves were meat eaters, and they found ample food among the weak, sick moose.

After a few years the number of wolves on the island had increased to approximately twenty-five. By hunting in packs, they were able to kill enough moose to feed themselves. Enough wolves were born each year to replace the ones that died of old age or were killed by natural enemies. According to conservationists who work on Isle Royale, the number of wolves there has become stable.

The moose herd has been much

better off since the arrival of the wolves. The size of the herd is stable at about 700 moose; the herd no longer exceeds the carrying capacity of the island. The trees, shrubs, and other plants on the island now have time to grow, thus providing adequate browse for the moose. The herd is healthier than before and is also younger because the wolves kill off the old and weak animals. Conservationists who study the moose on Isle Royale say that very few of them have died from disease or lack of food since the timber wolves came to the island.

What has happened in the Kaibab National Forest and on Isle Royale is an excellent lesson in ecological balance. Where natural predators have not been allowed to flourish, regulated hunting has become the accepted method of controlling the population of their prey. But, as on Isle Royale, where predators and their prey stay in balance, the predators should be allowed to live.

The Work of Insects

F. C. Smith

Insects play an important part in the balance of nature. When attempts are made to destroy some of these tiny creatures, unexpected things can happen.

A famous insect scientist has said that there are one hundred times as many *kinds* of insects in the world as there are single stars which you can see in the sky—and those are countless. Insects seem to be everywhere in the world around us. They are different from most other animal life because they go through several forms as they grow. A baby deer or rabbit looks something like its parents, but a butterfly, for example, was once a caterpillar.

The lives of the millions of insects in all their forms are closely bound up with plants. Plants provide food for most kinds of insects, at least when they are young. Caterpillars, cutworms, grubs, beetles, grasshoppers, aphids, and many others eat leaves, stems, plant juices, or roots. Bees, butterflies, and young wasps use nectar, the sweet juice of flowers, for making food. And some insects devour the insects which are plant eaters.

Plants furnish homes for many insects. Twenty thousand tiny plant lice, or aphids, may live on one tree. A young praying mantis makes its home in a bush on the underside of a branch, and many caterpillars do, also. Tent caterpillars build white webs in wild cherries or other trees. Some insects hide their eggs in little bumps on leaves or stems of plants until they hatch. Even wasps use wood from plants to make the paper with which they build their homes.

Many insects can hide themselves perfectly on plants, and so find protection from enemies. Green aphids or grasshoppers can scarcely be seen against leaves and stems. The insect called a walking stick looks almost exactly like a brown twig.

But insects help plants, too. Without them, many plants could not produce fruits or some of our common vegetables. In fact, without help from bees, moths, and butterflies, some green plants would disappear from the earth. This is why: Within flowers is a fine yellow dust called pollen. In order to form seeds and produce more flowers and fruit from year to year, plants must pass this pollen from blossom to blossom. But flowers have no way of carrying pollen. Wind blows some of it from one blossom to another, but not all plants are able to catch wind-borne pollen. Insects carry the pollen of some kinds of plants directly from one blossom to another.

A bee lights on a flower to draw nectar from it and also to gather pollen, both of which it uses in making food. As the bee clings to the flower, yellow pollen sticks to the fine hairs of its legs and body. As the bee flies from blossom to blossom to draw more nectar, pollen from one flower rubs off on other flowers. So pollen spreads, making it possible for flowers to form fruit and seeds and produce new plants. Bees are by far the most important insect carriers of pollen. Some large fruit-growers keep honeybee hives in their orchards so that the bees will work there to keep the orchards bearing fruit each season.

Termites are tiny, antlike insects which almost constantly chew wood. Inside the termites live even smaller animals which change the wood into chemicals that the termites can digest. Termites can chew so much wood from a fence or a set of porch steps, or sometimes even the walls of a building, that it will fall down. But in the forests termites give useful service. Termites and wood-eating beetles help plants like bacteria and fungi to break down all kinds of dead plant matter into chemicals which can be reused in the soil and air. Bodies of dead insects, especially ants, also help enrich the soil, returning chemicals to it.

Many insects are little plows, or even little bulldozers. Ants and beetles which live in the ground make tunnels and holes. These openings allow air and water to enter the soil and help plants to grow. Ants burrow energetically. They bring deep-down soil up nearer the top where it can receive chemicals and become fertile for raising more plants. Ants are small but so numerous that they accomplish much.

When a robin sings outside your window, you can be glad that there are insects. Insects furnish food for thousands of birds and for some other forms of life including spiders, toads, snakes, and some four-footed animals.

They even furnish food for other insects. Ants get some food from the tiny plant lice called aphids. Ants do not eat these lice, but take from them a sweet liquid which the aphids make from plant juices that are their food. When an ant strokes an aphid with its feelers, the aphid releases a drop of this sweet juice called honeydew. The ant drinks this or even stores it in its extra stomach to carry back to other ants in the burrow. The insects who do this work are called ant cowherds. They actually take care of the aphids, sometimes carry them to pasture from plant to plant, and fight off the aphids' insect enemies.

This ant-aphid combination may not seem good for people, because aphids destroy some plants. But usually the work the ants do for the soil repays both plants and people.

From the point of view of human beings, some insects are harmful and some are helpful. Insects don't purposely decide which to be. They merely do things naturally, in a way that enables them to go on living. Sometimes they eat the fruit or grain that farmers raise, or like the malaria mosquito, they carry disease. Then men call them harmful. But many insect pests have developed because people have upset the natural relations of plant and insect life. And even though some insects are harmful at times, they all play their important part in nature, where every living thing is connected in some way with other living things.

Conservationists are working to learn the best ways of managing insect life. Like all other living things, insects grow in greater or fewer numbers according to the food supply

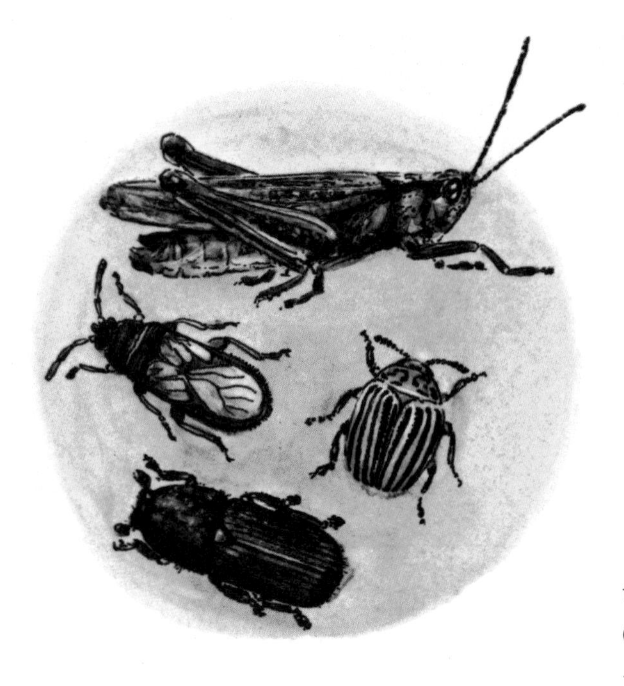

they can find. A meadow or woodland supplies food for fewer insects of one kind than the same land in grain. When men began to change woods and grasslands into great fields of cultivated grains and vegetables, some insects which ate these became so numerous that they were a pest. Grasshoppers sometimes stripped cornfields of leaves. Chinch bugs ate the wheat crops. Potato bugs feasted on acres of potato plants, boll weevils destroyed cotton, and borers grew plentifully in apple orchards. We are still trying to find ways of keeping some insects in check and using the help of others.

Have you ever heard the roar of an airplane and looked up to see a daring pilot flying back and forth dangerously low over a field or an orchard? That was a crop duster. The cloud of dust shooting from his plane was a chemical to kill insects that were damaging valuable crops. Other ways of killing insects are by trapping them, by destroying their breeding grounds, and by making use of their natural enemies.

Spraying poison is the most common way of killing insects, and it is sometimes a good way in cultivated fields and orchards. But farmers must be careful in the use of poisons. For they may also kill off too many of the insect pests' natural enemies, such as insect-eating birds, toads, or fish.

People think that little good can be said for mosquitoes. Indeed, in the arctic regions during summer and in some other places they are a dangerous pest, and in the tropics one kind carries the disease malaria. Yet mosquitoes in both the young and grown-up stages furnish food for many kinds of fish and birds, particularly for waterfowl in northern lakes and marshes, and for rare birds and valuable fish in southern and coastal swamps. In controlling mosquitoes, we must think of the natural environment and of all its wildlife.

In one large Florida swamp, men sprayed the water with poison for three years to kill mosquitoes. But dragonflies, birds, fish, and snakes—all mosquito-eaters—were also killed. In the third year more mosquitoes were there than in the first year. It is possible that some mosquitoes get so used to poison that it cannot kill them, but in this case ecologists believe that nature's mosquito controls—insects, birds, fish, and snakes—had kept the mosquitoes down better by eating them than the poison alone could do. The few mosquitoes that escaped the poison at first bred and multiplied in greater numbers than ever, with their natural enemies gone.

In some places it may be necessary to destroy the breeding grounds of mosquitoes by draining marshes and ponds, but draining too many of them may damage the underground water-storage places.

Natural mosquito eaters which you may see in your own yards and gardens are birds, bats, snakes, spiders, dragonflies, and praying mantises. These should not be killed.

Nor should the insects themselves be killed except when they become dangerous to us. Conservationists have found out that these tiny creatures play an important part in the total plan of nature. If we destroy even one species of insect, we run the risk of upsetting nature's delicate balance.

The Measure of Man

It has been estimated that
the most medium living thing
standing
exactly halfway in between
the smallest crawling gnat
and the tallest spouting
giant blue whale
is
man.

Of course on a different scale
say
ability to create
or greater yet
annihilate
there's
nothing
halfway
about him.

Eve Merriam

Their Time Is Running Out

George Laycock

Too often our relationship with wildlife has been careless and even destructive. But lately we have learned that there are ways to make up for some of the harm we have caused.

If you were to sit very quietly in a prairie dog town in South Dakota late in the evening, and if you were lucky, you would be one of the few living people ever to see the black-footed ferret. This member of the weasel family is one of the world's rarest animals. It is so rare that wildlife scientists know it is very close to extinction.

Its legs are short, and its long, thin body is like a fur-covered sausage. It has a small, rounded head with sparkling little dark eyes covered by a black mask.

What has brought the black-footed ferret so near the end of his days on earth? For one thing, he can't live unless he has prairie dogs around for neighbors. He lives in their burrows, and when he gets hungry he eats a prairie dog.

Also playing a part in the story of the ferret were great wandering herds of shaggy buffalo. They grazed across the plains and helped keep the grass short. Short grass was better than tall grass for prairie dogs. The buffalo was good for the prairie dog, and the prairie dog was good for the black-footed ferret.

Then along came man, who was not especially good for any of them. He swept across the grasslands through the heart of the country. First he killed the buffalo by the millions, until he had almost killed off the last of them. Next he began poisoning the prairie dogs. Today ranchers and farmers still spread poisoned food around prairie dog towns. They claim that the prairie dogs eat grass that sheep should get and that the burrows might break a horse's leg. All this is sad news for the ferrets as well as for the fat little prairie dogs.

Unless the ferret's luck changes soon, he may become nothing but a memory. His name may go down alongside the passenger pigeon and the Carolina parakeet, birds that are gone forever.

The black-footed ferret has a lot of company on the list of rare and endangered wildlife. In the last 400 years, which is not long as natural events go, the world has seen many kinds of mammals and birds pass into extinction. Today there are dozens of species of mammals, birds, and other animals close to the same fate. Some conservationists believe that one out of every forty of the world's higher animals is so rare that its name belongs on the danger list.

Our record in the United States is one of the worst. In North America during the last two centuries more wild creatures have become extinct or have come close to extinction than on any other continent. Within those 200 years we have watched as a dozen kinds of birds vanished from the scene. Included, besides the passenger pigeon and the flashy little green and yellow Carolina parakeet, were the heath hen and the great auk.

Meanwhile, grizzly bears have disappeared from state after state until perhaps only 850 remain today south of Canada. In the Arctic the great white polar bear is in danger. And in their ranges so are wolves, cougars, eagles, ospreys, pelicans, whooping cranes, and many other wild creatures.

Animals that live in the rivers and oceans have not escaped the danger list either. To the sorrow of salmon fishermen everywhere, the Atlantic salmon has its name on the United States government's official list of rare and endangered wildlife. This fish spends much of its life growing to weights of ten to fifteen pounds in the open ocean. Then it moves into the streams to lay its eggs. Pollution and dams have caused it serious trouble in many of the streams of New England.

But in the last few years Atlantic salmon have also faced other threats. Ships have recently searched out the salmon while they are in the open oceans. With drift nets and long lines carrying thousands of hooks, they have brought salmon into their boats by the tons. In the fishing streams of both Canada and Great Britain, fishermen no longer catch salmon in the numbers they once did. And conservationists now speak often of the Atlantic salmon's slide toward extinction.

Many of the great whales of the

open oceans are also disappearing rapidly. Among them are the Atlantic right whale, the Pacific right whale, and the bowhead whale. Included is the giant of them all, the blue whale, the largest animal ever to live on earth. So far, rules on taking these ocean giants have not saved them.

Still another endangered animal of the open oceans is the green turtle, which reaches weights of 300 pounds or more. Except in Hawaii, green turtles are almost extinct from the beaches of the United States. What brings the big turtle to troubled waters? Partly it is the fact that the females must come ashore to lay their eggs in the sand, where local people near the beaches hunt the eggs and rob the nests. Also, many of the turtle's nesting beaches have been taken over for homes, hotels, and swimming beaches.

How have we managed in so few years to make life impossible for so many of the wild animals we found here? First of all, we have changed the wild areas in which they live. Where the woodland animals depended on the trees for food and shelter, we cut down the forests. Then we burned and plowed the prairies. Next we drained and farmed the marshes, and dammed the streams to flood the green valleys. We ran chemicals, soil, and sewage into the rivers and oceans. We even filled in areas where rivers flow into the sea—areas that had been nature's cradle for sea fish and the small creatures on which they live.

At the same time we were attacking many kinds of wildlife directly. In the early days of our country there were few laws to protect our wildlife. Buffalo were shot by the thousands, sometimes just for their tongues. Birds were killed to get feathers for decorating ladies' hats. Eskimo curlews, heading south for the winter, were shot and hauled off to market by the wagonload. Prairie chickens and passenger pigeons were carted off by the barrel.

More recently, alligators have been killed illegally at night. Their skins are sold to make shoes and fancy handbags. In Africa hunters are killing off the last of the big leopards. This, too, is against the law.

In these cases it is not the law-abiding hunter doing the damage. At fault are the wildlife bandits who hunt outside the law. Modern hunting laws are intended to protect certain kinds of game animals. They do this by allowing hunters to shoot

Bald Eagle Pelicans Osprey

only the number of animals that can be replaced by births each year.

Today we have still other ways of killing wildlife. Special guns are set to shoot deadly chemicals into the mouths of coyotes. DDT and other chemicals harm such birds as eagles, peregrine falcons, ospreys, and pelicans. All of these birds are in danger of becoming extinct.

There is nothing new about extinction. Wild animals, including the gigantic dinosaurs, became extinct countless years ago. But scientists know that man has hastened extinction for a great number of creatures.

Some wild animals are better able than others to survive the changes men make in their surroundings. In general, the more kinds of food on which an animal can live and the wider the area over which it is spread, the better its chances of staying alive.

However, some animals are very specialized. And these are often the ones in serious trouble as the land changes around them. In the Florida Everglades lives a bird called the Everglades kite. It is also called a snail hawk because it eats nothing but snails. And not just any snail will do. Instead, it has fed on a single kind of snail for so long that it doesn't know to look for any other kind of food. This puts it in serious trouble when men begin draining the swamps. Wherever the big snails disappear, the kites also disappear.

Everglades Kite Passenger Pigeon Peregrine Falcon Whooping Crane

As a result, the Everglades kite is one of the rarest birds in the United States.

Other birds have met their downfall because they lived only in huge flocks. This allowed them to be easily killed by the hundreds. One such bird was the famous passenger pigeon, the last one of which died in the Cincinnati zoo in 1914.

Why worry about the vanishing wildlife? Scientists tell us there are a number of reasons, and some of them very serious ones. What is happening to these endangered wild animals is a warning for man. The more we change the world of nature, the more we make it unlivable for wild animals. And if we change the world enough, we may bring our own species—man—to extinction. Already scientists warn about such dangers as air pollution, water pollution, and the spreading of poisonous chemicals over the land.

Each living species is different from all others. Within its cells lie secrets of life that die if the species becomes extinct. And each species is related to other species in nature's system. Plants and animals are parts of complex food chains. Each has its job to do. The loss of a single species changes the whole natural system.

There is still another reason for saving every species. Each one is interesting to have around. Whenever a wild species is lost, mankind is a little poorer. There is less variety and beauty left in the outdoor world.

There is a bright spot in the middle of this dark picture. People everywhere have suddenly become interested in saving our endangered wildlife. Beginning in 1964, conservationists across the country started pooling their facts about our most seriously endangered creatures. These facts were brought together in a large report called "Rare and Endangered Fish and Wildlife of the United States."

Then Congress provided money for conservationists to begin studying the rare and endangered species more closely than they had been able to do before. Wildlife specialists are now studying the California condor. Others seek out the rare birds of the Hawaiian Islands and the vanishing black-footed ferret in South Dakota. In Texas and Maryland conservationists study the famous whooping cranes, the tallest birds of North America. It is hoped that the numbers of these birds will continue to creep upward.

How much all of this will help remains to be seen. But we realize now that we still know far too little about the life secrets of most endangered species. And the faster we can gather information, the better the chances become for saving them.

Already we know what steps to take for a few of the endangered species. Sometimes setting up a special refuge is all that is needed. In a corner of Montana the Red Rock Lakes National Wildlife Refuge was created in 1935. Its big job was to rescue the trumpeter swan, the world's largest water bird. Down to perhaps fewer than seventy birds at the time, these big white swans were believed to be close to extinction. But the refuge protected them from both people and animals and helped save them. Today the trumpeters are no longer on the endangered list. There are even extra birds to take from Red Rock Lakes to other refuges.

A similar system is being tried for the whooping cranes. All of the world's remaining wild whoopers spend their summers in the wilderness of northern Canada. Then, for the winter months, they travel down across the country to the Gulf of Texas. There they get full protection in the Aransas National Wildlife Refuge. Over the years, as the whooping cranes lived on the edge of extinction, people everywhere followed their progress. Their story was told so often that the whooping crane became everybody's endangered bird. It stood for all threatened wildlife.

In 1969 President Nixon signed into law the Endangered Species Act that had been passed by Congress. Conservationists everywhere hope this law will help save our wildlife. The law was written to stop people from bringing endangered creatures, or any parts of them, into this country. It is hoped, too, that the Endangered Species Act will bring an end to alligator killing by making it illegal to ship alligator skins from one state to another.

New York State has passed a law to halt the sale of products made of alligator hide. This same law also forbids selling products that use the skin or fur of such endangered animals as the cheetah, leopard, and polar bear.

What has been done to help the whooping crane and trumpeter swan is needed for other rare, wild creatures. People must become concerned and decide that these wild species will not die. Then we just might save them from joining the passenger pigeons. And, in the process, we might save ourselves.

Afterthought

A good way to learn to care about the welfare of wild animals is to discover what is going on around you. What are some of the problems faced by the wildlife in your community? How did these problems arise? What is being done to overcome them?

Which of the projects on the following pages can you or your class do as first steps in learning to care about wildlife?

Organize a field trip around your school or neighborhood. Make a list of the different birds, insects, and wild animals you see.

Make a map showing all your state parks, forests, and wildlife refuges. If your state has national parks, forests, or refuges, put these on the map also.

Build a small wildlife sanctuary in your own backyard or schoolyard. You will need to find out which trees and shrubs will thrive in your area and which creatures you can expect to attract to your sanctuary. Your state conservation agency and the local branch of the National Audubon Society will have information to help you in this project.

What are some of the restrictions your state puts on hunting, trapping, and fishing? Why are the restrictions needed?

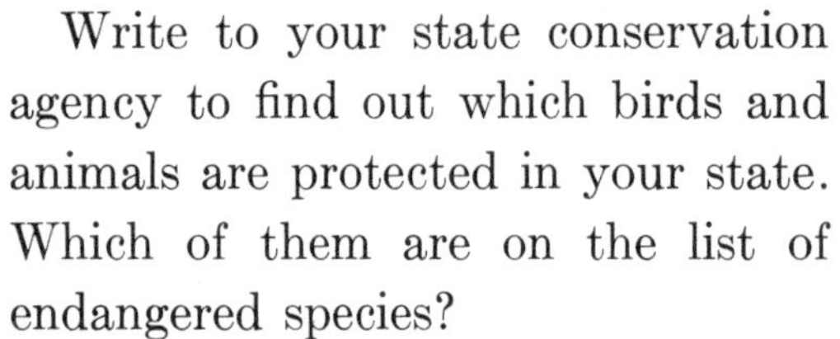

Write to your state conservation agency to find out which birds and animals are protected in your state. Which of them are on the list of endangered species?

Make a list of some of the insects you can find in your community. Which are harmful to humans, and which are useful? In what ways are they harmful and in what ways useful?

Your teacher may wish to invite a ranger or wildlife officer to speak to your class about the wild animals in your area. What questions would you like to ask?

Build a birdhouse and a feeder for your backyard or schoolyard. Find in an encyclopedia the kinds of houses various birds can live in and the kinds of food to put in the feeder. Make a list of the birds that come to your yard in the summer and another list of those that come in the winter. Which birds stay the year around?

Stupidity Street

I saw with open eyes
Singing birds sweet
Sold in the shops
For the people to eat,
Sold in the shops of
Stupidity Street.

I saw in vision
The worm in the wheat,
And in the shops nothing
For people to eat;
Nothing for sale in
Stupidity Street.

Ralph Hodgson

Operation Bird Wash

Percelle Leidy Coryell

Wild animals are able to overcome many of the natural dangers they face. When the dangers are created by human beings, they may need a little help from their friends—friends like Kim and Jana in this story.

Kim Dawson watched in horrified silence as the thick mass of oil spread shoreward, turning the blue-green water of the Gulf of Mexico black. Offshore, the massive hulk of a crippled oil tanker sprawled across the sandbar it had struck during the night. Heavy crude oil continued to pour from the gaping hole in its side.

Work crews toiled in the shallows in a desperate attempt to keep the black slick from coming ashore. The weary crews had worked since dawn, dumping straw over the sides of small, flat-bottomed boats to soak up some of the oil. But the oil slick moved closer and closer to the shore.

Kim's friend, Jana Rosten, shifted uneasily on the seawall beside Kim. Shielding her face with one sun-browned arm, she groaned, "Wow! What a mess. Why don't they just set fire to that stuff and burn it off?"

"Come on, Jana!" Kim answered. "Crude oil like this won't burn. It's got to be warmed and thinned first. Don't you remember? We just learned that in science class."

"I forgot," grinned Jana sheepishly.

Kim's concern turned to startled alarm as she suddenly caught sight of tiny movements in the oil slick. Pulling Jana with her, she jumped off the wall. Together they waded toward the floundering objects.

"Birds!" cried Kim. "Ducks trapped in the oil!" She scooped up one of the struggling creatures.

"Look at them," said Jana. "There must be a hundred of them. They'll never be able to get themselves out of that oil."

Kim called to one of the workers who was spreading the straw.

"Hey, mister! There are birds stuck in this oil. Please help us get them out."

The man looked up wearily and said, "Sorry. I sure would like to help you, but we need everyone to try to stop this oil. The farther it spreads, the more trouble we've got."

"But these birds will die," pleaded Kim. Jana, meanwhile, had waded farther out. And one arm now cradled two of the oil-covered little birds.

"I'm afraid more than those birds will die if we can't stop this oil," replied the man. "This stuff is poison to everything in the water."

Kim turned around, her feet slimy from the oil and her heart heavy with fear for the birds. Jana's face was grim with the effort of maintaining her balance and holding onto the slippery birds.

The girls climbed slowly back up onto the seawall, clutching all the birds they could hold snugly against their chests. Kim felt a frustration that she had never before experienced. Her thoughts were cut short by the striking of the clock on the old fishermen's meeting hall.

"Phew! Four o'clock already," she muttered. Suddenly her eyes widened. "Jana, we're supposed to go camping tonight. My mom will be looking all over for me to help load the station wagon. We'd better go up to the hall and phone home."

It was no easy job maneuvering their bikes up the sandy road, while keeping the struggling birds from falling out of their bike baskets. They finally arrived at the low white building, and Kim breathlessly made her phone call. But as she dialed, she had an idea. When her mother answered, the words tumbled from Kim's mouth.

"Mom, please bring the girls down to the waterfront. We can go on a camping trip any weekend, but we just have to try to save these birds now."

"Slow down, Kim," Mrs. Dawson said. "What birds?"

Kim caught her breath and explained to her mother. They discussed what supplies would be needed. Kim remembered reading of other similar incidents and tried to recall, step by step, what had to be done for the birds. Mrs. Dawson promised to collect what they would need and bring all the girls to the waterfront as fast as she could.

The bicycle ride back to the waterfront seemed much shorter to Kim and Jana; but they didn't talk much. Each was busy with her own thoughts. Kim's heart skipped a little as she looked at the oil-blackened ducks in her basket. She thought of all the others unable to escape from the slick.

The girls had barely arrived back at the waterfront when Mrs. Dawson's station wagon pulled in. Quickly Kim put Operation Bird Wash into action. She divided the girls into two groups, and headed one toward the water to pick up the birds while the others set up cleaning stations and small fires along the beach.

The rescuers scooped up bird after bird and passed them over to the girls on the shore. The girls were gentle, but the birds were terrified and struggling. However, the weakened birds soon quieted down, as though they knew they were being helped.

The cleaning job was a slow and painstaking one.

"Are you sure salad oil is the right thing to dump on a bird?" asked Jana doubtfully.

"You sure can't clean the oil off with detergents," answered Kim, without lifting her eyes from the duck she was working on. "That would remove too much of the natural oil from their feathers, and they wouldn't be able to float."

"Well, that sure seems like funny stuff to put on a duck," muttered Jana again as she ran back toward the water.

Hour after hour they worked, applying salad oil time and time again to each bird in order to dilute the heavy black crude oil. Kim's back and arms grew almost numb. But each time she looked up and saw Jana and the others waist-deep in the slimy Gulf, she forgot how tired she was and worked with renewed effort.

After the salad oil applications, the girls dusted fine cornmeal on the birds' feathers to soak up the oil. Then they gently wiped it away and repeated the entire process several times on each bird. When they felt that each bird was clean enough, they dried it with a soft towel and placed it in a carton near one of the small fires to keep warm.

"This is the part that worries me the most," Kim said. "After the scrubbing these ducks have had, it sure would be easy for them to get pneumonia."

A bit after midnight, Jana and the girls in the water waded slowly to shore.

"They could use a good scrubbing, too," thought Kim, looking at her friends with a weary smile. But the black Gulf didn't look so menacing now. A full moon glided out from a cloud bank, shooting darts of silver around the work crew in the boats. The fresh breeze peppered Kim's nostrils with a clean, salty spray, carrying away the heavy tar smell of the oil.

"I guess that about does it," called Mrs. Dawson as she wearily wiped her eyes with the back of her arm. "All your feathered friends seem to be present and accounted for, Kim. Are you ready to pack up the gear?"

"We can't just leave the birds here, Mom," Kim said. "They have to be kept warm for a couple of days."

"Let's take them home," suggested Jana.

Kim's face brightened at the idea. "Great! When they are strong and dry again, we can take them to the lagoon, where the water is safe and clean."

Shouts of agreement echoed through the dark waterfront. The tired girls, arms and boxes filled with birds, piled into the wagon. Mrs. Dawson started the engine and headed the car up the sandy road toward home.

Afterthought

1. What effect does an oil slick have on sea life?
2. Why did the girls take the birds home after they had cleaned them up? Was this a good idea?
3. What would you have done if you had found ducks trapped in an oil slick?

Remember Tomorrow

Proverb

What is bitter to stand against today may be sweet
to remember tomorrow.

Carl Sandburg

The Loner

Ester Wier

The Loner is a boy without a name, a family, or a home. The only person who was ever kind to him is killed in an accident, and the boy starts hitchhiking west. After traveling many miles, he stumbles into a field, exhausted. A woman rancher finds him and takes him to the wagon where she lives while tending her sheep. The part of the story you will read takes place the next day.

When the boy awoke in the morning, he was startled by his surroundings. Slowly it came back to him. He lay snug and warm under the blankets, examining the room. Boss had left her bed on the long bench neat, the blankets pulled smooth and the soogan folded lengthwise. The hinged window above his bed was held open a crack by a short stick, and he pulled himself up to look out.

There was no sign of Boss or her sheep, only the hills beyond covered with dried brown grass. He got out of bed and walked the length of the wagon to the window set in the upper half of the door. The view from here was a slope leading down to a stand of trees. A road cut through the middle of them and ended at the foot of the hill on which the wagon stood. There was no sign of life in that direction either, only a light wind bending the trees which stood pale and golden in the thin sunlight. The brush among the trees was a flaming orange, and here and there were wild currant and serviceberry bushes.

He turned to find the beans and a pan of biscuits warm on the stove. There was a note on a piece of paper tacked to the dish cupboard but, since he couldn't read, he only looked at it curiously. Opening a biscuit, he heaped beans into it and ate, standing beside the stove, the long flannel nightshirt dropping in folds upon the floor.

The woman called Boss had told him not to go out in his thin clothes. He turned the handle of the door and sniffed the air outside. It was brittle-cold and he withdrew hurriedly. Next, he examined the stove, opened the dish cupboard, then tested the sliding bracket of the lamp, standing on his toes to reach it. Discovering the table hinged to the bed, he lifted it and placed the leg under it upright on the floor. He found that when raised it rested on the two benches, and he lifted and lowered it several times. Seeing the rope ring on the hinged short bench lid, he thrust his finger through it and raised the trapdoor. In the grub box were tins of milk, bags of sugar, beans, coffee, and some dried fruit.

Satisfied, he returned to the bed and slipped under the blankets. It was time to think about where he was and what he should do next. Boss hadn't asked him where he had come from. She wasn't nosy like some of the people who had given him rides along the highway. He had told them all something different, anything that popped into his head, but nothing about Raidy or the digging machine or the pickers' camp. He couldn't talk about that.

He had to be getting on to California, before the winter set in. Somehow he must have got turned in the wrong direction, so he would have to go back and find the highway again. He looked around the sheep wagon. It was all right here, nice and warm and there was plenty of food to eat. Boss was all right, too. She had given him her bed and this nightshirt, and she had even covered him up. No one had ever bothered so much about him before, no one but Raidy. He lay back and closed his eyes, suddenly tired again.

When he awakened, a man was standing in the doorway looking at him. The man was young, with dark weather-beaten skin and very light-blue eyes. His clothes were rough and well-worn. He held a pipe in one hand and a bag of flour and tins of food under his arm. Closing the door behind him, he came to the short bench and laid the articles on it.

"Where's Boss?" he asked, and the boy immediately knew he was a Texan. He had the same way of saying words, drawling them slow and easy, like the overseers in the bean fields.

He sat up. "Out with the sheep," he said, feeling comfortable with this man right away.

"When I saw smoke from the chimney, I wondered if she was sick." The man removed his greasy hat and extended a hand. "I'm Tex," he said, "camp tender."

His words meant nothing to the boy but they shook hands. "I've got kerosene and wood and more groceries in the truck outside. Some mail here." He removed it from his pocket. "If it's all right with you, I'll make some coffee and warm myself up a bit." Without waiting for a reply, he took off his coat, filled the coffeepot from the bucket, and sprinkled a handful of coffee into the water. Setting it on the stove, he lighted his pipe and sat down on the bench.

"You know what a camp tender is?" he asked.

The boy shook his head.

"My job is to come up here every week to see how Boss is makin' out and to bring provisions. Now, there's snow blowin' up in the northwest, so I'm bringin' supplies in early. Tell Boss we're in for some weather, first of the season, and that Bezeleel's dog was rabid. Must have been bit by a coyote before he turned on the old man. And tell her—"

The boy interrupted him. "Who got bit by a coyote?"

"The dog that belonged to the old feller who used to be herder here."

"What's rabid?"

Tex laughed. "You sure got a lot of questions. Say, I thought everyone in Montana knew what rabid meant."

The boy shrugged. "Is that where I am?"

"Sure. Where did you think you were?"

"I didn't know, but it didn't seem like what I'd heard about California. Wasn't warm enough. Any crops to pick around here?"

"Whoa, boy. You asked me a question. Rabid means the coyote was sick and he bit the dog and made him sick too; then the dog bit the old man."

"I don't like dogs," the boy said.

Tex looked at him, surprised. "Don't believe I ever knew a boy before who didn't like dogs. I wouldn't let Boss hear you say that. Jup and Juno are the best friends she has. And two of the best sheep dogs in these parts."

"Friends?" the boy said scornfully. "I'd never have a dog for a friend. I been throwing rocks at dogs as long as I can remember. And hitting them, too."

"Why?"

It seemed strange to the boy that Tex didn't know why. "We were both after the same food, that's why." He boasted, "But I usually got it."

Tex stood up and went to the stove. The coffee was boiling and he took a cup from the dish cupboard and filled it with the strong black liquid. When he was sitting down again, he said, "Yes, you're in Montana. But there's no crops to be picked here now. Did you run away?"

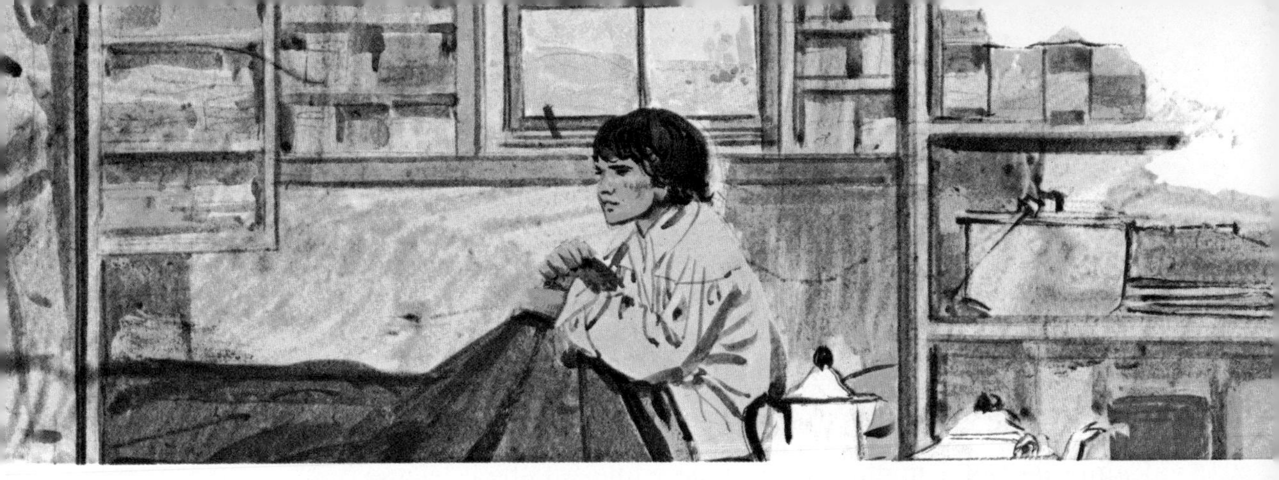

The boy considered the question. "No. I just left."

"What about your folks? They'll be worried."

Amazement showed in the boy's eyes. "Worried about me? Nobody's going to be worried about me. I never had any folks."

"Who takes care of you?"

"Takes care of me? I take care of myself, always have."

Tex chuckled. "You sound like a real loner for sure."

"A loner? What's that?"

"Best way I can explain is to tell you how I grew up. I didn't have folks either, nobody to worry about me. I grew up in an orphans' home."

"One of those places?" The boy was horrified.

"Oh, it wasn't so bad. You might say I was a loner too. One of those who didn't believe anyone cared about them or wanted to help. I figured it was up to me to take care of myself and I didn't need help from anyone."

The boy nodded. This man understood.

"Let me tell you, boy, that's a poor way of livin'. A mighty selfish one too. Somebody will care if you just give 'em a chance."

The boy thought of Raidy.

"There's always people who need you as much as you need

them. Don't you forget that. All you got to do is find 'em. And when you do, you find you're happier carin' about someone else than just about yourself all the time." Tex took another long swallow of hot coffee. "You thinkin' about stayin' around here? This is mighty pretty country. It's sheep country."

The boy thought it over. "I was planning to get on to California but I might stay a little while—if she'll let me."

Tex leaned back and laughed. "You know what I think? I think Boss has got herself a bum lamb."

"What's that?"

Tex raised his eyebrows into an arch. "Guess you don't know nothin' about sheep raisin'. Let's see how I can explain it. At lambin' time in the spring, the ewe—"

"The what?"

"The mother sheep. Well, sometimes her lamb dies. Or sometimes the ewe dies. Now everybody knows ewes are healthier and happier if they've a lamb to raise, and lambs are better off if they've a mother. So the lambers take an orphan lamb—they call 'em bum lambs—and give it to the ewe that lost hers. Understand?"

"Sure," the boy said. "The mother needs a baby and the baby needs a mother, so they put them together. The ewe adopts it the way they say people do sometimes for kids in those orphan homes."

Tex shook his head. "That's where you're wrong. The ewe knows the scent of her own lamb, and sometimes she won't take a bum lamb. Sometimes she'll even trample it to death."

"What do they do then?"

"They fool the ewe. They skin her dead lamb and put its wool on the bum. They make slits for the legs and one for the neck, and then they slip it over the bum and give him to the ewe. Funniest thing you ever saw. The lamb has two tails and eight legs."

The boy laughed. "Does she take it then?"

"Sure," said Tex. "Just as soon as she sniffs that wool and decides it's her own lamb. And she makes it a real good mother, too. Yes, sir, I think it would be good for Boss to have a bum lamb now."

He drew on his pipe and took a swallow of hot coffee. "You stay here with Boss for a while if she'll let you, hear? But don't tell her I said so. Ever since Ben was killed, she don't take kindly to people figurin' out what she should do."

"Who's Ben?"

Tex didn't answer for a few minutes. He teetered back on the bench and his eyes looked far off. He seemed to be making up his mind. Finally he decided and he leaned forward.

"I'm goin' to tell you about Boss so you'll understand her a little better. She won't tell you, that is for sure. She don't talk much and never about herself. Maybe later on she'll get around to explaining to you about Ben, but I think you should know now. Don't you tell her that I've been talkin' about her." He finished the mug of coffee and rose to refill it. "Ben was her son. He was killed by a grizzly, a bear, two winters back when he was out huntin'. Boss spent a whole year lookin' for that bear and never did find it. There was never anyone in the world like Ben to her. Sometimes I think that's why she took old Bezeleel's place here when he got bit, just so she could be out here and find that bear. Angie said she should try to hire a herder but she wouldn't listen. These ewes in her flock are the best on the ranch, the real money-makers, so it's a special job and Boss decided to do it herself."

The boy was confused. "Who's Angie?"

"Ben's wife, Ben's widow now. She lives on the ranch and teaches school in town. Angie got real upset about Boss comin' way out here alone with the sheep for the winter. That's what I mean by sayin' Boss don't take kindly to people tellin' her what she should do. The more Angie talked, the stubborner Boss got, and I ain't never seen anyone could beat her at bein' stubborn." He slapped his leg. "There I go again. One thing Angie can't stand, bein' a schoolteacher, is someone saying ain't. I been tryin' my best to get over it but it slipped out again."

The boy wanted to hear the rest of the story. "Did you think Boss should have come out here?"

Tex whooped with laughter. "Me? I'm only a hired hand for now. I kept out of it. I'm just here to tend the camps of the herders and to do chores around the ranch. But someday . . ."

His eyes looked far off again. He reminded the boy of how the old man had looked driving down the highways. As though there was something beautiful way past the next hill that no one else could see.

"Someday," Tex said, "I'm goin' to have me a sheep ranch, too. Sheep as far as you can see, dottin' the hills all around my ranch." He slapped his leg again and stood up. "I've talked enough for one day. Got to go now. I'll bring the food and kerosene in and lay the wood under the wagon." He moved toward the door.

"You still a loner?" the boy asked.

A grin spread over Tex's face. "I been gettin' over it lately; that's how come I gave you all that good advice. You better get over it, too." He winked. "You put up with Boss as long as she'll have you. When she does talk, you'll hear a lot about Ben and about the bear and about sheep, but I reckon you can stand that. Seems to me you two belong together, a nice old ewe and a bum lamb." He threw up his hands and let out a loud whoop. "Don't tell her I said that, though. She'd skin me alive for callin' her an old ewe." He left, laughing.

When Tex finished his chores, the boy watched him walk down the hill and get into the provision truck. He watched until the truck disappeared down the road between the cottonwoods and the quaking aspens and willows.

The boy thought about Ben and Boss, the bear, and Angie, and Tex for a long time. Tex had advised him to stay here if he could. It made sense. If he kept wandering around the country alone, someday someone would find out he didn't belong anywhere, and they'd put him in one of those homes Tex had grown up in. Women who came to visit the pickers' camps were always threatening to put the children in homes somewhere. They said the children ought to be where they could go to school regularly and live like other people. Well, he'd had too much freedom in his life to like the idea of that. Maybe Tex was right. If Boss would have him, he'd like to stay here for a while, maybe until next spring.

He began to study how to make Boss want him to stay. He remembered how she'd made him wash last night. That must mean that she liked for people to be clean. All right, if he had to be clean to stay, then he'd get used to it. Finding the pan he had washed in before, he poured water into it from the bucket. The water was warm from standing near the stove, so he used it as it was. He stripped off the nightshirt and dropped the soap into the pan. Then, with the end of the towel, he washed himself thoroughly, better than he ever had in his life. Some of the crop-pickers had had portable tubs and he had seen them bathing on Saturday nights, in the middle of their shacks, the whole family waiting in line for their turn. No one he had ever traveled with had carried a tub. The ones he had known had left it up to each person to do what washing he wanted to at the spigot that supplied the whole camp with water. There in the sheep wagon the boy used the towel to dry himself, and put his nightshirt back on again. He threw the water out the door as he had seen Boss do.

He ate another biscuit with beans and climbed back into bed. His body cried out for sleep and rest and he curled up under the blankets, grasping the bag of potatoes close to him although the wagon was warm now. There was no way of knowing what time it was and, even if he had known, it wouldn't have mattered. Boss would be home at sundown. Until then he would sleep.

Afterthought

1. What words or phrases made you understand that the boy is a migrant worker?
2. How could Tex see so quickly the problem that the boy has to overcome?
3. Why did the boy trust Tex enough to listen to his suggestions?
4. What makes you think that Tex has learned to care about other people?
5. How can you compare the boy's taking a bath to putting a dead lamb's skin over a bum lamb?

City Hall

Nellie Burchardt

The children in the Housing Project think the rule against pets is not fair. All of them work hard getting people to sign a petition to change the rule. Now the day has come for the hardest part of all.

"Now let's all be real quiet," said Betsy when they arrived at City Hall. "They'll never let us see the mayor if we sound like a bunch of wild Indians."

The children climbed the steps of the huge stone building. Down the long marble corridor to the mayor's office they walked. The sound of their footsteps was lost in the great, high-ceilinged hall.

As they approached the mayor's office the other children held back more and more, leaving Betsy in front.

"Please, miss," she said to the lady at the desk by the door that said MAYOR, "we'd like to see the mayor."

"Do you have an appointment?" asked the lady, looking up from her typewriter.

"No. We didn't know you had to. But we have a petition for him."

The lady held out her hand. "I'll take care of it. You needn't wait," she said.

The children looked at each other doubtfully. Ellen shook her head at Betsy but did not say anything.

"No," said Betsy. "We want to see the mayor in person."

"I'm sorry, but the mayor is very busy at a City Council meeting."

The children eyed each other again.

"We'll wait," said Betsy.

"I said the mayor is very busy," said the lady, beginning to sound annoyed. "You can't see him now."

"That's all right, miss. We have lots of time," said Betsy. "We'll sit down and wait till he's not busy." She turned and led the way to a bench against the wall. The other children followed her and sat down in a row on the bench.

The lady at the desk pushed back her chair and stood up.

"Now, listen here, all of you," she said. "I told you that you *can't* wait. The mayor is too busy to have a bunch of noisy kids hanging around his office."

The lady seemed quite angry. Betsy wished the other children would not leave all the talking to her.

"We'll be very quiet, miss. Please—we just *have* to see him," she pleaded. "It's very urgent."

She stood up but hesitated to leave when she saw a door open behind the lady's back. A tall, rather stout man stood in the doorway. He started to fill his pipe from a pouch he took out of his pocket. In the room behind him Betsy could see people walking around, talking to each other.

The lady did not see the man. She walked toward the children with her arm raised, pointing at the door down the hall where they had come in.

"I said no! Now, out with you!" she said.

The man stuffed the tobacco pouch back into his pocket and stepped forward.

"Come, come, Miss Witherspoon," he said, "that's no way to treat a group of future voters."

Miss Witherspoon spun around. "Oh—Mr. Mayor!" she gasped. "I didn't realize you were there. I'm so sorry if we disturbed you. I—I—I was just trying to persuade these children to leave, but they absolutely refuse to."

"Have you tried twisting their arms?" asked the mayor, with a wink at the children.

"Twisting their arms!" exclaimed Miss Witherspoon in a horrified voice. Then she giggled. "Oh—you're joking again. I just never know when you're joking."

"But I'm glad you didn't persuade them to leave," continued the mayor. "It's not every day that I get a chance to talk to a group of my younger constituents."

The children exchanged puzzled looks.

"Now don't tell me that you didn't know you were my constituents," said the mayor.

The children shook their heads.

"Well, don't let it worry you. It just means you're the people I represent. You know what that means, don't you?"

The children nodded their heads.

"Now," said the mayor, "out with it. To what do I owe the honor of this visit?"

Ellen gave Betsy a shove, and Betsy had to take a step forward to keep her balance.

"Yes?" said the mayor.

When he looked at her, her stomach felt shaky. He had not seemed so enormous in the picture she had seen in the paper.

"We—we—we have a petition here for you, M-Mr. Mayor," stuttered Betsy. She was surprised to hear how little and shaky her voice sounded. She handed him the papers covered with signatures.

The mayor took the papers from Betsy with one hand and with the other he reached into his pocket and pulled out his glasses. He adjusted them on his nose and read the petition, then turned the pages of signatures one by one and examined them carefully.

Finally he looked up at Betsy and said, "So I can have a pet and you can't, is that it?"

"Yes, sir," said Betsy in a tiny voice.

"And you don't think that's fair, eh?"

"N-n-no, sir."

"What kind of pet would you get if you could have one?"

Betsy took a deep breath. "A cat. You see, there's this poor little cat that has a lame paw—"

Suddenly the other children found their voices and all started speaking at once.

"—and we've been feeding her—"

"—and she's going to have kittens—"

"—but we're not allowed to have pets—"

"—and the weather's getting too cold—"

"Whoa! Whoa!" shouted the mayor over the babble of voices. "One at a time!"

The children fell silent.

Now that he could make himself heard, the mayor looked right at Betsy and said, "This seems to be something of an emergency. Is that it?"

"Yes, sir," said Betsy. "She's going to have her kittens any day now. And Ellen's mother says if she has them outside she'll hide them somewhere and we won't be able to find them before winter comes."

"What do you say to that, Miss Witherspoon?" asked the mayor. "Kittens all over the place!"

Miss Witherspoon looked up from her desk, where she had gone back to her typing.

"Pardon me, sir?" she asked.

The mayor raised his voice. "I said we're going to have kittens all over the Project. Are we going to allow that?"

"Oh—no, sir," gasped Miss Witherspoon.

"You're absolutely right!" said the mayor. "Kittens all over the Project, scaring away the birds and digging up the flower beds. We certainly can't allow that!"

Betsy's heart sank. Maybe they should not have come. And the mayor had seemed so nice at first.

"You know what I'd like to do?" the mayor asked.

"N-no, sir." Betsy's voice was small and scared.

"I'd *like* to insist that you children take those kittens in and give them decent homes."

Betsy gave a sigh of relief. He was nice, after all!

"*But*," continued the mayor, "there's only one catch."

Betsy and her friends exchanged worried looks.

"What's that?" asked Betsy.

"I don't make the rules. The City Council has to approve any change in the rules for the Project. You know, you're not the first ones who have said the rule against pets was unfair. Now—I wonder what we could do about it." He puffed at his pipe in silence for a moment.

The children watched his face anxiously.

"Hm-m-m—yes. It just might work," he said at last. He looked at Betsy. "What's your name, little girl?"

"Who? Me?" Betsy looked around, hoping he meant some other child.

"Yes—you."

"Oh. Betsy."

"All right, Betsy. Do you think you could go in there to the City Council meeting and show them the petition just the way you showed it to me?"

"Oh—no!" Betsy stepped back toward the protection of the rest of the group. "I'd be too scared."

"You weren't too scared of me, were you, Betsy?"

"No-o-o." She remembered she *had* been afraid of him. But that seemed a little silly now. He was not the least bit fierce or grumpy.

"Do you want to keep that cat, Betsy?" he asked.

"Oh—yes! I do!"

She bit her lip. That cat was certainly leading her into doing a lot of things she would have been too scared to do last year—talking back to Ellen, ringing all those strange doorbells to get signatures, talking to the mayor. And now he wanted her to face the City Council! Well, she'd come this far. She couldn't give up now.

"All right. I *guess* I could do it," she said.

"That's the girl!" exclaimed the mayor.

As Betsy and the mayor entered the room, the council members went back to their seats. Betsy almost changed her mind when she saw all those strange grown-up faces staring at her from around the big council-room table. The council members looked like the kind of people who could say no to almost anything.

The mayor sat down in the chair at the head of the table and told her to stand beside him. He picked up a little wooden mallet and rapped on the table for silence.

"I'd like to make a change in the order of business," he said. "I want to introduce a very determined young lady to you. Her name is Betsy—uh—Betsy, what's your last name?"

"Delaney."

"Her name is Betsy Delaney, and she has a problem for you."

To be called determined made Betsy feel a little braver. She tried not to think of all those grown-up eyes looking at her. She tried to think instead of the cat's green-and-gold eyes.

Once she started talking, it was not as hard as she had thought it would be to explain about the petition and the lame cat the children had been feeding. When she had finished and had passed around the petition for all of them to examine, the mayor motioned to her to lean closer to him.

He whispered in her ear, "This isn't a promise, Betsy, but if I were you, I'd go home and catch that cat and lock her up before she starts having kittens all over the place."

Betsy grinned. "Oh, yes, sir!" she said.

As she turned to leave, she saw the mayor very distinctly wink at her. She winked back. It seemed silly now that she had been so scared of him at first.

I'm as bad as the cat, she thought. I get scared of things before I know if there's really anything to be scared of.

She was not sure, but she thought that two of the council members were smiling. She was not quite brave enough yet to look right at all those strange grown-up faces. But she *had* gotten them to look at the petition. That was the main thing.

And Then What?

Shirley L. Arora

Out of every rupee Raman earns for his family, he may keep one naiye-paise to buy books with. He plans for the day he will become a scholar and live in the city on the plains. But an American lady asks Raman a question that makes him wonder whether he should change his plans.

The days passed. The coins tied in the cloth and tucked behind the loose brick numbered thirty-eight now, but Raman did not think of buying one of Tumbuswamy's paper-covered books. True, he stopped by Tumbuswamy's stall each time he went to the bazaar. But he never glanced at the shelf where the little pile of books lay. He had eyes only for that gold-titled book that lay on its bed of tissue paper at the front of the glass case.

"Someday I am going to buy that book," Raman would say each time as he was ready to leave. Let Tumbuswamy laugh if he wished! But the old bookseller did not laugh. He only nodded his head and repeated his usual answer:

"Someday, Thambi, perhaps you will."

"But maybe it won't be here by then, Tata."

"Maybe it won't, Thambi, but maybe it will."

Things were going well now. Every week or so the bus driver brought a brown envelope for Raman to take home to his mother. To be sure, the money was not enough for all the things they needed, but at least they need no longer fear that there would not be rice to eat. The baby was warm in new winter clothes now, and another water vessel had replaced the old one that had been leaking for so long.

Raman did not gather pine cones anymore, for there was almost no market for them anyway. Instead he devoted his time to hunting flowers for the Merkin lady. As time went by, it became harder and harder to find new kinds of flowers, and he had to go farther and farther beyond the lake to look for them. But sometimes the Merkin lady was particularly pleased when he found a flower that was rare, and then she would add extra coins to those she usually gave him. And one day when he brought a lily plant that he had found growing halfway up a cliff, she gave him a whole rupee for that flower alone.

Whenever Raman had time, he stayed to watch the Merkin lady at her painting. It was fun to see how the deft strokes of the brush made the flower grow and bloom where once had been only blank white paper. And the Merkin lady seemed happy to have him stay.

"You give me a chance to practice speaking Tamil," she told him one day.

"Amma speaks Tamil very well," Raman said shyly. It was true that sometimes the words the Merkin lady used seemed strange to his ears, and she spoke slowly, as though she were speaking in English, which was a slow language compared to Tamil. But Raman could always understand what she meant. It was not often that one heard the Merkin people speaking Tamil.

"Thank you, Raman. I think it is a very difficult language to learn. But in my school we must teach only in Tamil."

"Amma teaches school?" Surprised, Raman forgot to be

shy. He could not picture the Merkin lady standing before a class with a pointing stick in her hand, like Munuswamy the schoolmaster.

"Yes, indeed." The Merkin lady seemed amused at his surprise. "We have a school down on the plains, a very big school; a college, really, for older boys and girls."

"Girls!" Raman echoed, astonished. "You have girls in your college?"

"Certainly. Why not?"

"But girls do not need to read and write. They will just marry and keep house, and the learning will be wasted." The reasoning he had always accepted and repeated, parrotlike, from his elders sounded strangely hollow to his ears.

"Ah, there you have it!" the Merkin lady exclaimed. "But it will not be wasted. They will marry and keep house, it is true, but they will teach their children, and those children will teach their children, and so on. And then too, Raman, in our school we teach many things besides reading and writing: how to farm, how to raise better crops, how to build better houses; and for the girls, how to prepare better meals, how to care for those who are ill. . . . Then those who have learned in our school go back to their villages to teach others. That is the real importance of it all."

"Oh, Amma, if only I could go to a school like that someday!"

The Merkin lady's eyebrows lifted. "Who knows? Perhaps you will. How old are you, Raman?"

"Twelve. Almost."

The Merkin lady nodded. "It will be quite some time before you are old enough, then. But in the meantime if you work hard—tell me, do you go to school here?"

"Oh, yes, Amma, I have been going for a year now—that is, I was going to school, until my father went down to the plains. Even now I keep up with my reading, and when my father returns I shall start school again. Perhaps even before. I am anxious to go back. Already by the time I left, I had caught up with the others my own age."

"You must have studied hard indeed, to do so much in one year."

Raman nodded agreement. "I like the reading most of all," he went on, the words tumbling over themselves in his eagerness. "In my school I am the best in reading. And I am the first in my family to learn to read." He said this proudly, and paused to see whether the Merkin lady was impressed.

She was eyeing him thoughtfully. "That is a great responsibility."

Raman had already opened his mouth to say more, but he stopped and closed it instead, disappointed. He had expected her to say more than that, to show more admiration.

"I am going to be a great scholar someday," he continued after a moment. "I shall read many, many books. And I shall own the books myself. Shelves and shelves of them. I want to learn many, many things."

"Good," the Merkin lady nodded. "And then what?"

Again Raman stopped short, puzzled. He shifted feet a trifle uncomfortably.

"What will you do then, after you have learned many things?" the Merkin lady repeated. Her blue eyes searched his face keenly.

"Why—why then I shall know them, that's all," he answered, stammering a little.

For a moment he thought the Merkin lady was going to say something else, but instead she only nodded again and turned back to concentrate on her painting. Raman watched, first absently and then with closer attention, as with the skillful strokes of green and yellow and brown the flower began taking shape on the paper. With sudden courage Raman asked a question that had been in his mind for a long time.

"Why does Amma paint pictures of the flowers?"

For a while the Merkin lady was silent, intent on her work, and Raman bit his tongue, regretting the question that it was surely not his place to ask. If he had angered her—! But then she glanced up with her usual smile. "I am going to make a book, Raman," she said, "a book with pictures of all the flowers that grow in these hills."

Make a book! Raman's eyes widened. To read a book was one thing, a fine thing, to be sure. But to write a book! Of course, he knew that all the books he had ever seen—the paper-covered ones he owned, the books on the shelves in the Merkin lady's bungalow, the wonderful book in Tumbuswamy's glass case—all were written by someone. But here he was, face to face with a person who was actually writing a book. Someday these pictures he had watched grow on paper would be printed on shiny pages and bound in a book like those on the shelves inside the bungalow. And in a way he, Raman, had helped.

The thought was a pleasing one, but something else puzzled him. "Amma," he asked hesitantly, "why not paint the flowers from the garden? They are much more beautiful."

The Merkin lady put the final delicate touches on the painting and then set down her brush and sat back in her wheelchair. She looked at Raman. "Perhaps the garden flowers are more beautiful," she said slowly. "They are larger, more brightly colored. But they do not belong here. The hill flowers belong here, and so, even though many of them may not seem so beautiful, they are more important. I want people to know about them, and that is why I am writing a book about them.

"That is something you should remember, Raman," she went on, eyes on the painted flower now, yet seeming to look

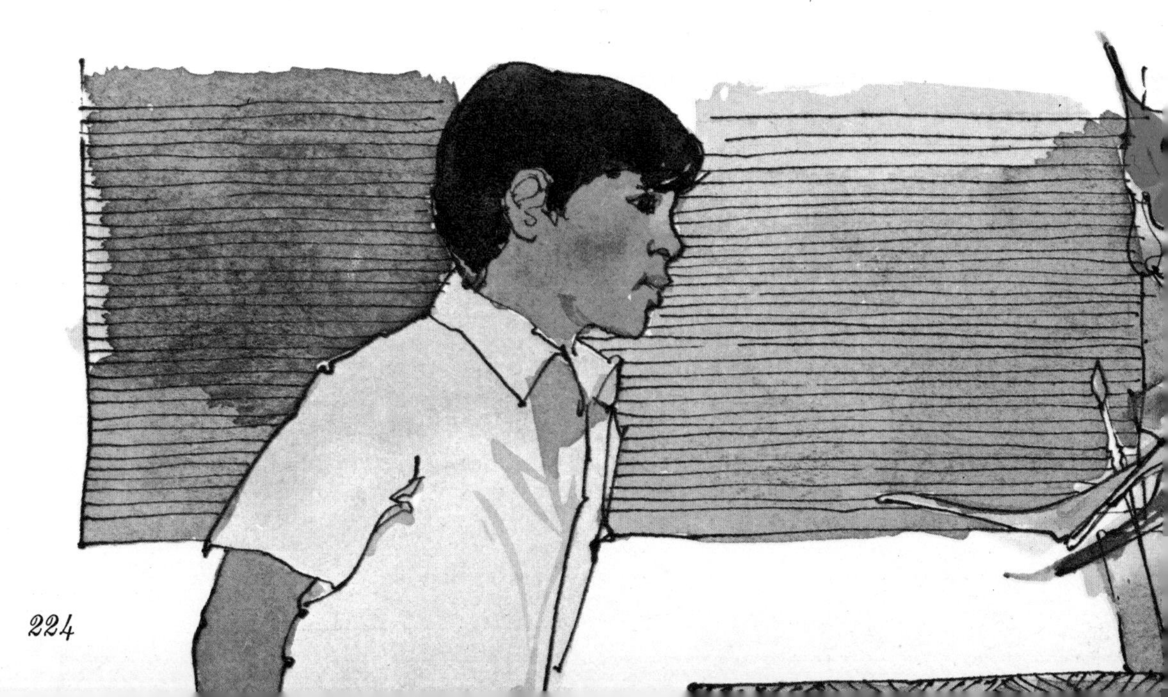

beyond it. "These things which belong here, which are a part of these hills, of this country—they are important, simply because they do belong. That is true not only of flowers but of many other things. Even of people. You belong here, Raman. I do not belong here, even though I have come many times to the hills and spent many months in this bungalow, and many more in my school on the plains. Still I do not belong, and someday I shall be going away. When I teach the boys and girls in my school, I think of that. I am their teacher, and yet they are more important than I, for they belong here, and long after I have left they will still be here, to go on teaching others. You also, Raman," she turned to look directly at him, "you also belong here, in these hills, in this country, and so you, too, like the hill flowers, are important."

She leaned forward again suddenly and began to clear away the painting things from the table, putting the tubes of paint and the brushes away in the box again. Raman sprang to help. By now he knew exactly what needed to be done: the glass of water emptied, the board with its still-wet painting

carried carefully into the bungalow and set on the shelf above the fireplace to dry, the table shoved back into its place on the veranda, the box of paints put away.

"Amma," Raman said when the work was done, "when the book is finished, do you think—could I see it?"

"Of course. But it will take a long time. I shall be leaving in three more weeks now, when my leg has healed enough, and that is not time enough to finish all the flowers. Next year when I come, I shall paint some more. And the year after that, perhaps the book will be finished."

"I like books very much," Raman confided. "I save all the money I can to buy books to read." And the next moment, in a rush of excited words, he was telling the Merkin lady about the book in Tumbuswamy the bookseller's glass case, about the gold letters on its cover, the brightly colored illustrations, the wonderful stories it must have inside.

"Someday I shall buy that book," he boasted. "Someday it will be mine."

"It must be a very wonderful book."

"It is," said Raman. "It is a book that a real scholar would own."

The Merkin lady was studying him keenly. What was she thinking? She smiled then. "Good luck, Raman," she said gently. "Good luck. I hope someday you will have your book."

It was the last week of the Merkin lady's stay in the hills. Soon there would be no one for whom to hunt flowers, and there would not be a coin to add every day to the pile in the hiding place in the wall. Raman could go back to gathering pine cones with Vasanti, but so few, so very few of the bungalows were occupied that he would be lucky to sell two or three bags a week. There was no worry about rice, with the bus driver still bringing regularly the brown envelope from the City. But Raman's heart sank when he thought of the weeks ahead, when it might take days to earn a single rupee. He had fifty-seven naiye-paise now, more money than he had ever had in his life. But that was just a little over half of one rupee. And he needed six and a half rupees to buy the book!

One afternoon Raman sat alone outside the house, leaning against the wall and looking out over the vegetable garden that was now mostly dried, straggling stalks of plants. He picked up a thin twig and bent it in half and then in half again and again until it was so small it would not bend anymore, and then he broke each section off and tossed it into the air, watching as it fell back into the dust. Six and a half rupees, he thought. There must be some way to get six and a half rupees.

He did not hear Vasanti approach until she sat down beside him. "Uncle gave me some sweets, Enna. Do you want one?"

Raman shook his head. He wanted to be alone, to be able to think, think about some way to get six rupees more.

"You are so sad these days, Enna. Is it because you can't go to school?"

"No." He did not mean to sound so gruff. He saw the hurt in Vasanti's eyes and turned away from his own thoughts to look at his sister closely. He remembered suddenly the day they had gone hunting for mushrooms, just after their father had left. He remembered Vasanti's wistful voice saying, "You are lucky, Raman, to know how to read. I wish I could."

"Girls have no need for schooling." That was what he had

said, and Vasanti had agreed. She too had heard it said so often! But now Raman thought of the Merkin lady, who not only read but could write books and teach school also; and of the Merkin lady's school, where girls as well as boys could learn not just reading and writing but many other things as well. Vasanti could scarcely hope to go to a school like that—but why should she not learn to read just the same?

And suddenly Raman heard his own voice saying, "Vasanti, would you like to learn to read?"

Vasanti stared, openmouthed.

"I said, would you like to learn to read? I'll teach you."

"Enna, do you mean it?" He saw the joy light her whole face.

"Of course, why else should I say it?"

"But girls—"

"There's no reason why girls shouldn't learn to read," Raman said firmly. "And I'll teach you. We'll start today itself."

Half an hour later Vasanti had finished her first halting pages out of the old, worn booklet from which Raman had

first learned to read. Then their mother called Vasanti to bring twigs to start the fire, and Vasanti, her face still shining with pride, ran off down the slope to find them. Raman sat alone again. He was conscious of a strange, warm glow, unlike anything he had ever felt before. It was like having a power, he thought. A power to give knowledge to someone. A power to teach.

I could teach Dasan, too, he thought. And then another thought crept in, unbidden: I won't be the only one who knows how to read anymore. It gave him a somewhat empty feeling. It had been fun to think, to say, "I am the only one, the first one in my family and in my village, who has learned to read."

But this is better, he decided. This feels even better. Still conscious of that warmth within, he stood up and started slowly down the slope to help Vasanti gather sticks for the fire.

Afterthought

1. What was your first clue that the setting of this story is not the United States?
2. What did you learn about India from reading this selection?
3. Why would a scholar be a very important man in a place where many people cannot go to school?
4. What will Raman give up if he decides to become a teacher? What will he gain?
5. How will Raman's decision affect his country?

Child of the Silent Night

Edith Fisher Hunter

Laura Bridgman could not see, hear, or talk; and she had almost no sense of taste or smell. Her bright mind was trapped inside her. Old Asa Tenney had taught her to use her hands and feet to learn about stones and birds' eggs and the pond. But Laura needed to learn more. Dr. Howe thought he knew of a way to teach her.

It was Columbus Day, October 12, 1837, just a few weeks before her eighth birthday, when Laura Bridgman started out on her great adventure. Seated in a light carriage, called a chaise, between her father and mother, Laura was tense with excitement. Where was she going? No one could tell her.

Why had she helped her mother put the best of her old clothes and many new ones in a large trunk that she knew was in the carriage with them? Why had her treasures been taken out of her boot and put in a box in among her clothes?

Laura knew that something very unusual was happening. Exactly what it was she did not know, but at least her parents were with her.

The trip from Hanover to Boston was a long one in those days. The Bridgmans had to change from the chaise to a stagecoach and spend several days along the way. Never had Laura been on such a long journey; never had she felt herself in the midst of so many strangers. She tried to hide behind her mother's skirts and her father's greatcoat. When would they get to wherever it was they were going?

After what must have seemed to Laura an endlessly long time, the

coach finally stopped. Mr. and Mrs. Bridgman and Laura were helped out. Laura clung to her mother as they went up a short flight of stairs and into a building. In another moment Laura felt her small hand once again held by the large hand that belonged to the unusually tall man who had visited her once in Mill Village. Was this his home? What was she doing here? No one could explain, of course.

Then Laura felt a woman's soft hand take hers. Laura could not know that this was Miss Jeannette Howe. Laura and her mother took off their coats and bonnets. Following the strange woman, they walked along—what was it? A room? A hall? Laura could somehow sense the largeness of the rooms. She was accustomed to small, low-ceilinged rooms at home. She felt very small and lost in so much space. She clung to the strange but friendly woman on one side of her and to her mother on the other.

Now they had entered a smaller room and she was allowed to feel about. There was a bed, a rocking chair, a washstand, and a little table. The furnishings here were not unlike those in her own room at the farm. She was encouraged to help her mother take her dresses and other

clothes out of the trunk in which they had been placed at home. Were they perhaps going to stay here for a visit? Where was her mother's bag?

There, now they had come to her box of treasures. She felt her mother take it and place it on the table by the bed. Was this going to be her own room? Would her little brothers, Addison and John, be coming too? Would her treasures be safe on the table? No one can know whether questions such as these passed through Laura's mind and no one, of course, could have made her understand the answers to them.

Now they were going back through the long hall to the large room from which they had come. Laura was led over to a low chair near her father and the tall man and given a cup of milk and a cookie. When she had finished eating she sat quietly in her chair.

Then she felt people getting up around her. Her father leaned down and patted her. Laura started to jump up. That pat usually meant that he was going away. His firm hand pushed her back down into the chair again. Now her mother leaned over and patted her.

Laura was terrified. This too was a good-bye pat. Surely her father and mother were not going away! Surely they were not going to leave her in a strange place! Laura struggled to get out of the chair. But now it was the large hand of the friendly man and the gentle hand of the woman that were holding her back.

Laura felt a door close. She was allowed to get out of the chair, and she rushed madly in the direction in which she knew the door lay. It was closed. Laura let out a loud unpleasant sound. It sounded almost like a wounded animal. She began crying and pounding on the door with her little fists.

"We must let her tire herself out some with her grief and tears," said Dr. Howe to his sister. "She is already tired from the long journey, and the fear and sorrow of this separation will exhaust her further. In a little while we must take her to her room. Her box of treasures and her clothes at least will be familiar to her."

"Oh, Sam, it is so pathetic to see her frightened and upset," said Miss Jeannette. "If there were only some way to let her know that it is all for her own good that she has come here." Dr. Howe and his sister watched the terrified little girl crying, beating the door, feeling about the room for some familiar object or person. When she came near them they tried to comfort her, but each time she would draw away.

At last, when they felt that Laura would allow it, they led her to her

room. They left her there and locked the door. When Miss Jeannette returned in less than half an hour, she found Laura sound asleep on her bed.

"We can expect that there will be several more scenes like the one we have just witnessed before Laura will accept the fact that she must stay here," said Dr. Howe to his sister.

"Of course!" said Miss Jeannette. "Can you imagine how she must feel? Suddenly, with no warning—for how could anyone warn her?—she has been taken from the familiar surroundings of the farm, separated from her father, her mother, her little brothers, and her good friend Mr. Tenney. Why, it is as if she had been suddenly plunged into an even darker prison than the one she has always lived in: still no light, no sound, almost no smells or tastes, and now not even the familiar things and people around her to touch!"

"I had thought of having Mrs. Bridgman remain here at the school for a few days," said Dr. Howe. "But I decided that since Laura is so bright and friendly, she would recover from the shock of separation quickly and I could begin her education sooner if we did not have to wean her gradually from her mother. I hope I am not wrong about this."

"She *is* bright and friendly, Sam," said Miss Jeannette enthusiastically. "I could see that even in the little while before her parents left."

And Dr. Howe was right in thinking that Laura would quickly recover from the first shock of separation. In less than a week Laura began to be her own lively self once more. She began to reach out with her wonderful hands to learn all she could about her new home.

The room that had been given to Laura was in Dr. Howe's own apartment, and he and his sister quickly became another father and mother to her. In a very short time she began learning, through her hands of course, to identify every member of the school family. There were more than forty people: blind children and teachers. Laura soon knew every one of them by touch.

At the end of two weeks Laura was so happy in her new surroundings that Dr. Howe felt he could begin the experiment he had planned. The night before he began, he discussed his plans aloud with his sister.

"My goal is perfectly clear to me, Jeannette," he said. "I am going to try to bring into Laura's mind the idea that there are twenty-six different signs or letters that everyone uses. This is our alphabet. I want her to know that by combining these letters into words, we can share our thoughts with each other."

"But Sam, how in the world are you going to 'tell' Laura that?" asked Miss Jeannette, puzzled. "If she were just blind, you could have her feel the raised-up letters with her fingers and tell her their names. Or, if she were just deaf and mute, you could show her letters. But she is blind and deaf and mute, so what can you do?"

"I know just exactly how I am going to try to do it," said Dr. Howe, smiling. "You may attend the first class with Laura tomorrow morning and see for yourself."

The great day dawned. When the first lesson began, Laura was seated at a table across from Dr. Howe. Beside her sat Miss Drew, who was to be Laura's own special teacher. Miss Jeannette Howe sat watching nearby.

The doctor had arranged a row of objects on the table in front of him. There were a large key, a spoon, a knife, a fork, a book, a cup, and a few other things with which he felt sure Laura would be familiar.

First Dr. Howe put the key into Laura's hand. It was a very large key. He let her handle it and feel it all over. She knew immediately what it was. The key at home with which she locked her boot in the cupboard was very much like this one—except for one thing. Her sensitive fingers paused as they felt the long key. There was something *on* this one.

Dr. Howe had fastened a paper label on the key. On the label the word *key* was written in a special kind of raised lettering or embossing that was used at that time in writing for the blind. The Braille system, now so widely used, had not yet been adopted. Dr. Howe guided Laura's fingers over the raised lines of the letters several times. She had no idea, of course, what the letters were.

Then he took the key away from Laura and handed her a spoon. She took it, felt it, and immediately recognized it as a spoon much like the ones with which she set the table at home. Again there was one important difference. Along the handle of the spoon Dr. Howe had pasted a label with the letters S-P-O-O-N written in raised type. Dr. Howe guided her fingers carefully over this word several times.

Now the doctor took away the spoon and gave the key back to Laura. He directed her fingers to the label on the key again. Then he gave her back the spoon and directed her fingers to the label on the spoon once more. He wanted Laura to feel that the shape of the lines on the key label and the shape of the lines on the spoon label were just as different from each other as the key and spoon themselves were different from one another.

Somewhere, thought Laura, I have felt lines like these before, but where? Was it on my plate that Uncle Asa gave me?

Now the doctor did something else. He took away the key and the spoon and gave Laura just a piece of paper with some raised letters on it. The letters were K-E-Y again. Taking the key once more, Dr. Howe directed Laura's fingers to the label on it.

An expression on Laura's face made it quite clear that she recognized that the raised letters were the same on both papers, the one on the key and the separate label. Dr. Howe went through the same process with the spoon and a separate label that read S-P-O-O-N.

The rest of that first lesson was spent letting Laura feel the remaining objects—cup, knife, book, and so forth—and the labels for these, both those pasted on the object and

those that were separate. From that time on, Laura had lessons every morning and afternoon. She seemed to enjoy them thoroughly and to consider them just a game, not work. It was difficult for Dr. Howe and Miss Drew to get her to stop "playing" this game.

By about the third day, Dr. Howe and Miss Drew were delighted to see that Laura had grasped the important point that the separate label for *key* somehow went with the key and the label that was separate from the spoon went with the spoon. That she understood this was shown by the fact that she could take a separate label, such as the one spelling *book*, and feel about until she found a book without any label. Then she would place the label on the book.

In a very few days Laura could reverse this process. She could pick up an object such as a spoon, search through a pile of loose labels on the table, feel them until she found the one that read S-P-O-O-N, and then put it on a spoon. She could do this for any object for which she had been taught the feeling of the word.

Dr. Howe was greatly encouraged. He felt sure that he was going to succeed with Laura; his only question was how long it was going to take him. In a report that he once wrote about his work with her, he said: "It sometimes occurred to me that

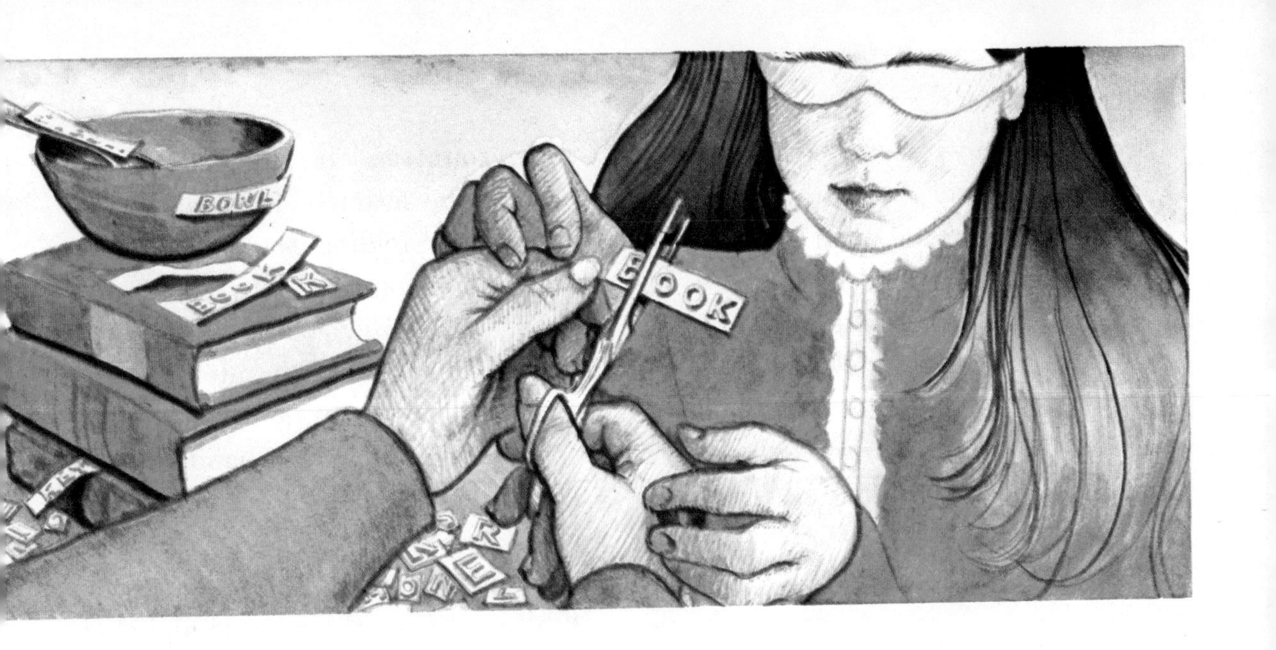

she was like a person alone and helpless in a deep, dark, still pit, and that I was letting down a cord and dangling it about, in hopes she might find it, and that finally she would seize it by chance, and, clinging to it, be drawn up by it into the light of day and into human society."

The lessons were going so well that Dr. Howe felt Laura was ready to take another important step forward. He had Miss Drew cut the labels for the words *key*, *spoon*, *knife*, and so forth, into separate letters. Up until this time, Laura had seen words as wholes. Now he wanted her to learn that they are made up of parts—letters. Laura was allowed to follow closely, with her hands, all that Miss Drew did. After the words had been cut into separate letters, her hands followed Miss Drew's as she arranged the letters back into words.

In an astonishingly short time, Laura had grasped the point of this new "game." If Miss Drew handed her the letters O, S, N, O, P, in a flash Laura could arrange them in the correct order to spell S-P-O-O-N. If Miss Drew gave her Y, K, E, Laura arranged them into the word K-E-Y. O, K, O, B and I, K, E, N, F were equally simple for her. After a few more lessons, Laura could do this with all the words in her vocabulary, and soon after that she could take from a whole pile of loose letters whatever ones she wanted and spell correctly any word she wished of those she had been taught. This would have been a great accomplishment for any eight-year-old. How much more remarkable it was for a little girl like Laura Bridgman!

Dr. Howe thought it would be easier for Laura to arrange the letters if there were some kind of form into which they could be fitted. Therefore he had metal letters—types, he called them—made for her, and a frame with grooves into which the letters could be fitted. He had four complete sets made of the twenty-six letters of the alphabet. Within a short time Laura was using the metal letters to build all the words she knew.

Two months had passed before Dr. Howe felt that Laura was ready to take the final step that he had planned for her. Miss Drew was sent to the home of a Mr. George Loring, who was a deaf-mute, to learn the manual alphabet. She learned it in one afternoon.

The manual alphabet is a way of forming the twenty-six letters of the alphabet with the hands. In the United States the one-handed manual alphabet is used. There is also a two-handed system used in some countries. In the one-handed system the letter *a*, for example, is formed by folding the four fingers over and keeping the thumb straight. *B* is formed by holding the fingers straight up with the thumb folded in. In only a few cases, as with *c* and *y*, for example, does the hand form a shape that very much resembles the shape of that letter as we write it.

A deaf person who has been "talking" with the manual alphabet for a long time can "say" with his hand as many as 130 words a minute. A deaf person who is skilled at watching another person "speak" with his hands can easily "read" 130 words a minute.

Laura, of course, would not be able to see the letters. Miss Drew would have to form them in Laura's hand, so that she could feel them.

But how could she teach Laura that the various positions in which she held her fingers meant the letters of the alphabet that she had already learned with raised letters and metal types? This is how Miss Drew did it. She picked up the key and let Laura feel it. Then she took the letter K from the set of metal types and let Laura feel that. Then she shaped the letter *k* in the manual alphabet into

Laura's hand, her first two fingers up and bent forward, the next two fingers folded down, and the thumb up. She made Laura feel the way her fingers were held. Then she let Laura feel the metal letter K again.

The same procedure was followed with the letter *e*. First Laura must feel the metal type of the E, then Miss Drew formed *e* in the manual alphabet, all the fingers folded over and the thumb folded down, and then back to the metal type again. Finally the letter Y was taken from the metal types and Laura allowed to feel it. The manual *y* is formed with thumb up, little finger up, and other fingers all folded down. This one almost looks like a *y* as we write it. Now Miss Drew had set the metal types K-E-Y in the form. She let Laura run her hand over the whole word. Then she formed again, in the manual alphabet, the letters *k-e-y* in Laura's hand, and she placed the key itself in Laura's other hand. This was done with the spoon, the cup, and the key again.

And then it happened! For two months Laura had been "playing" these games with letters and words almost the way a trained dog performs certain tricks. Now, suddenly, it was different. Dr. Howe always said that he knew almost the exact moment when Laura's face showed that she at last really understood what all this meant. Suddenly it seemed to become clear to her that every object had a name, that these names could be spelled by letters, either in raised letters, metal types, or, most easily of all, by the manual alphabet.

In one of his yearly reports about his work with Laura Bridgman, Dr. Howe wrote:

> . . . Now the truth began to flash upon her, her intellect began to work, she perceived that here was a way by which she could herself make up a sign of anything that was in her own mind, and show it to another mind, and at once her countenance lighted up with a human expression . . . I could almost fix upon the moment when this truth dawned upon her mind and spread its light to her countenance. . . .

Laura had found the rope that Dr. Howe was dangling before her. She had caught hold of it at last and could be drawn up from the dark pit in which she lived into the light of day!

Afterthought

In the title of this selection the phrase "the silent night" stands for the words deafness, muteness, and blindness. Instead of "Child of the Silent Night" the selection might have been titled "The Child Who Was Deaf, Mute, and Blind." Decide which title you think is better; think of several reasons for your choice and be ready to discuss them.

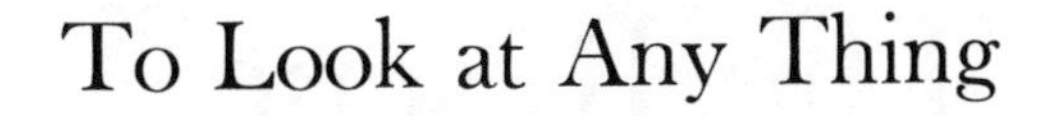

To Look at Any Thing

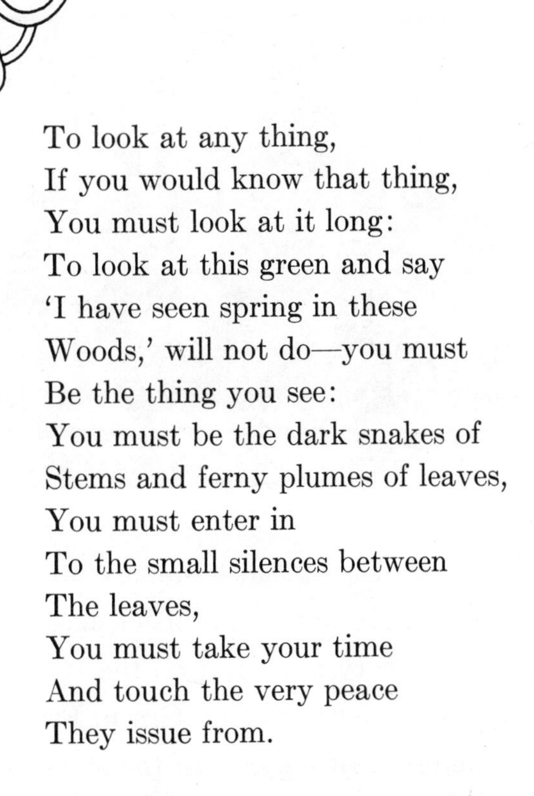

To look at any thing,
If you would know that thing,
You must look at it long:
To look at this green and say
'I have seen spring in these
Woods,' will not do—you must
Be the thing you see:
You must be the dark snakes of
Stems and ferny plumes of leaves,
You must enter in
To the small silences between
The leaves,
You must take your time
And touch the very peace
They issue from.

John Moffitt

The Rescue

William O. Steele

Flan Taylor had too many problems to make a good pioneer. He was small for his age, clumsy, and afraid of almost everything. But on the Wilderness Trail with the Long Hunter Chapman Green, Flan got a chance to believe in himself. In the part of the story you will read, Flan and Mr. Green are traveling with Mr. Rhea, a trader.

He woke early next morning. He'd sort of hoped he wouldn't be so stiff and sore this day, but as soon as he sat up in his blanket his muscles started aching.

The Long Hunter was already up, and in a few moments the trader threw back his fur robe and sat up. He and Flan went down to the spring together to get a drink. They ate the remains of the turkey for breakfast.

"I got meal for ashcake," said Mr. Rhea. "But there's no use wasting it when we got turkey breast. We may need that meal afore long. Game's scarce." Chapman Green agreed and handed Flan a piece of the breast. The white meat was dry and fine-textured, and it was almost as good and satisfying as bread. Mr. Rhea had gathered some beechnuts, and he gave Flan a handful to eat as they walked.

While the trader was getting his truck together, Mr. Green handed Flan his rifle.

"Here. There's a big knot over on that hickory tree. See if you still got that shooting eye."

Flan took the rifle, but glanced uneasily at Mr. Rhea. The trader was busy getting his pack onto his horse and seemed to be taking no notice. Flan picked out a handy tree to steady the rifle and aimed carefully.

He fired three times. The first time he hit the tree near the knot. The second time he missed completely. The third time he hit the black knot square in the center.

"Now ain't that fine shooting for a lad that never fired a rifle but once up till yesterday?" asked Mr. Green proudly.

Flan swelled up fit to burst.

Mr. Rhea came and examined the knot. "How come a boy like you ain't learned to shoot afore this?" he asked.

He looked at Flan accusingly, and Flan felt himself turning red.

"Well," Mr. Green answered for him. "He's got some big brothers that figured they could shoot so good he didn't have no call to learn how. When he tried, they like to bust theirselves open laughing at him, instead of helping him do better. But he's a natural-born shot."

Mr. Rhea shook his head. "Aye, when brothers laugh at brothers, they're bound to come to grief sooner or later. When I was a boy I laughed at my oldest brother for a story he told, till he up and left home. And now I know it was the truth he spoke, and I ain't never laid eyes on him again to make amends."

He looked very doleful. Flan wondered if he was going to tell what the story was that the brother had told. The horses were ready now, so they set out down the trail.

"My oldest brother was a hand for traveling in strange parts," said Mr. Rhea slowly. "He come home with tales about this and that, and we always believed him. All except me, that is, and I'd laugh at all his tales and say they were lies. It was

because I was the same as he was, I reckon, and I was a-hankering to be off to new lands myself.

"It made me feisty to hear him come back and tell of those places, and me not able to go and see 'em. So no matter what he told, I'd laugh and hold my sides and say it was the tallest tale I'd ever heard."

He sighed and ate a beechnut. "So when he come home a-telling how he'd found bones as big as cabins, I 'lowed that was the best tale of all. I laughed till I cried. I told my other brothers and my relations and all the neighbors he was addled in the head, for he claimed he'd seen the bones of animals as tall as mountains.

"I laughed at him and guyed him till the others took it up, and every time we'd see him coming we'd yell, 'Oh, Jack'—for that was his name, Jack—'Oh, Jack, we just seen a 'possum twelve feet tall down at the spring!' Or some such thing. And after a spell he got so riled up, he left the cabin one day and vowed he'd never come back."

"Didn't you never see him again?" asked Flan.

"Never laid eyes on him till this day," answered Mr. Rhea.

"But two, three years ago, when I was up in Kentuck country with another feller, we come on a marshy place there. And lying about on the earth was the biggest bare bones I ever hope to see. Rib bones so tall a man could stand inside 'em and stretch his rifle up as far as he could and still not touch the top. Leg bones taller than a horse. It fair give me a turn to stand in that quiet place with all them great white bones lying about. Me and my partner left out of there, but I stayed long enough to know my brother'd been telling the truth."

"You never seen any of them animals alive, did you?" asked Flan a little fearfully.

"No, and I hope I never do," answered Mr. Rhea fervently.

"What kind of critters do you reckon they was?" asked Flan.

"Oh, now, game grows to right good size in Kentuck," spoke up Mr. Green calmly. "I expect these was a couple of rabbits or squirrels some wildcat had for his supper and left the bones there in the swamp."

He grinned at Flan and Flan grinned back.

They made good time for the rest of that day and all the next. Flan was proud because he could keep up with the two men. They never had to slow down or wait for him at all. Or anyway he didn't think they did. And his muscles were toughening up. After a day's hard walking, he would be plenty tired and his legs stiff, but they were never sore anymore.

Mr. Green made Flan take a few shots with the rifle whenever they stopped to water the horses or for a meal. He hardly ever missed now. Mr. Green said it was time he learned to load.

"Put the powder in the pan first off. That way you ain't apt to forget it," the hunter explained. "Just a dab, then close the pan cover."

Flan could see that it wouldn't take much, for the pan was shallow, but he was worried about how much to pour in the rifle barrel.

"Now there's some that measures the powder they put in the barrel," Mr. Green went on. "That's fine, if you got all the time in creation. But if Injuns is a-coming or a bear, you'd be better off pouring the powder straight from the horn. So you might as well learn that way right off."

Mr. Green placed the small end of his powder flask in the muzzle and shook powder down it once, twice. "A couple of quick shakes like that. It ain't hard once you get the hang of it."

He reached inside his shot pouch and took out a patch made of coarse tow cloth. "It's best to keep you a few patches already cut out, but they're no trouble to make. Put one on the muzzle and center the lead ball on it. Then you start it down the barrel with your thumb, like this. And push it on down with your ramrod. Not hard, mind you. Just send it down easylike till it'll just touch the powder. Now you try it."

Flan tried. He stuck his tongue out and worked hard. The day was hot, and water dripped from his forehead and chin till finally Mr. Green laughed.

"You can't fire a rifle with wet powder, Flan," he teased, and Flan grinned at him.

But he sweated on and loaded his gun. After that he loaded every time he shot. He made mistakes sometimes, but he didn't mind. Mr. Rhea said he'd never be a fine shot because his eyes were too close together. Flan knew he would in time. He was getting used to the rifle now, and the quick jolt of the recoil against his shoulder was a good feel. If he sometimes poured too much powder in the pan so that when the cover closed the extra powder was knocked to the ground and wasted, Mr. Green never said a word.

At first Mr. Rhea watched him shoot, shaking his head sadly at every mistake the boy made. Then as Flan improved, Mr. Rhea didn't pay any more attention to his practice.

Mr. Rhea was a strange-looking man with narrow green eyes, and he didn't miss a thing along the trail. He was always on the lookout for something a little different, a little odd. He showed Flan queer rock formations, double leaves, a tree strangled to death by a vine, a hollow sycamore where swallows nested by the thousands. In his shirt he carried a white squirrel fur, the dried wing of a bat, some big brown beans with a sweet smell.

Flan liked the things Mr. Rhea showed him, but he didn't like to listen to the trader's tales. They were always sad or scary, about people who got drowned or snakebit or killed by Indians. Sometimes it seemed like Mr. Rhea was the gloomiest man in creation.

His packhorse's name was Stella. He had named her that because she had a star on her forehead, and once a man had told him that Stella was Latin for Star. She was a tall bony horse, as odd-looking as her master, with a funny patchy coat, but Mr. Rhea said she was the smartest horse in the States.

The third day they traveled with Moses Rhea was as hot a day as Flan ever remembered. He struggled along the trail up and down the rolling hills with his linsey shirt clinging to his back. He was grateful for every patch of shade and cool stream they came to. The horses too lingered at the springs, their hides dark with sweat.

Mr. Rhea tugged at Stella's lead thong. "She's skittish today," he explained. "She smells Injuns for sure."

"She smells a storm more likely," said Mr. Green, and Flan hoped he was right. The very thought of meeting a band of Indians turned him to stone. He'd never be able to run from the savages. He'd do the wrong thing and get them all killed.

Sure enough, in the early afternoon dark clouds billowed up in the sky to the southwest. Lightning flashed in the black sky and distant thunder grumbled, but the day stayed as hot as ever.

"We'd ought to make it to Cumberland Gap by night," said Mr. Green. He scanned the sky. "We'll get wet afore we get there, I reckon, but I won't mind. I'm as dry as the old well right now."

They walked on steadily. Flan felt baked, he was so hot. He drank at every spring they came to, and still, ten paces along the trail, his mouth would be as parched as ever. To their right the long blue line of the Cumberland Mountains stayed in sight but came no closer. Mr. Green quickened his pace, and Flan set his teeth and forced his legs to move faster.

Then the wind came whistling over the hills and hit them sharply as they trudged along. Brown and yellow leaves flew through the air, and the dust swirled about their legs.

As they came to the top of a hill, the wind roared through the valley below them, bending the yellowing tops of the trees and making a wild noise. A great limb broke from a hickory tree and fell to the ground just behind them. Flan jumped, thinking it might be Indians. He knew he was too tired to run.

He drew in great breaths of the cool air. It was sweet with the smell of coming rain, and the forest was alive and excited. Every leaf and twig spun and fluttered in the wind. A flock of pigeons flew over, were caught and hurled through the sky by

the great gusts of wind. A buck and two does splashed across a creek and into the shelter of a thicket.

The Cumberland Mountains loomed right overhead now, gaunt and dark, and the gloomy thunderheads piled up. A spattering of rain fell and a flash of lightning split the sky.

The thunder growled and rumbled constantly, and the wind blew so Mr. Green had to shout to them, " 'Tain't much further to the Gap, now. There's a cave there I know of. We can sleep dry in there."

Flan hoped it wasn't far. It was so dark he could hardly see to walk, and the wind was so strong that when it hit him he staggered. They were going uphill now. He pulled himself along by the bushes that grew close to the trace.

"Here it comes," shouted Mr. Rhea and began to run.

Flan heard the new noise, a deeper roar than that of the wind, and saw the white mist of rain come driving toward them through the twilight. Then it was on them, pounding against the side of the mountain like horses' hooves. It fell on him in a drenching torrent, and in a minute he was wet to the skin. The rain stung his eyes and he stumbled forward, blinded, frightened, and half-drowned.

Chapman Green guided him by the shoulder. "Come on," he shouted.

They stumbled on. Flan could hear his sobbing breath, and his chest felt like it was splitting for lack of air. In the next lightning flash he could see the mouth of a cave in front of them.

"Here," shouted the Long Hunter. "Hold these horses, Flan, whilst we get the powder in the cave."

Mr. Rhea had already tied Stella beyond the mouth of the

cave. Now he came back, and the men quickly unloaded the powder and disappeared into the black hole in the rocks.

Lightning and thunder ripped through the sky. The horses shuddered and tossed their heads nervously. It was all Flan could do to hold them. In the flashes of lightning he could see the foam on their great mouths. He had thought the horses were his friends, but now he scarcely recognized them in these huge wild beasts who reared and whinnied and jerked at the reins.

In a moment Mr. Green took the thongs from his hand. "I'll tie 'em over yonder," he shouted, nodding to a place below the cave. Flan didn't wait to watch but scooted into the entrance. It was so low he had to stoop to keep from bumping his head.

Mr. Rhea was squatting on the floor of the cave, holding a blazing splinter in his hand for a torch. Chapman Green came lumbering in, all bent over.

"I tied them horses good," he announced. "I hope you tied Stella pretty stout, Rhea. All this thunder and lightning's liable to send all three of them nags straight over to Chickasaw country. We don't want to have to spend tomorrow looking for 'em. Not but what the critters wouldn't break a leg sure getting down this mountain in the rain."

Mr. Rhea held his splinter higher and looked around. "Some friends left us a fire in here," he said in a strange voice. "Still a-burning."

Mr. Green checked his rifle, putting fresh powder in the pan. Then Flan watched as the two men examined the floor of the cave, especially the sand over to one side where a little stream flowed from the back of the cave and then out the mouth.

Chapman Green straightened up. "I reckon I'll go outside and take a look around for them friends," he said at last. "It was neighborly of 'em to leave a fire, but they had no call to throw a broken arrowhead down for us to find."

Injuns! Flan began to shiver in earnest and crept closer to the fire.

"If they aim to come back and use this fire tonight, I aim to know about it before they get here," Mr. Green said as he went out.

Mr. Rhea began to walk around the cave, looking for dry sticks to use on the fire. He found a few and built up the fire a little.

"I'm a-going this way," he told Flan, indicating a passage with his torch. "I might find some more wood back there. You want to come?"

Flan shook his head miserably. But after the trader had disappeared, he wished he'd gone with him. The leaping flames made odd shadows on the walls of the cave, and the sounds of

the storm came to him weirdly from outside. He hoped Mr. Green came back soon.

Finally he went to the front of the cave and crouched there, looking out into the night. The rain had slackened a good bit, but the lightning was dazzling bright and the thunder was deafening. He could see the dark shapes of the horses, Stella on one side, Mr. Green's horses on the other side, further away.

Suddenly there was a terrible blazing light all around him, a hissing, crackling sound, and then such a roar of thunder that it seemed to fling him back into the cave. He pressed himself against the rocks and peered out. The lightning had struck a tree, a dead pine tree standing not twenty yards from the cave entrance. And in spite of the rain it was burning fiercely.

And then in the light from the burning tree, Flan saw Meg and Brownie. Terror-stricken the poor beasts reared and plunged, jerking at the halters that tethered them. Fiery splinters from the burning tree fell around them and on them. They shrieked and lashed out with their hooves. Stella whinnied in alarm, but she was tied safely out of the way.

Flan knew in an instant that someone would have to loose the horses. If the lightning-fired tree didn't fall on them and burn them, they'd kill each other rearing and fighting that way.

"Mr. Green!" he bellowed. "Mr. Rhea!"

But he knew neither of the men could hear nor get to the horses in time if they heard. The horses would be killed, and the powder they'd brought this long way would never get to James Robertson.

With a despairing cry, Flan ran toward the plunging, maddened horses.

He kept his eyes on Meg as he ran. She was the nearest; he would free her first. He circled wide to avoid the plunging hooves, slipping and stumbling over the rocks. Once a branch, heavy with rain, slapped him across the face and sent him sprawling among the wet underbrush.

One of the horses screamed.

"I'm a-coming, Meg," he panted, struggling on. His wet buckskins made him slow and awkward.

Finally he reached the spot where Meg was tied. Just beyond, the fire roared and crackled. He put up his arm to shield his face from the heat. In the red glow of the burning tree the horses looked as big as mountains. Their lips were pulled back from the great yellow teeth, and their eyes rolled madly. Again and again they reared before him and came plunging back to earth. Those flashing hooves could crush his skull like a puffball.

Flan began to work at the knot, picking at it with trembling fingers. He worked slowly for he had to watch Meg, stopping often to duck away from the snorting, thrashing mare.

He couldn't seem to get hold of the wet leather, and finally he began to claw desperately at the thong, wishing Mr. Green hadn't tied it so tight, or that Meg wouldn't pull it tighter every time he tried to loosen it.

He glanced up at the flaming tree, towering over him in the

blackened sky. It couldn't burn much longer. The top at least was bound to fall in another moment, and they'd all be burned to death. He had to do something quick.

His knife! What a woodenhead he'd been! Frantically he snatched out his hunting knife and reached for the leather thong.

There was a sudden sharp crack that made him jump. A limb broke from the burning pine and hurtled to the ground. A big flake of blazing wood lit on his hand, and he dropped the knife. Half-sobbing, he crouched to pick it up, snatching among those wicked hooves and at last seizing it.

He pulled himself up by holding on to Meg's tree. He could feel it tremble as Meg jerked in panic. Her eyes were wild and staring, and foam fell from her lips.

He slashed again at the leather thong. A shower of sparks sent the horses shrieking and rearing worse than ever. He cowered back for a second, but then he was sawing away at the thong again, standing as far back from the horses as he could.

But the knife didn't cut. There was something wrong with the knife his pap had given him. It wouldn't cut the thong at all.

With a rush of relief he saw that he had got the knife blade turned around and was trying to cut with the dull thick backside. In an instant he turned the knife over and hacked at the leather.

Then Meg was free. He heard the hard sound of her hooves on the rocks as she vanished. He turned to Brownie.

Brownie was wild with fear. There was an ugly red mark across his nostrils. In a frenzy he lashed out at Flan, his big hooves grazing the tree to which he was tied. Sweating with fear, Flan thrust at the thong again and again, but he couldn't get close enough because Brownie bit at him.

Any moment that tree would fall. Desperately he lunged forward and slashed at the thong where it circled the tree. He cut it cleanly and jumped away. With a final terror-filled whinny, Brownie sped away!

"Run, Flan! The tree! Run!" Chapman Green's voice from the trail was hoarse.

Panic-stricken Flan stood in the circle of glaring light. A moment before, he had known the tree would fall on him. Now each way he turned he was sure that was the way the tree would fall. He was trapped. He could not move.

Mr. Rhea called sharply from the cave entrance, "This way, Flan!"

His wet leather breeches were like iron clothes. His knees couldn't bend in them, and they were heavy as bars of lead. He didn't know how he ever managed to make his way over the slippery stones to the mouth of the cave. It seemed like a year till Mr. Rhea grabbed his hand and pulled him inside.

There was a crash and a moment of wild flaming light, and a million stars seemed to fly through the night. But he was safe. He lay on the floor of the .cave, panting and gasping, until Chapman Green bent over him.

"Be you all right, lad?" he asked anxiously. "You ain't burnt?" He pulled the boy to his feet, asking again, "Be you all right?"

Flan shook his head. "I ain't hurt," he said finally, though there was a blister as big as a frog on the back of his hand.

They walked back into the room of the cave. Flan took off his wet clothes and sat wrapped in his blanket while Mr. Rhea brewed him a hot drink.

"Put some mud on that burn. It'll take the sting out. I ain't got anything for a burn but that," Mr. Green told him.

Mr. Rhea poured the tea into Flan's horn cup and explained, "I went off a-looking for dry wood, and I come on a room just full of all sorts of rock shapes. Curious looking as all git. I broke off an icicle for you, Flan." He handed over a small brown stalactite sparkling in the firelight. "Time I got back here, I found Flan gone and heard them horses squealing and taking on. I never figured he'd get out of that alive."

"He's a brave lad," said Mr. Green. "I made sure the Injuns had you when I seen the fire and heard the horses taking on so."

He set a flat stone down in the edge of the ashes to brown the ashcake. "I come up the trail as quick and quiet as I could and there's the boy risking his neck to loose the horses. I said then he was as brave a lad as I ever seen. He's tough. A mite puny, but he's tough."

Flan listened sleepily, his heart pounding with pride. He'd done the right thing for once. He'd done a good thing, a brave thing. He'd risked his life and won out, and he was as tough as hickory. He reckoned he could do most anything out in the woods, shoot a rifle, rescue horses, anything.

Afterthought

1. Find places in the story to show that Mr. Green thought praise, jokes, and patience would help Flan solve his problems.
2. Why would Mr. Rhea have been a poor one to help Flan gain confidence?
3. How will Flan's experience in the storm help him the next time he is scared?
4. How might remembering what you've read in this unit help you with your own problems?

Metaphor

Morning is
a new sheet of paper
for you to write on.

Whatever you want to say,
all day,
until night
folds it up
and files it away.

The bright words and the dark words
are gone
until dawn
and a new day
to write on.

Eve Merriam

Free to Be . . .
You and Me

There's a land that I see
Where the children are free.
And I say it ain't far
To this land, from where we are.

Take my hand. Come with me,
Where the children are free.
Come with me, take my hand,
And we'll live . . .

In a land
Where the river runs free—
(In a land)
Through the green country—
(In a land)
To a shining sea.

And you and me
Are free to be
You and me.

I see a land, bright and clear,
And the time's coming near,
When we'll live in this land,
You and me, hand-in-hand.

Take my hand. Come along,
Lend your voice to my song.
Come along. Take my hand,
Sing a song . . .

For a land
Where the river runs free—
(For a land)
Through the green country—
(For a land)
To a shining sea—
(For a land)
Where the horses run free.

And you and me
Are free to be
You and me.

Every boy in this land
Grows to be his own man.
In this land, every girl
Grows to be her own woman.

Take my hand. Come with me,
Where the children are free.
Come with me. Take my hand,
And we'll run . . .

To a land
Where the river runs free—
(To a land)
Through the green country—
(To a land)
To a shining sea—
(To a land)
Where the horses run free—
(To a land)
Where the children are free.

And you and me
Are free to be
You and me.

And you and me
Are free to be
You and me.

Stephen Lawrence and Bruce Hart

The Southpaw

Judith Viorst

Sometimes being free requires courage, patience . . . and a sense of humor.

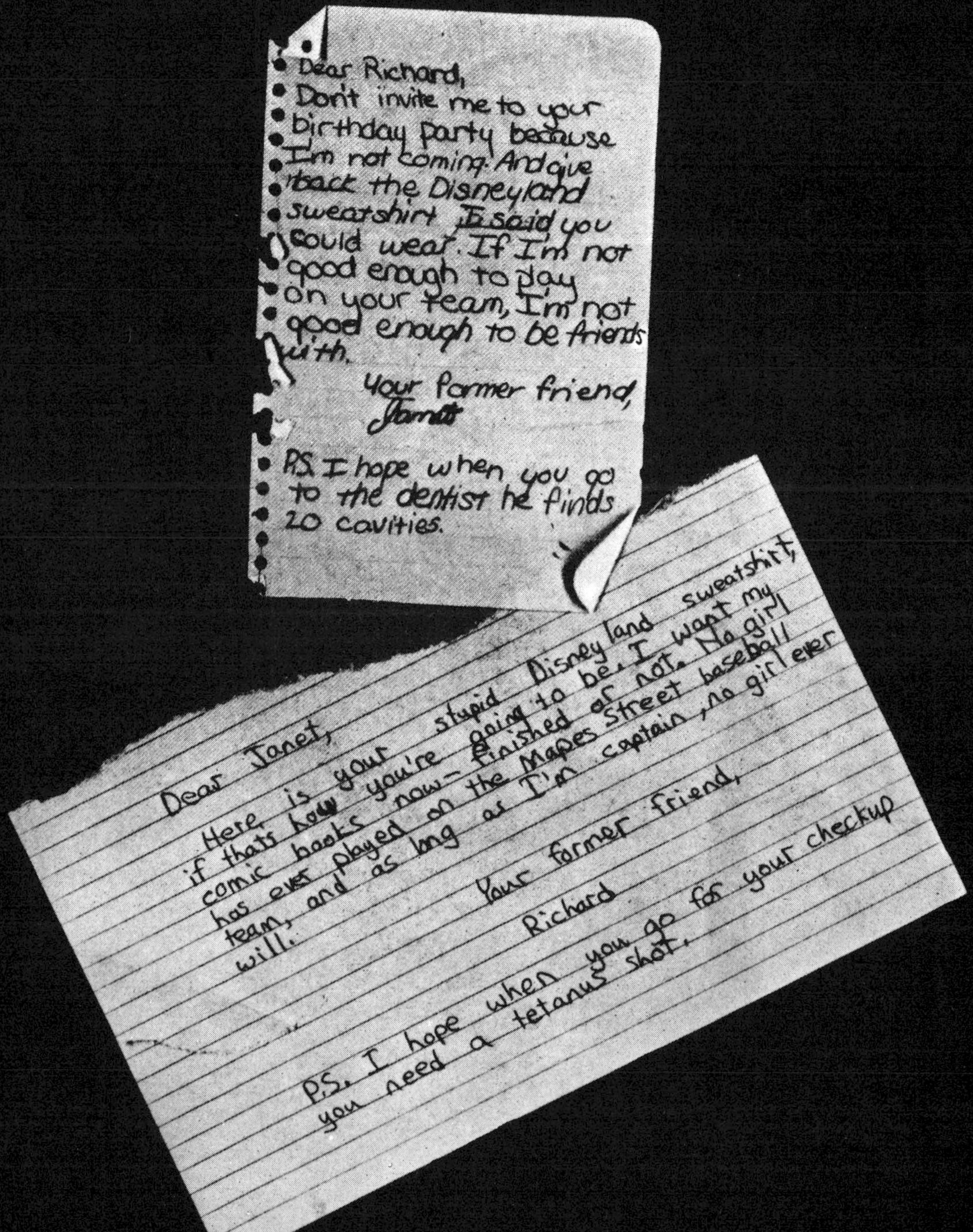

Dear Richard,
Don't invite me to your
birthday party because
I'm not coming. And give
back the Disneyland
sweatshirt I said you
could wear. If I'm not
good enough to play
on your team, I'm not
good enough to be friends
with.

Your former friend,
Janet

P.S. I hope when you go
to the dentist he finds
20 cavities.

Dear Janet,

Here is your stupid Disneyland sweatshirt,
if that's how you're going to be. I want my
comic books now — finished or not. No girl
has ever played on the Mapes Street baseball
team, and as long as I'm captain, no girl ever
will.

Your former friend,

Richard

P.S. I hope when you go for your checkup
you need a tetanus shot.

Dear Richard,
I'm changing my goldfish's
name from Richard to
Stanley. Don't count on
my vote for class
president next year.
Just because I'm a
member of the ballet
club doesn't mean I'm
not a terrific ballplayer.
Your former friend,
Janet

P.S. I see you lost
your first game 28-0

Dear Janet,

I'm not saving anymore seats for you on
the bus. For all I care you can stand the
whole way to school. Why don't you just
forget about baseball and learn something
nice like knitting?
your former friend,

Richard

P.S. Wait until Wednesday!

Dear Richard,
My father said I could
call someone to go
with us for a ride
and hot-fudge sundaes.
In case you didnt
notice, I didnt call
you.
Your former friend
Janet

P.S. I see you lost your
second game, 34-0.

Dear Janet,
Remember when I took the laces out of my
blue-and-white sneakers and gave them
to you? I want them back.
Your former friend,
Richard

P.S. Wait until Friday.

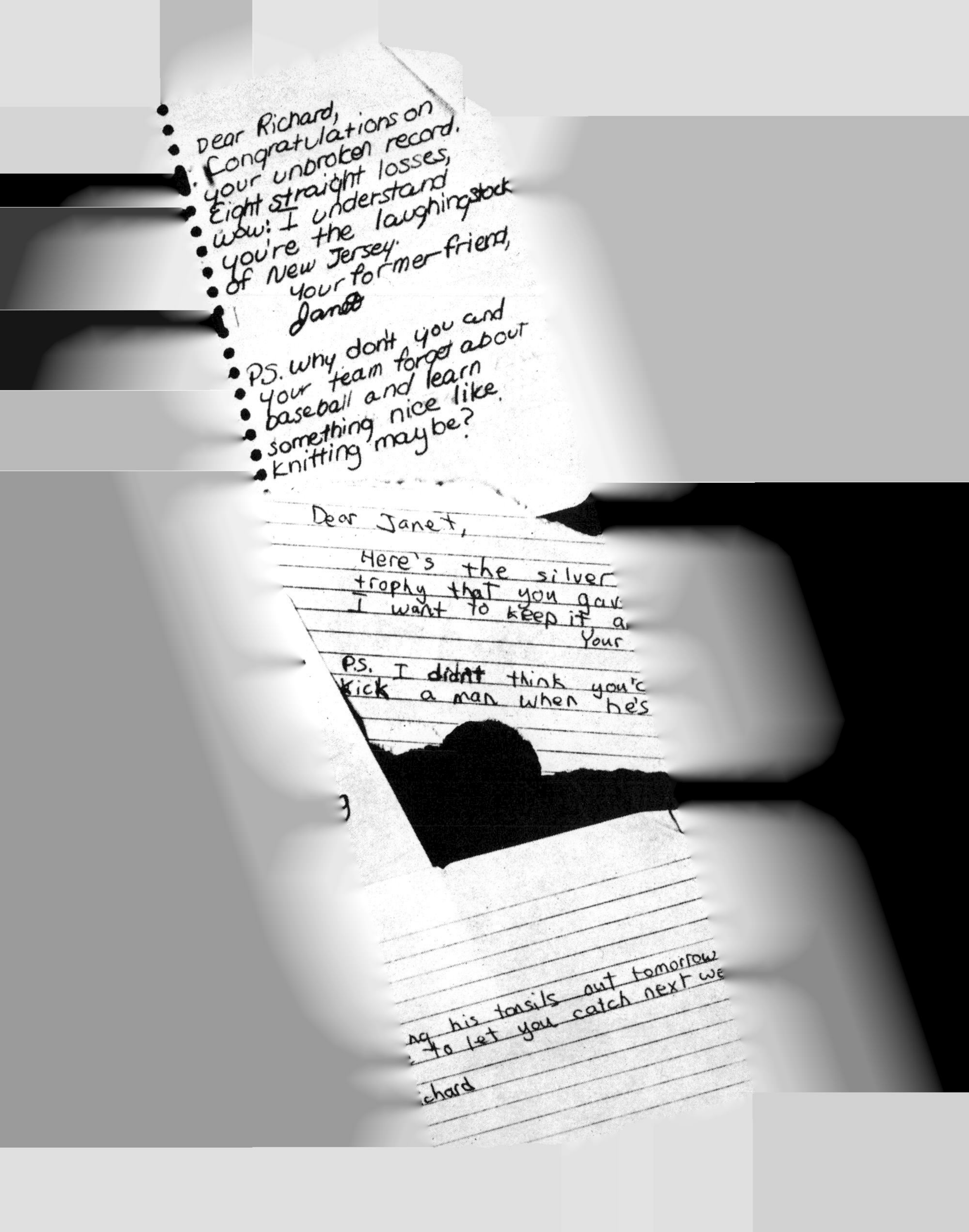
Dear Richard,
Congratulations on
your unbroken record.
Eight straight losses,
wow! I understand
you're the laughingstock
of New Jersey.
Your former friend,
Janet

P.S. Why don't you and
your team forget about
baseball and learn
something nice like
knitting maybe?

Dear Janet,
Here's the silver
trophy that you gav
I want to keep it a
Your

P.S. I didnt think you'c
kick a man when he's

g his tonsils out tomorrow
to let you catch next we

chard

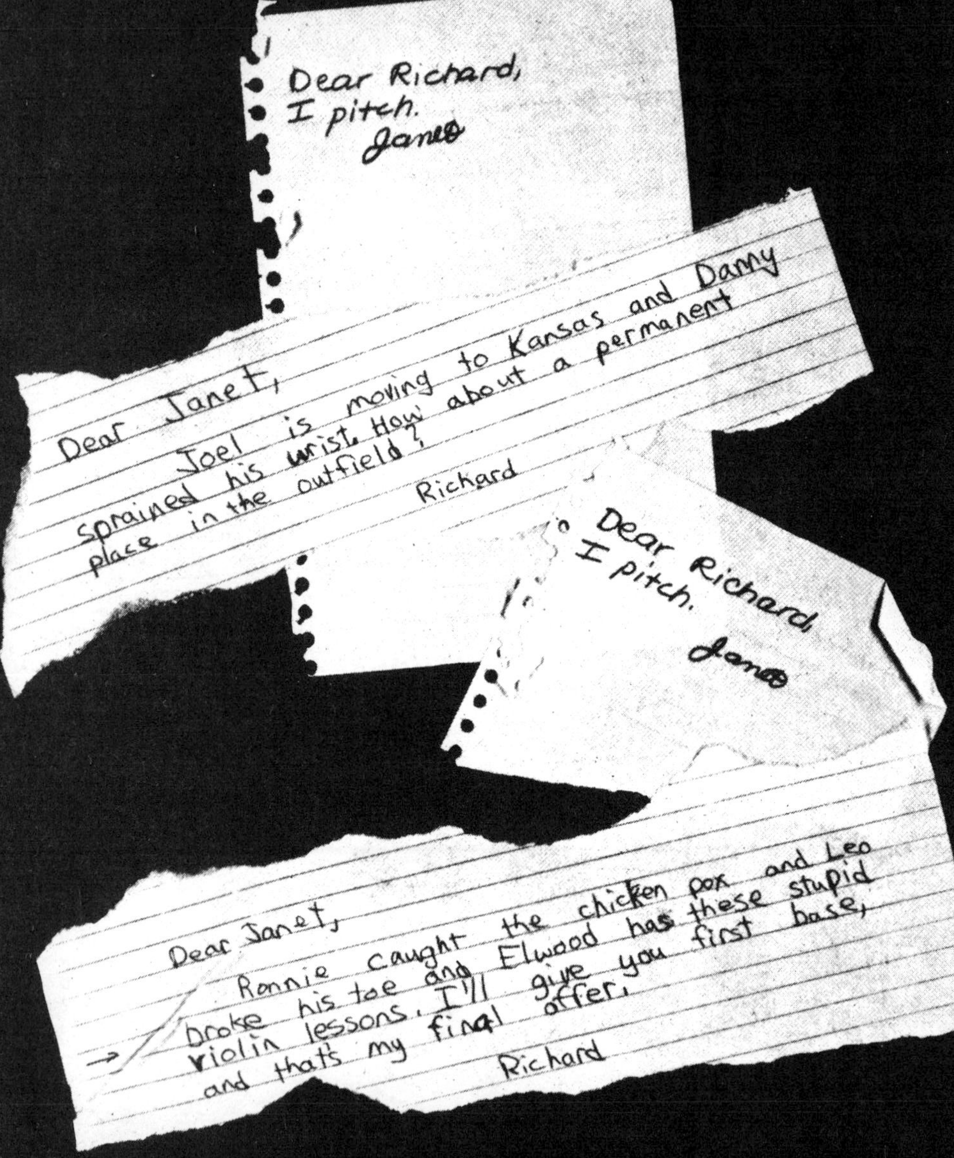

Dear Richard,
I pitch.
Janet

Dear Janet,
Joel is moving to Kansas and Danny sprained his wrist. How about a permanent place in the outfield?
Richard

Dear Richard,
I pitch.
Janet

Dear Janet,
Ronnie caught the chicken pox and Leo broke his toe and Elwood has these stupid violin lessons. I'll give you first base, and that's my final offer.
Richard

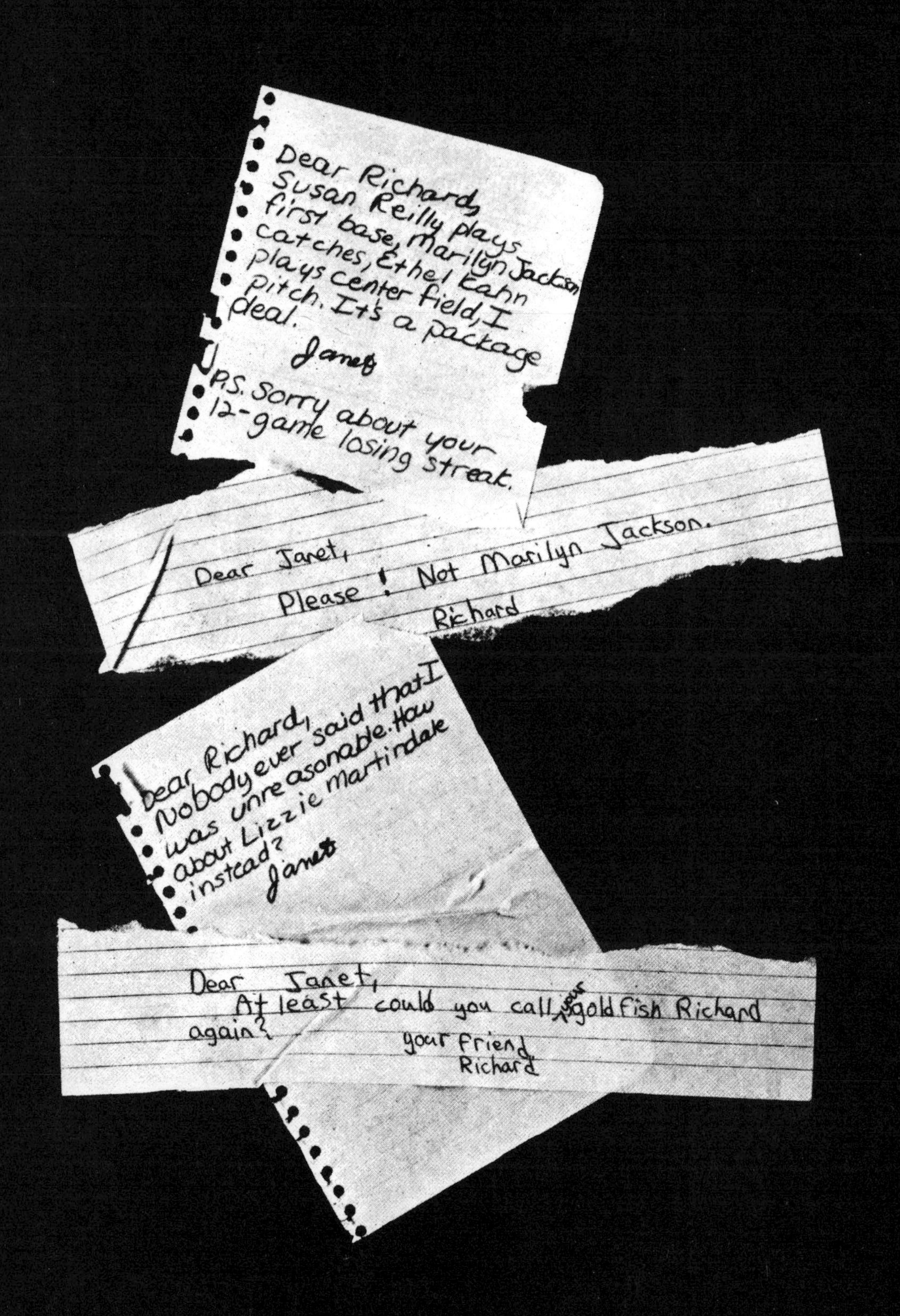
Dear Richard,
Susan Reilly plays first base, Marilyn Jackson catches, Ethel Kahn plays center field, I pitch. It's a package deal.
Janet
P.S. Sorry about your 12-game losing streak.

Dear Janet,
Please! Not Marilyn Jackson.
Richard

Dear Richard,
Nobody ever said that I was unreasonable. How about Lizzie Martindale instead?
Janet

Dear Janet,
At least could you call your goldfish Richard again?
your friend
Richard

Call of the Sea

Kansas Boy

This Kansas boy who never saw the sea
Walks through the young corn rippling at his knee
As sailors walk; and when the grain grows higher
Watches the dark waves leap with greener fire
Than ever oceans hold. He follows ships,
Tasting the bitter spray upon his lips,
For in his blood up-stirs the salty ghost
Of one who sailed a storm-bound English coast.
Across wide fields he hears the sea winds crying,
Shouts at the crows—and dreams of white gulls flying.

Ruth Lechlitner

Earth's Wonderful Sea

You may never have seen the sea. But, like the Kansas boy, you can hear "sea winds crying" no matter where you live. The following article will help you hear the call of the sea.

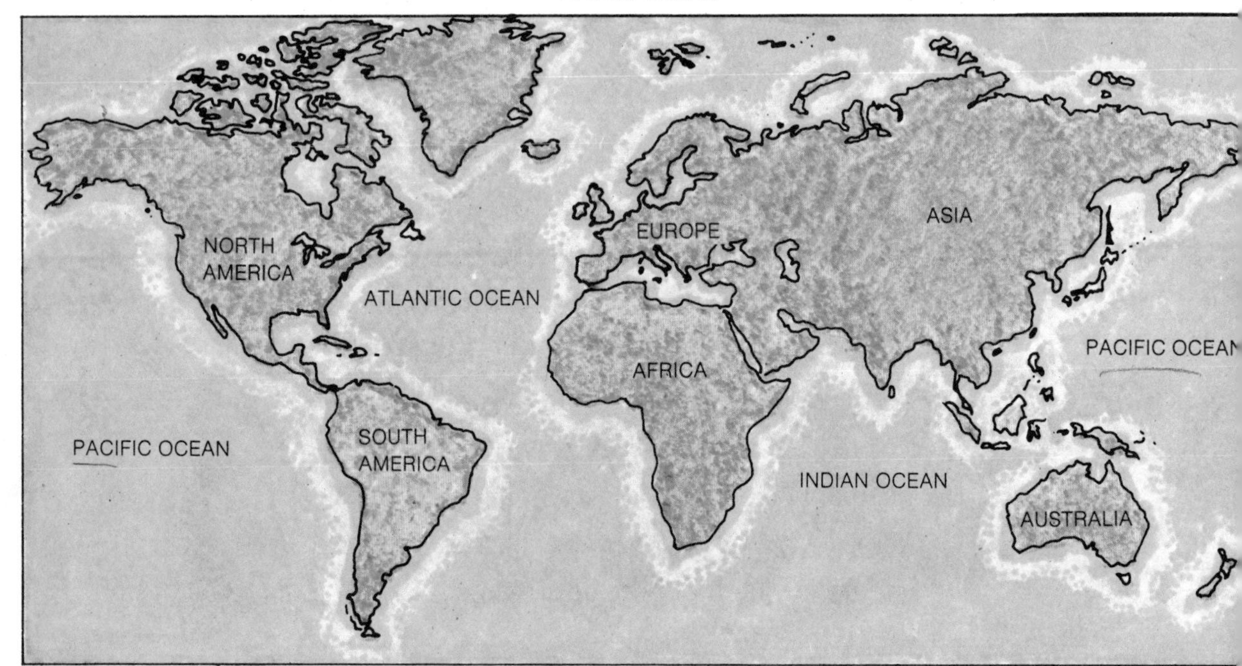

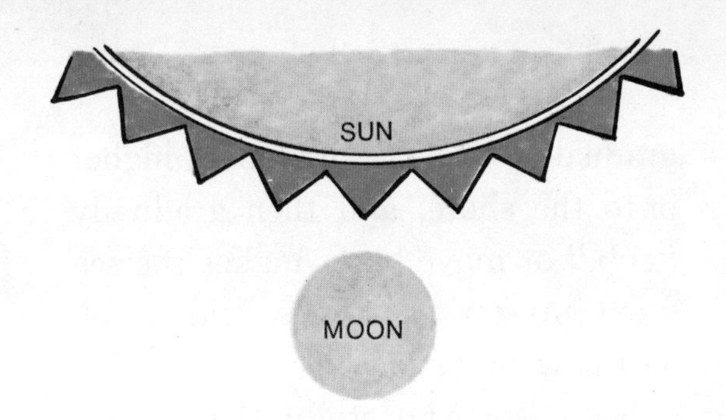

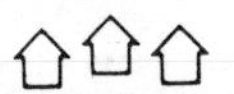

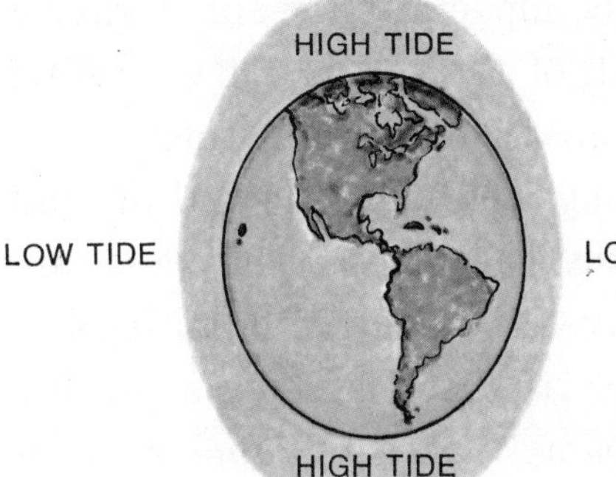

Continents and Oceans

The surface of our planet, Earth, is covered with bodies of land and water. The larger land masses are the continents, and the larger bodies of water are the five oceans—Pacific, Atlantic, Indian, Antarctic, and Arctic. Here and there, dotting the waters of these oceans, are found smaller land masses. These are the islands of the earth.

The five huge oceans and some smaller bodies of water—seas, gulfs, and bays—are connected. Together they form one vast body of salt water that covers almost three-fourths of the earth's surface.

The Surface of the Sea

Down through the ages this great ocean has been referred to as "the sea." It is so vast that it reaches entirely around the earth, and it has many strange and interesting features. Among these are the tides, the waves, and the currents of the sea. And strange indeed are the lands that lie beneath its surface.

Anyone who has visited the seashore has noticed the ocean tides. Watching the water in the sea gradually "flow," or move higher onto the shore, and then gradually "ebb," or move back, makes the sea seem mysterious. These tides ebb and flow twice each day.

Scientists who study the oceans, oceanographers, say that the tides are caused by the pull of gravity from the moon and the sun. Gravity pulls all of the earth, but we see its effect most clearly in the tides.

Among the most beautiful and impressive features of the sea are the waves that move across its surface. Earth has few sights lovelier than foamy whitecaps dancing across a sunlit sea. And when we watch the huge waves that crash against shore during a storm, we begin to realize how immense and powerful the sea is.

The sea's waves are, of course, caused by winds blowing across the water. Winds also help to cause one of the most interesting and important features of the sea—the currents. But the winds that affect the currents are steady winds that blow all the time. The currents also move all the time, flowing thousands of miles across the oceans. So steady and regular is their movement that they have been called the "rivers of the sea."

Some of the sea's currents are warm; others are cold. These currents help to regulate temperatures in different areas of the earth.

Perhaps the most famous current is the Gulf Stream. It flows up the Atlantic coast of North America from the Gulf of Mexico. After leaving the coast of America, this amazing stream moves across the Atlantic Ocean to warm the coast of northern Europe before it finally disappears.

Lands beneath the Sea

So far we have talked only about the surface of the sea. What of the

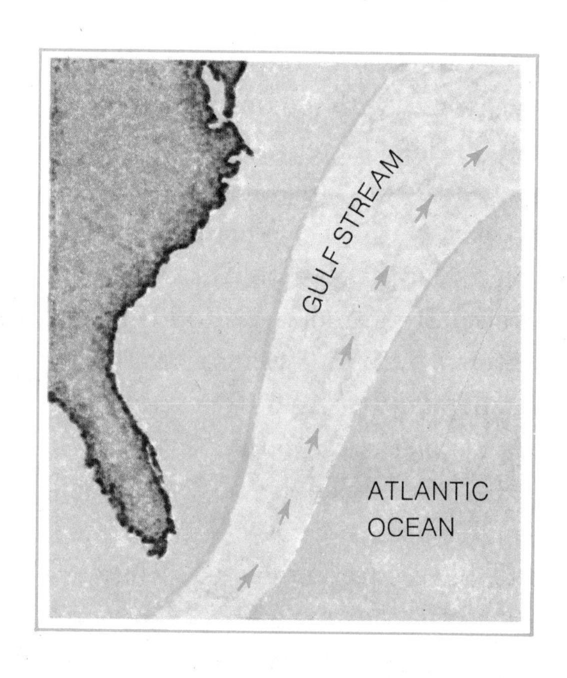

land beneath it? Early sailors believed that most of the land below the sea was a smooth and level plain. Today we know that there are not only plains but also wide valleys, deep canyons, enormous mountain ranges, and even volcanoes.

Scientists generally think of the land under the seas as divided into three types. There are the continental shelves, which are lands lying under shallower waters next to the continents. At the edge of these shelves are underwater lands that drop steeply to the deepest parts of the oceans. These steep lands are the continental slopes. And then there are the mysterious, sunless deeps of the abyss, the ocean bottom.

For many years oceanographers have been at work measuring and mapping the lands below the sea. Sounding lines have long been used to measure the ocean depths. A sounding line is a weighted rope marked off in fathoms. It is dropped over the side of a ship to measure the ocean's depths.

The newest and best instrument for measuring the deepest areas is sonar. This instrument beams a sound wave from a ship to the bottom of the sea. After it strikes bottom, the sound wave bounces

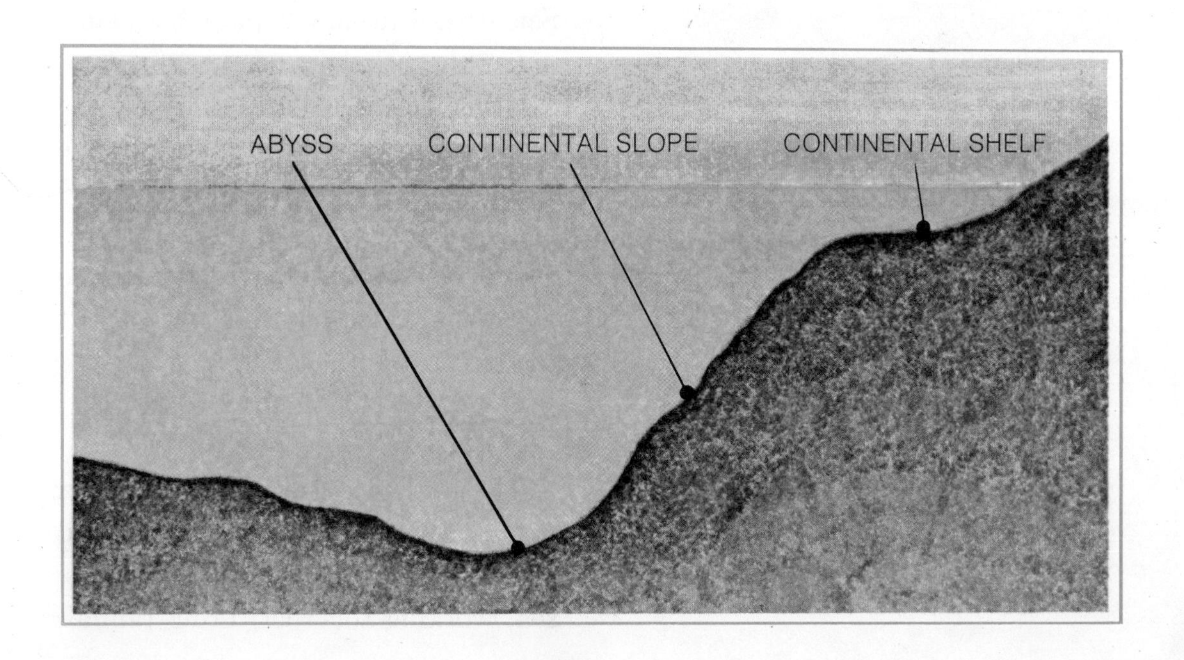

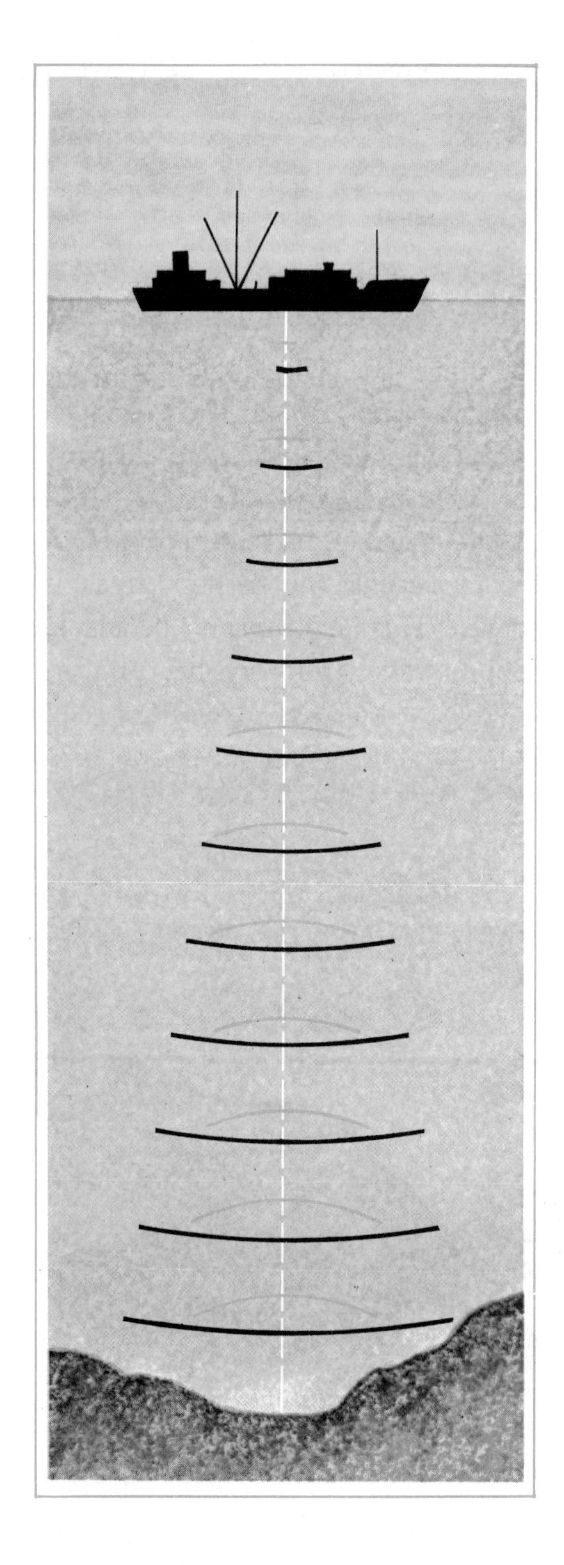

back to the ship. The time it takes for the sound wave to reach bottom and return to the ship tells the scientists how deep the ocean is at that point.

The deepest sea area measured by sonar is a trench near the Mariana Islands in the Pacific. The depth of this trench has been found to be over 35,000 feet, or nearly seven miles.

Until recently not very much was known about the lands under the Arctic and Antarctic oceans, because ice covers these oceans all year round. The invention of atomic power has made it possible for submarines to go under the ice and remain for long periods of time. Scientists can now explore the lands under the polar oceans.

Other scientists are studying the kinds of rock that make up the ocean bed. They are taking samples of these rocks and studying them. They expect that the rock samples will someday tell us still more about the nature of the earth.

Effects of the Sea

The sea is very important to us. In fact, without it there would be no life on the earth. The wind and the sea, working together, bring rainfall to the land. And without water there could be no plant or animal life on the earth.

The winds over the sea evaporate and absorb moisture from the oceans. When these winds move across the land and come in contact with cool air, they drop some of their moisture. It falls onto the land in different forms. It may fall as rain, hail, sleet, or snow.

The sea's currents affect the climate of different areas of the earth. Currents of cold water flowing near hot lands help cool these lands and make them livable. And warmwater currents help to warm lands that otherwise would be too cold for life.

Uses of the Sea

Aside from the many effects the sea has on climate and weather, the sea is important to us in other ways. Seawater is a source of many chemicals and minerals. The sea helps supply us with food. It provides us with a "roadway" for traveling from one place to another. And certainly the sea is one of our favorite playgrounds. Think of the many water sports—swimming, water skiing, skin diving, fishing, and sailing. Many are the uses of the sea!

So important is this vast body of water that many nations are at work exploring the sea. With the help of the scientific instruments of our age, we are always learning more about the mysteries of the earth's wonderful sea.

Wild Are the Waves

Wild are the waves when the
But fishes in the deep
Live in a world of waters,
Still as sleep.

WIND BLOWS;

Walter de la Mare

Sea Meadows

Ferdinand C. Lane

If you were at the seaside, you would not be able to see most of the sea plants and animals floating in the water. Many of them are too small to be seen without a microscope, and the sea hides many of the larger ones. But the meadows of the sea are swarming with life.

Perhaps you have walked in a meadow on a warm summer day. The grass was like a green carpet dotted with yellow buttercups and white daisies. How beautiful it was—how full of life!

Or you may have seen those sandy wastes that we call deserts. Perhaps a few withered plants were struggling to keep alive in the hot sun. But still the landscape seemed empty, as though it were dying if not already dead.

The sea also has its meadows and its deserts. True, sea meadows are quite different from those we find in Vermont or Wisconsin. Sea plants are far more numerous. But because they are so small, you might sail among them and never know that life was all about you.

Scientists like to explore these meadows of the sea. Like fishermen, they use a net. Only their net is of woven silk. With this net trailing behind a moving boat, they skim the waters for some of the tiny plants and animals that swarm there. These are called plankton, which to the old Greeks meant "wandering." The name is well chosen, for plankton are carried about by winds, tides, and currents.

The most useful of the plant life that this silken net skims from the waves are diatoms. If you could place one of the largest of these on clear glass, it would be like a speck of dust. Diatoms are unbelievably tiny. They are so small that a quart of water drawn from the Kiel Canal in Germany contained more than six million diatoms.

With a microscope, we can make these tiny plants appear larger. In this way we can study them and learn more about them.

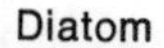
Diatom

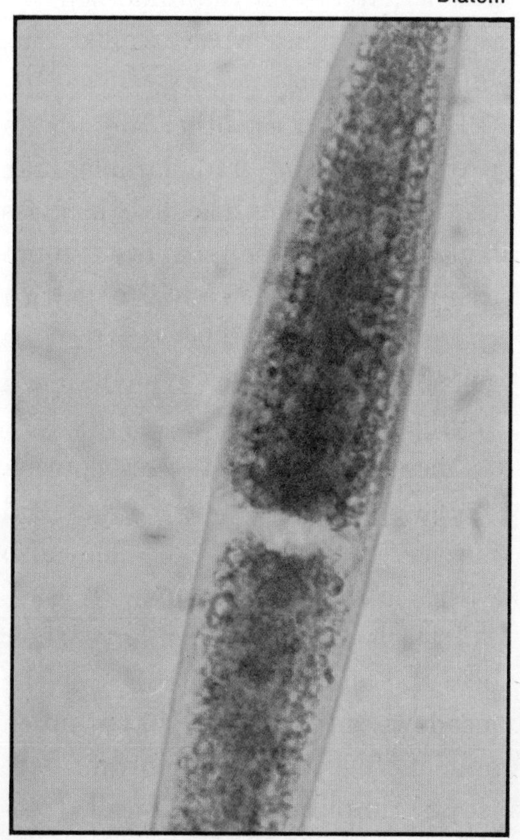

Actually diatoms are of many shapes and sizes. Each one is enclosed in a tiny glass case marked with beautiful designs. Diatoms seem almost like fairy dishes but are very much alive. In Polar Seas they swarm in such numbers that they color the water a glassy green. If you could rub some of this water between your fingers, you could get the gritty feel of the diatoms.

Diatoms are true plants and form the food of many small sea animals and fish. Sometimes they grow in yellow patches on the underbelly of the great blue whale called the sulphur-bottom.

Even lovelier are other tiny plants with a long name—radiolarians. Like the diatoms, they also live in glass houses. But these are even more richly ornamented. They bristle with spikes and spines. They glitter like gems. But no jeweler ever designed anything half so fine.

These meadows of the sea flourish in the spring just as the grass and flowers do in upland fields. They also wither in the summer sun.

Just as upland fields have their bees and ants and dragonflies, so the meadows of the sea have much animal life. Most important are tiny shrimplike creatures called copepods. They usually make up two-thirds of the yield of a plankton net. One of these copepods may swallow no fewer than 120,000 diatoms in a single day.

And as they eat, they too are eaten. For more than 60,000 copepods have been taken from the stomach of a single herring. Both fish and whales eat them. Whales swim along the surface with their mouths wide open, then strain the copepods through ribbons of whalebone that hang from their upper jaws like whiskers. Whalers call these copepods "brit."

In the Polar Seas where copepods are so numerous, they sometimes color the water as though with floating brick dust. More than 300 gallons of "copepod soup" have been taken from the stomach of a great blue whale.

Such is the life that swarms in the meadows of the sea. But there are other even stranger creatures. Some have big heads and horns and staring eyes. Some give off light like fireflies. A ship passing through them at night seems to stir a trail of smoldering fire.

Then, too, there are the eggs of fish and baby clams and oysters and lobsters, which float for a while until they settle down upon the bottom.

Most tiny floating plants are useful, but a few are dangerous. One species along Pacific shores forms reddish streaks in the water and glows at night with a pale-green light. Fish and shellfish that eat these plants might poison us if we ate them.

Just as the uplands have their deserts as well as their meadows, so has the sea. There are waste spaces where plant and animal life are scarce. Much of Hudson Bay is poorly supplied and so are great regions of the open sea.

Less important than the tiny plants that float upon the surface are those other plants that grow along the shores. They are called seaweeds, which isn't a very good name. For a weed is one of those harmful or useless plants in our garden. Seaweeds are merely the larger plant life of the sea.

Upland plants are almost always green. That is because of the wonder substance, chlorophyll, in their leaves. With this substance and the sunbeams, the leaves make sugar, starch, and even wood mainly out of air and water.

Some seaweeds are green, such as the sea lettuce and other algae. Some are blue green. And many are red. But the larger plants are olive green or brown.

They grow only in shallow waters where the light soon fades. Below a certain depth they cannot grow at all. For all plants, except a few like mushrooms, need the sun.

Unlike land plants, seaweeds have no roots, and few have blossoms. They get all their food from the water, none from the soil. Many cling to rocks, but that is merely to keep from being washed about by the waves. The giant kelp of the Pacific has great floating leaves, and its stems may be 200 feet long. It grows in beds all the way to Alaska. No African jungle swarms with so much life as these strange jungles of the sea.

One kind of giant kelp grows off the shores of the Aleutian Islands. It holds fast to the ocean floor by a stem so tough that Eskimos once used it for fishlines. From a central floating bladder, rubbery leaves spread out like a big blossom fifty feet across. This strange plant is called sea-otter's-cabbage. For the sea otter, which swims about for fish, climbs upon that floating bladder. There he loves to doze as though in a cradle rocked by the ocean swells.

Many other seaweeds have air-filled spaces which act as floats. Some break loose from the rocks and drift far from shore. Sometimes they gather where the surface is not disturbed by the great rivers of the sea.

The strangest of all these lonely places stretches across the Atlantic from near the Azores toward Bermuda. It covers an area two-thirds as large as the United States. It is called the Sargasso Sea because of a kind of seaweed called sargassum. This seaweed has collected in floating fields sometimes several feet in thickness with broad lanes of water between.

Many weird stories have been told about the Sargasso Sea. In the early days it was thought that sailing ships might be caught there and never get away. But we now know that they can sail through such weedy waters. Even Columbus crossed a part of the Sargasso Sea and wondered at the queer life he found there. For tiny crabs crawl about, and odd fish hide in the weed.

As in the upland meadows, much of the plant life of the sea has its seasons. And as it flourishes, so does the animal life that feeds upon it.

Afterthought

Discuss ways the meadows of the sea are like fields on land. You might want to begin by comparing the Kansas boy's cornfield with a kelp bed.

Sea Creatures

Sam and Beryl Epstein

Sea animals need the plants in the sea meadows. As you read the following article, you will discover that the animals of the sea also need each other.

Every once in a while a fisherman finds in his net a creature no one has ever seen before. Experts are called in to study the new discovery. They learn all they can about it and give it a name. Then they add it to the list of animals known to live in the ocean.

That list keeps growing all the time. No one can say how long it would be if it included every one of the animals that makes its home in the sea.

We know already that those animals range from the tiny shellfish called a copepod, no bigger than a pinhead, to the giant blue whale that may weigh close to a hundred tons. We know that they range from the barnacle, which does not move at all, and the snail, which slowly inches its way across the bottom, to the swift marlin that streaks through the water at a speed of fifty miles an hour. We know they range from the graceful porpoise to the awkward horseshoe crab and from the most brilliantly colored tropical fish to the ugly bigmouthed toadfish.

The animals that live in the ocean are of as many different varieties as those that live on land. Each variety has its own habits. Usually each variety inhabits a particular part of the ocean.

Some live near the surface, where there is very little pressure and where the water is lit up by the sun. Others live far under the surface, where the pressure is very severe and the water is entirely dark. The light from the sun only faintly illuminates the water at a depth of 1,400 feet. At 1,700 feet below the surface, there is no light at all.

Some ocean inhabitants can survive only in warm water. Others die if a current sweeps them away from the icy waters where they make their home. Some live only in very salty water like that of the Red Sea. Others prefer brackish water, only faintly salty, found where a freshwater river empties into the ocean.

In other words, the ocean is divided into separate life zones by pressure, light, temperature, and saltiness. Each zone has its own population.

Animals that can live in two different kinds of zones—in both salt water and fresh water—are rare. Eels can do this.

Eels are born far out in the salty ocean. When they are still tiny, they make their way toward bays or the mouths of rivers. The young female eels travel on into fresh water, while

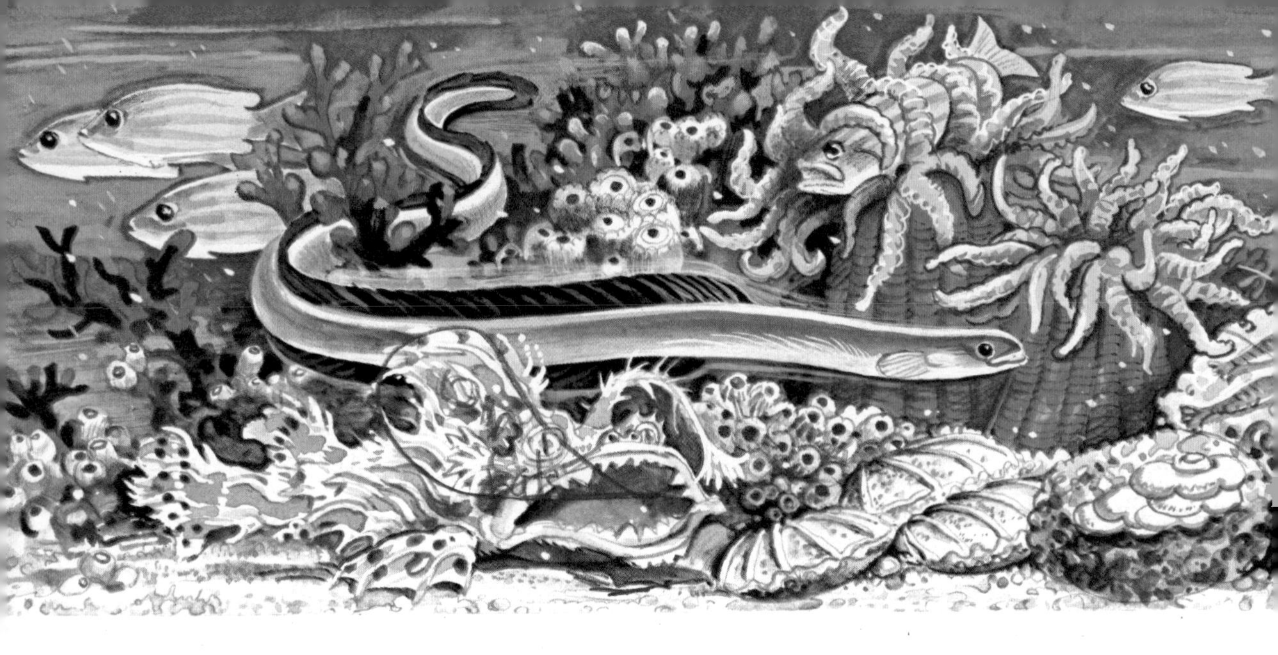

the males remain where the water is brackish. After several years both males and females swim back to the place where they were born. There their eggs are laid and hatched. Soon the new baby eels set out for the rivers and bays that their parents came from.

The whale can also move back and forth between two different zones. This huge creature is a mammal—not a fish. It does not have gills. Therefore it cannot breathe underwater. It must thrust its head above the surface in order to get its air. But when a whale has filled its huge lungs, it can dive more than half a mile down into the ocean, where the pressure is tremendous. Then it can shoot up to the surface again as swiftly as it dove. If a human diver surfaced that fast, even from a two-hundred-foot dive, he would probably die from the dreaded diver's disease known as the bends.

Even animals that spend their whole lives in one oceanic zone usually move about constantly inside that zone in their search for food.

Some sea animals live on plants. The tiny copepod, for example, and other small shellfish live on the very tiny one-celled algae. That is why small sea animals and algae are often found together in plankton.

But most of the animals of the ocean live on other animals, smaller or weaker or more helpless than themselves. Herring, for example, live on copepods. Mackerel live on herring. Tuna fish live on mackerel.

When human beings eat tuna fish, they are completing a food cycle

that begins in the sea with the tiny plants called algae.

The best-known ocean animals are those that live in the shallow water above the continental shelves, or in the upper 600 feet of water above the continental slopes and the deep ocean floor.

Among these are hundreds of different kinds of fish, from the tiny guppy to the big whale shark that may be fifty feet long. Most fish have balloonlike sacs in their bodies, which keep each creature afloat at the water level best suited to its way of life. All fish take in their food through their mouths, though they do not all have teeth. Nor do all fish have eyes! Those that have none find their food, at least in some cases, by their sense of smell. Some fish move by undulating their whole bodies. Others travel through the water by moving their fins only.

The swordfish carries its own bony weapon on the front of its head. The porcupine fish has an armor of bristling spines. The little sea horse, about three inches long, is covered with tough bony plates. Other fish, not so well equipped to fight off their enemies, are protected by a kind of camouflage. Certain striped fish, for example, become almost invisible if they remain motionless among seaweed. Many fish are white on bottom and dark on top to help make them invisible to enemies either above or below them.

But fish are only one group of the inhabitants of the sunlit upper waters. Living among them, or in the sand and mud of shallow bottoms, are many varieties of one-shelled animals such as barnacles, two-shelled animals such as clams, crustaceans such as shrimp and lobsters, and odd plantlike creatures such as the sea peach and the sea cucumber.

Each of these animals has its own way of getting the food it needs, of moving about or holding fast to the place it has chosen, and of protecting itself from its enemies.

The pretty little two-shelled scallop opens its shells, takes in water, strains out the tiny plants and animals it can digest, and pumps the water out again. The scallop's shells are also useful when it must move about on the shallow bottom of bays and tidal creeks where it lives. When it snaps its shells shut and ejects a stream of water, the force of the stream shoots the scallop backward in a kind of jet-propelled leap. The scallop's shells are also a protection against its enemies.

The single curling shells of snails, whelks, and other similar creatures serve as protective armor but do not help them move about. A snail or a whelk moves by putting a fleshy sort of foot through its shell opening and prodding itself along the bottom. Most of these creatures, which move so slowly that they cannot catch living prey, eat the small dead animals they find littering shallow bottoms. But some of them have tough hard tongues, as rough as a file, which can cut through even a hard oyster shell and reach the soft meat inside.

Some crabs move quickly in a sort of sideways scuttle. Their speed helps them catch their prey, although crabs as a rule live mostly on bits of dead animals they find on the bottom. The crabs' speed is more important in helping them escape their enemies. Their tough shells are a help too, and so are their two strong, nipping claws. Some types of crabs are very well camouflaged. A sand crab motionless on the beach is almost invisible because it is almost exactly the color of the damp sand itself.

One crab that can move only very slowly is the horseshoe crab. But its shell protects it from many faster animals. Its thin tail, as stiff and pointed as a dagger, gives it the appearance of a prehistoric creature. And that is what it is. This same species of animal existed long before the time of the dinosaurs. It is one of the most ancient animals in the world.

Starfish are among the most interesting of all the ocean's animals. A dead starfish, lying on the beach, is as hard and stiff as if it were made of clay. But a live starfish can move by means of its flexible pointed arms. Those arms are fitted with many tiny suction cups, and they are very powerful. Wrapped around a tightly shut clam or oyster, they can slowly force the shells to open. Then the starfish's stomach, pushed between the opened shells, surrounds the soft meat inside and digests it. Starfish consume so many clams and oysters that they are a menace to the men who make their living gathering those shellfish.

The names of the sea peach and the sea cucumber tell us what these creatures look like. The sea cucumber has a long body quite a lot like a garden-grown cucumber. The sea peach has very much the shape and color and size of a real peach. Like all sea squirts, it has two tubes through which it squirts jets of water when it is in danger.

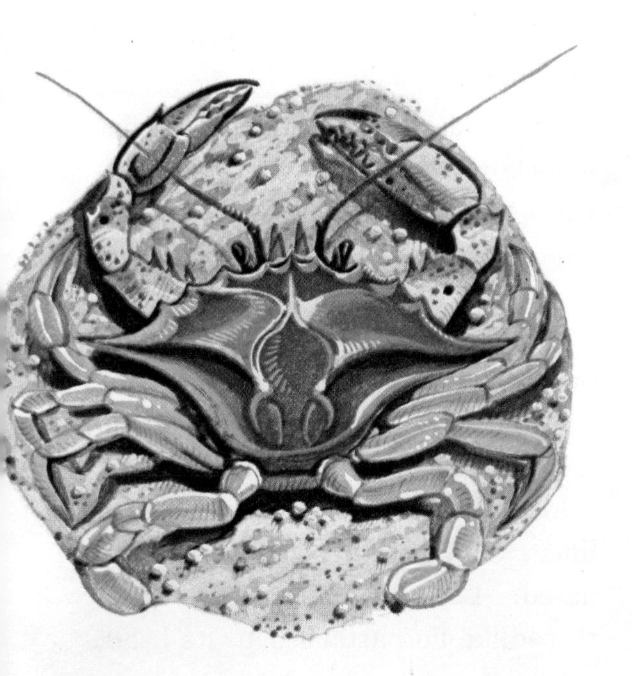

There are flowerlike animals in the shallow coastal waters, too. The best known are the many varieties of the sea anemones, whose small stalklike bodies are crowned with slender, waving tentacles. A sea anemone is not as delicate as it appears. It can sting and trap almost any small creature that swims within reach of its tentacles.

One tropical relative of the sea anemone is the coral. It is no bigger than a pinhead and has a tiny limestone skeleton. Thousands of these skeletons sometimes form shapes that look like trees or bushes. Sometimes they collect in such numbers that they form great islandlike reefs. The most famous of all coral reefs is the Great Barrier Reef off the coast of Australia. It rises about 500 feet from the ocean floor to the surface of the water. It is more than a thousand miles long.

The animals that live in the upper levels of the ocean are well known partly because they have long been useful to human beings. Men began to learn a great deal about the fish and shellfish of these waters when they started to catch them for food thousands of years ago. And as soon as men discovered the value of sponges and pearl-bearing oysters many hundreds of years ago, they began to dive into the coastal waters in search of those creatures. Divers for pearls and sponges were probably the first men who saw the animals of the ocean moving about alive.

Today the animals of the coastal waters are being watched and studied by divers using aqualungs. Many skin divers who took their first dive for fun became so fascinated that they made a career of oceanography or of the study of fish.

Man's knowledge of the animals that live in the deeper parts of the ocean is still quite scanty. A century ago it was widely believed that the cold, dark, lower waters of the sea were entirely empty of life.

But in 1930, when Charles William Beebe made his first descent in his bathysphere, he saw living creatures more than 2,000 feet below the surface. Since then, weird dagger-toothed fish, and jellyfish, and squid of strange shapes have been seen at much deeper levels of the ocean.

An underwater listening device has shown that some of these creatures make odd noises that sound like drumming, crackling, mewing, shrieking, and moaning.

Many deep-sea animals carry their own lights with them through the dark waters. The lanternfish, which has rows of glowing spots along its sides, looks like a miniature ocean liner with all its portholes illuminated. The oceanic angler has a threadlike line attached to its head, just above the mouth, with a light like a bit of shining bait at the end of it. It swims with its mouth open, ready to snap up any small fish that is attracted to the shining light at the end of its line.

Afterthought

1. Think of ways in which the physical features of the sea are important to the sea's plant and animal life.
2. Be prepared to discuss ways in which sea creatures you have read about are suited for living in the sea.

The Big Spring

Jean Craighead George

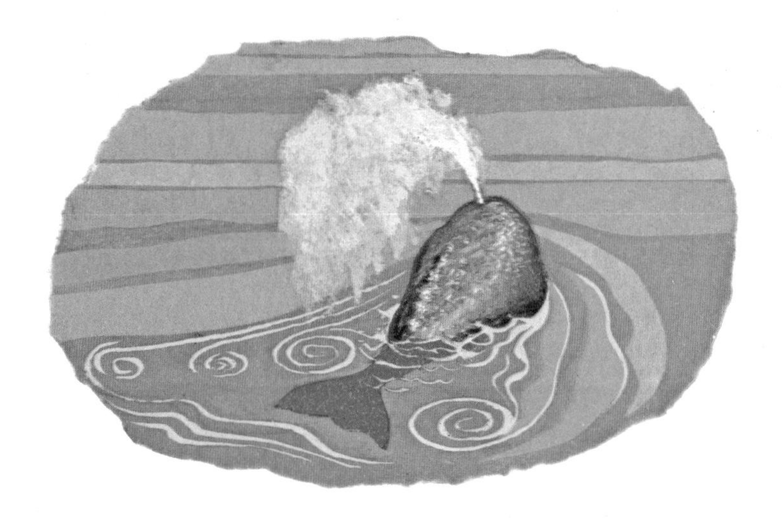

When spring comes to the ocean, the plants and animals give signs of new life. As you read about the adventures of a mother whale and her baby, notice details that are signs of spring.

Off the west coast of the United States a gray whale surfaced. Her nostrils emerged first and blew a spout of air and water fifteen feet into the air. The column swooshed with a roar that could be heard for half a mile. Having exhaled, she then inhaled. The breath came into her lungs with a whine, like wind rushing into a tunnel. Her nostrils closed over this salty gasp. She went under.

Four seconds later, her nose, which was on the top of her head, came up again. She gave four strong blows. The waves clapped around her. She snorted at them, then headed down into the Pacific Ocean.

The female gray whale was forty-three feet long. She weighed thirty-four tons. She was one of a group of animals that are the largest ever to live on this earth. Like all other whales, she was also hostess to many small beasts. On her back and over her belly lived thousands of barnacles. They pulled their feet in and stopped kicking food into their mouths when their great hostess surfaced to breathe. They adjusted to her rising and diving.

This animal plunged forward for a thousand feet. Then she surfaced and peered over the ocean. She had no language, she made no vocal sounds, but she spied now and then to look for her relatives.

Beside her swam her son, a twenty-foot baby. He had been born in January in a California bay. Now the two of them were on their way north to the Bering Sea—a long journey of 7,000 miles.

The mother plunged down into the green spring ocean and looked around. She was following a canyon wall that she knew as well as you know your own street. She had traveled along it every year for twenty years of her life. The canyon was gray and dark, and lay like a great highway up the continental shelf. The whale knew exactly where she was.

Ahead of her loomed a sand barrier. She quickened her pace, for she knew she was coming to a cove. Once more she blew and looked around. She saw no other gray whales and sensed she was behind the main migration. At the sandbar she tasted the silt of Coos Bay. Because she could not feel the currents from her baby, she slowed down, then stopped.

Her son was looking at a giant squid. The mother got his attention by crunching her wide teeth, the only sound she could make. The baby spurted to her side. He whooshed friskily to the surface and peered around. He saw boats and lighthouses. This was his first trip to the summer meeting of the gray whales—The Bering Sea. His mother was teaching him the underwater landmarks. In the fall he would have to travel back alone.

The mother whale swung over the delta at the mouth of the bay and crunched her teeth again. Her son came down to her. She was taking the water from the bay in and out of her mouth. He did likewise, and the taste of the bay was forever imprinted on his senses. Each bay and cove and canyon had to be memorized in this manner—by taste, by sight, and by currents. For each was different in every inlet along the coast.

The mother plunged over the sandbar. The whale child followed. For a moment they lingered in the different water pressures, feeling all the details of this place with the openings under their necks that were sensitive to pressures.

The mother delayed long here as if to impress this particular spot on the youngster. From here they would take out to sea. From here on, it would be all pressure memories. The whale child circled gently, biting the sand, filtering the water in, and learning.

Then they hurried on—a thousand feet at a run. They swam to the edge of the continental shelf.

Suddenly the whale child looked back. He whirled in panic. Coos Bay appeared different from the north. He turned and flipped back to the sandbar. He tasted the salts and minerals once more, feeling the water, trying to learn well. When he was satisfied, he tailed out to meet his mother. But she was gone.

The life of the gray whale is silent for the most part—a grind on their teeth, a noisy blow. Over the sea-canyon walls, ticking like the beat of a tin cup on a wooden table, came the "distress" sound made by the baby whale.

He was lost. He surfaced, blew a great column of air and water, and pulled himself skyward so high his whole chest was out of the water. All he saw was a boat harvesting fish. He saw no mother. He glanced at the boat again. It was big; it might be a whale. He headed for it, spying as he went.

The boat was gray like his mother and covered with barnacles. Rising and blowing, he came up to the object. But the whale child drew back. The wooden whale was too small, the wrong design, the wrong scent. The water that surrounded it was not warmed by the mammal body. And oil seeped from it.

The young whale fled in terror, diving into hills and valleys. His eyes rolled as he searched. Schools of fish felt him and wheeled away. He plunged on but saw no sand barrier, tasted nothing familiar.

He cried into the ocean, tapping out his bleat that traveled swiftly for hundreds of yards and then faded against the coastal reefs.

As the sun went down, the giant child circled and circled the empty waters. He spied out and looked until he was tired. Finally he slept. His flippers hung down into the sea. His tense nostrils were barely above the surface.

Two hours later the young whale awoke. His skin was cold, and he turned sleepily to nurse. Then he remembered his mother was not around. He swirled in panic. He saw the land and knew this was where he must begin to retrace his steps. He swam south.

No adult gray whales eat on the long eight-month migration. Nor do they eat in the bays where they give birth to their young. The gray whale swims constantly while starving, with the exception of the babies that nurse on the trip north.

So the giant whale child sucked in the ocean because he was hungry and weak. He filtered out the plankton through odd rows of teeth that were more like sieves than teeth. Then he rolled southward in fear and fright.

At noon he found Coos Bay. He knew its taste. His mother had taught him this. Swimming to the familiar barrier, he tapped his jaws together and called. There was no answer in all the vast ocean. The young whale drifted into the cove. It was familiar. He had been born in a cove, in the low hot waters of a California bay. The young whale spied upon the shore. It was different from his first home; there were tall trees and lush plants. The strangeness alarmed him, and he went under for ten minutes. The bars, the shallows, and the light that flickered from the sun down into the bay were comforting. But he saw no whales. There had been thousands in the bay of his birth.

The young whale felt strong instincts pulling him. He swam to the mouth of the bay and looked north, for gray whales work on appointments with their needs. They must give birth to calves in the protected lagoons. They must depart on schedule to travel the 7,000 miles to the only food they eat—the plankton of the Bering Sea. And they must get there on time, or they starve to death. Again in the fall they must leave on schedule in order to have their babies in the protected waters.

The young whale child tapped his teeth and circled Coos Bay. He had been born in January, a magnificent male of sixteen feet. He had been immediately nuzzled by his giant mother, who, without arms to hug him, expressed her love by circling him. She led him to the surface to blow. Then, tipping her body, she showed him where to find her milk.

The rest of the two months in the lagoon were reassuring

to the young whale child. Hundreds of other whales slept and rolled with him. Each one awakened instinctively before the tide went out and beached him, an event which means certain death to a whale. The whale child learned to tell when the tide was leaving and how to avoid being stranded. He met other young whales, and by meeting them, knew what he was.

In March there were fewer and fewer of his kind in the bay, for the great migration had started north. Finally his mother beat her tail, crunched her teeth, and led him around sandbars, over hills, and out into the sea. He stayed close to her big side. She paused beyond the bay channel to teach him the tastes and pressures of his birthplace. Then she spanked him forward to keep her schedule with the burst of spring in the Bering Sea.

The young whale felt pressures and tastes in Coos Bay similar to those he knew as an infant. And so he lingered, blowing and swirling over the bottom. By night he would swim toward the shore. By day he would surge to the entrance, feeling the pull toward the dark waters of the north. But he did not know how to go.

He stayed where he was.

The days passed. His mother did not return. The huge child grew weak with longing and hunger. He could not know that they had lost each other as she had spurted forward to drive a killer whale from their path. Killer whales never kill adult gray whales, but they hurt the young. Over the ages the gray whale has learned to keep to the bottom. The killers keep to the surface.

But all life is chance. A killer whale and the whale child's mother had met, and she chased him. The mother moved instinctively north to keep her schedule with June in the

Bering Sea. And the child, following the instincts of the young, looked for familiar waters.

A week later the tired whale child came up to the shores of Coos Bay, where people moved and boats were tied. In loneliness he watched the boats. They were almost as big as his mother. One night he nuzzled one. And close beside its purring motors he fell asleep.

But as he slept, he breathed like a wind tunnel. The owner of the boat heard the strange sound and came out to see if a storm were brewing.

He looked down into the water and saw the young whale sleeping happily against his ship. He stared again to make sure, then paced the entire length of his deck until he came to the end of the baby. A whale tail lay under the water. He radioed the Marine Laboratory, and he radioed the Fish and Wildlife Service.

At dawn the lost whale child was a captive.

The excitement was great. During the night the men had enclosed him in a great wire fence. They all stood and stared at him as he snapped and rolled.

The scientists in Coos Bay were thrilled to be able to study a live gray whale. They measured and weighed him. They noted the movements of the whale child. They put microphones in the water to record any sounds he might make. They watched him judge the tide and swim to the deepest pocket of the cage when it went out. And they took his temperature and studied his blood.

To feed him, they poured nutrients into the water that were similar to those in plankton. The formula came from studies made on the stomachs of other gray whales that had washed ashore. The scientists were coming to a new understanding of this remarkable beast, and they were excited.

Meanwhile the remarkable beast grew weaker and weaker, for the plankton formula was not what he needed. He needed his mother's milk. He cried at night and eyed the men by day.

Then one night a small craft, sailing out into the ocean, was rocked by an enormous object just off the sandbar. The boat was thrown off course by the swell. Its crew peered into the water to see if they had struck anything, but the sea was black. Something big had passed down the channel into the bay. They gave the incident little thought, for their boat righted itself quickly and purred on out to sea.

The next morning when the scientists came, they found the fence crunched as if it were paper—and the whale child gone.

Far out at sea, a mother whale and her son blew four times and went under to follow green currents in the Pacific Ocean. The mother lingered to teach her son the pressure and weight of these waters. She was very patient, and her child was obedient.

A school of sharks circled them as they plunged over the edge of the continental shelf and thundered north. For the belly of the female bore toothlike gashes—as if raked by a wire fence.

As the gray whales followed the watery highways, the "roadsides" were spangled with the signs of spring. Diatoms bloomed, copepods glittered among the diatoms, and fish glimmered as they tossed their silver eggs to the sea. For it was springtime in the ocean.

Afterthought

1. What did you find out about gray whales in this story?
2. What details make the story believable?

Water-Front Streets

The spring is not so beautiful there—
  But dream ships sail away
To where the spring is wondrous rare
  And life is gay.

The spring is not so beautiful there—
  But lads put out to sea
Who carry beauties in their hearts
  And dreams, like me.

Langston Hughes

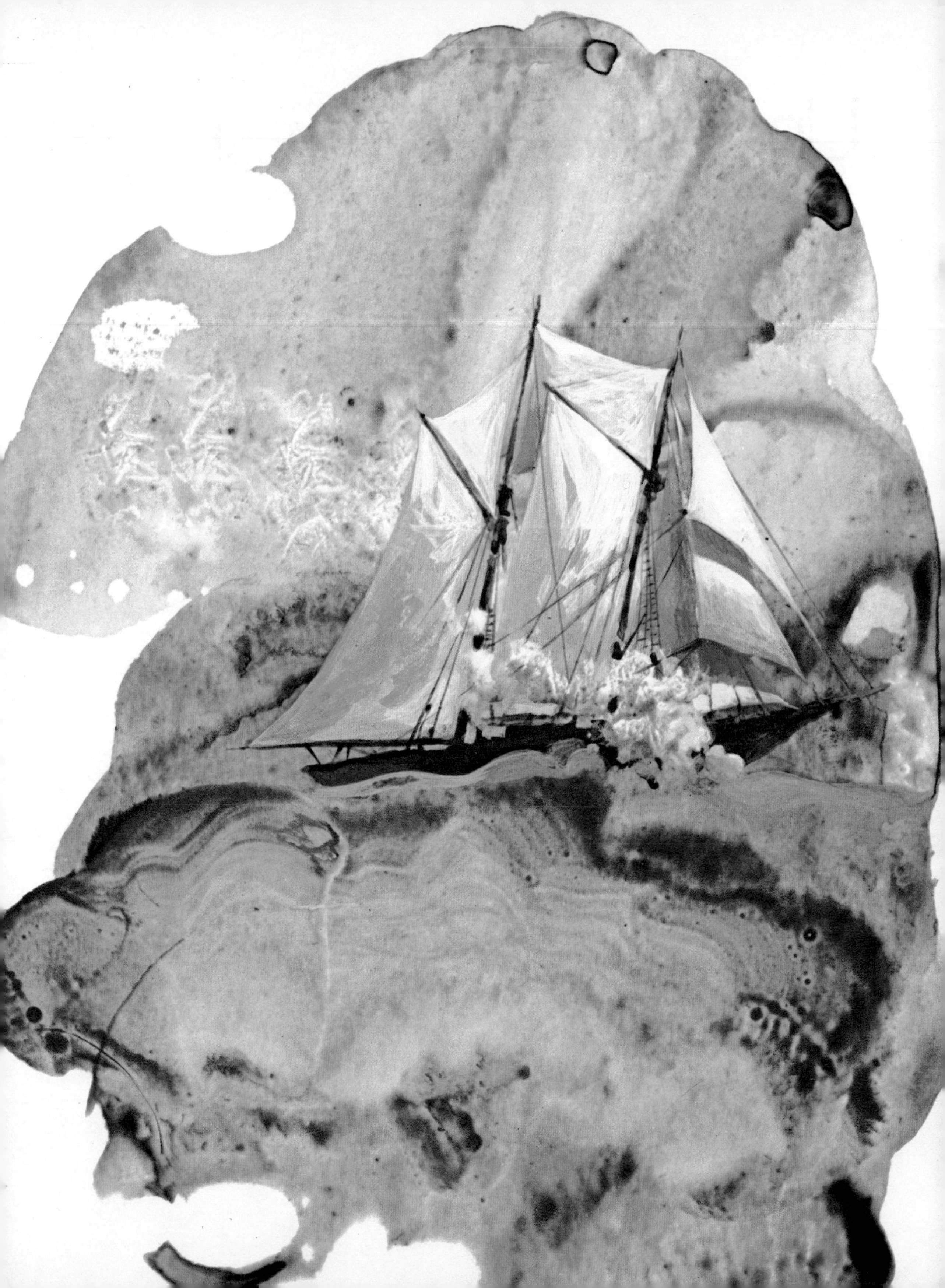

Underwater Harvest

Charles Coombs

Over the years whales have been a source of many products used by us—meat, oil, whalebone, and meal for cattle and poultry, to name a few. The day may not be far off when we will serve whale's milk at our tables. Read the following article to find out about other exciting products from the sea.

Half the world's three billion people are lucky to get one full meal a day. This condition exists today, but the future seems even more grim. By the year 2000 it is estimated that the world's population will be more than double what it is now. How many then will enjoy a full meal a day? How great will be the hungers? What will prevent widespread starvation?

Naturally, more lands will be put under cultivation. Scientific agriculture will increase farm production throughout the world. Improved methods of harvesting and processing will diminish waste. These things will help to put more meat and vegetables on the world's tables. But they will fall far short of keeping up with the increasing demand for food.

The biggest promise for the future lies not in the land but in the sea. The greatest storehouse of food is in the world ocean. It is estimated that four-fifths of the world's animal life is in the sea. This ranges from copepods to whales. All are rich in food value, although few species are considered to be tasty.

Still, man must soon turn to the sea for increasing amounts of his food. Certainly the supply seems limitless and is generally untouched.

This statement may seem unreasonable, for the great fishing fleets of the world fill their holds with rich ocean bounty. But for all the fishing being done, the main supply is scarcely being touched.

There are nearly 30,000 species of fish alone, and only about sixty are being caught commercially. They are the ones that gather in great schools and are easily hooked, netted, or trawled. And, of course, the flavor of fish caught must be suitable to the tastes of the public. This is particularly true in the United States, a meat-eating nation.

In the United States the annual consumption of seafood is about eleven pounds per person. This is low, considering that some nations depend almost entirely upon the sea for food. The daily survival of Japanese, Norwegians, Icelanders, and Eskimos depends upon harvesting the sea. There are few nations not somehow bound to the ocean for a major part of their existence.

No one really knows how much life there is in the sea. Some say that the sea produces about forty billion tons of new food each year. Others go so far as to double this.

These figures include the billions upon billions of tons of plankton. So far, plankton is of no direct commercial use as a food. Its buggy, slimy appearance and fishy taste make it a poor dish for home tables. However, the day when a juicy planktonburger will be considered a delicacy may not be so distant. Not all people would think a dried eel or the raw insides of a spiny sea urchin much of a treat. Yet many peoples of the world are delighted with such foods.

Of particular interest to us, though, is the familiar fish. It is estimated that sea fish for commercial use increase by about a billion tons a year. The annual world fish catch is only about forty-five million tons, or less than five percent of the possible supply.

Forty-five million tons is a lot of fish. Certainly it is ample to make fishing a big business. In the United States alone nearly half a million people work in the commercial fishing industry. Yet the United States is rated only fifth among fishing nations.

Fishing remains a backward industry. It has been slow to take full advantage of improvements in science. Commercial fishing still depends largely upon the same hook, line, and net methods that have been used for thousands of years. To be sure, there have been some improvements. Echo-sounding sonar locates deep shoals of fish. Nets made of nylon and plastic have replaced the old twine variety. Refrigeration has helped the fishing industry by allowing a ship to stay out until its holds are full. A modern tuna clipper may remain at sea for months before it has a full cargo. It will return, carrying more than 300 tons of fish. And every fish will be frozen-fresh.

Tuna fishermen have begun getting away from the old fishing-pole method of landing their quarry. They have turned to purse seining.

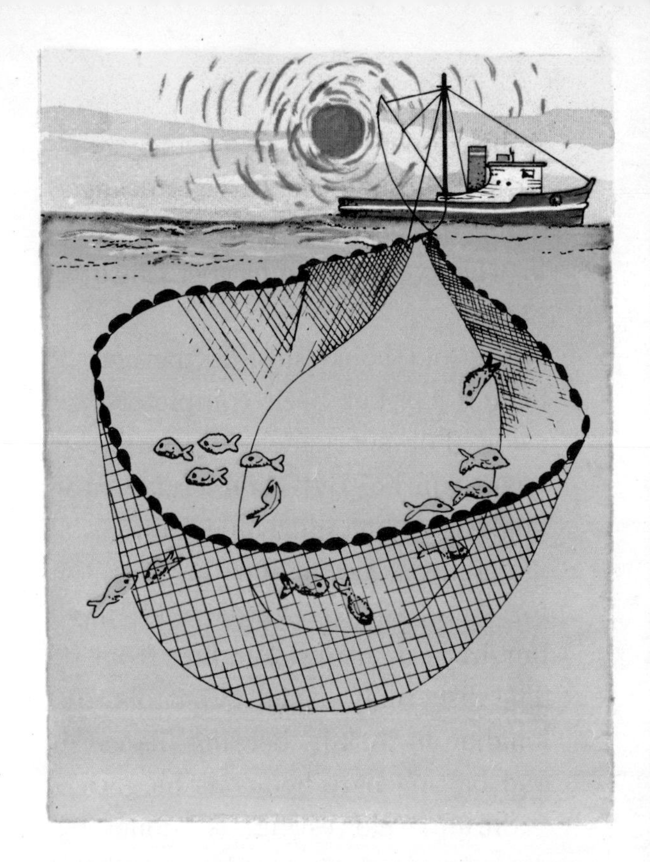

Small motorboats tow a huge net around a school of tuna. Cork or plastic floats support the top of the net on the water's surface. The bottom is weighted by a heavy chain that has metal rings for the ship's cable. When the dangling net has circled the fish, the net is "pursed in" by the cable. Thus the bottom of the net is drawn in tight, forming a purselike pocket that traps everything within it. Using this method, fishermen take in a large haul in one operation.

Trawling is another method of commerical fishing. A trawl is much like a butterfly net. Its gaping mouth is held open by weights and floats. Towed through the water or dragged along the bottom, the trawl gathers in whatever sea life happens into its path.

The old hook-and-line method of fishing has not been completely set aside. For sportsmen, of course, it never will be. But commercially the hook and line developed into the "longline." A longline may stretch for hundreds of yards and have hundreds of hooks dangling from it. The fisherman usually patrols the longline in a skiff, boating his catch and baiting bare hooks as he goes.

Shrimp harvesting is done by dragging bottom trawls along the ocean floor. Prawns and sea scallops also are trawled. Crabs and lobsters generally are caught in the same type wire or wooden traps that have been used for years. Clams, oysters, sea mussels, and other mollusks are dredged, raked, or dug from bottom sands and muds.

The harvest of the sea is not limited to its animal life. Various types of seaweed and kelp are useful. Peoples of some nations eat the plants either cooked or raw. Usually, however, they are processed for fertilizer or added to livestock food.

Kelp contains algin, which has made it quite valuable to many industries. Algin is able to absorb large quantities of water. For instance, a single tablespoon of algin in a quart of water turns the water as thick as cold honey. In powder form, algin is widely used in gelatins, toothpastes, soaps, vitamins, paint, ice cream, and other products.

Scientists are developing methods to improve harvesting and increase the catch. For example, boats have been rigged with suction pumps hooked to hoses dropped over the side. A bright light lures the fish toward the open end of the hose. Slurp! Fish are sucked through the hose and dumped into the hold. The general idea has much merit, but so far only small fish have been taken in this manner. The light does not penetrate far enough into the seawater to attract a large number of fish. The pumps are not powerful enough, nor are the hoses large enough, to suck in the big fish.

Small species of fish such as sardines and anchovies are being pump-landed. Bigger pumps and pipes, with some kind of sonic or electronic lures, may be developed to attract the larger quarry.

Remote-controlled trawls may one day cruise beneath the waves. When

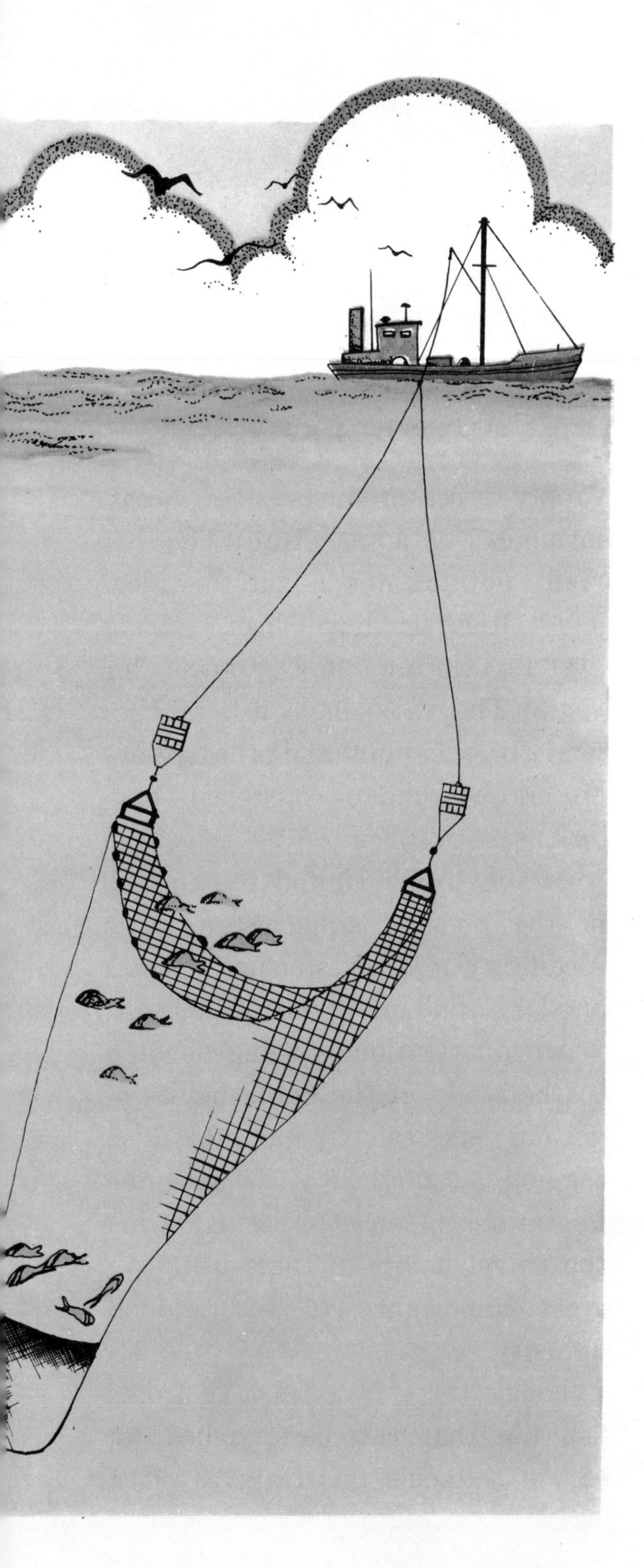

the trawl is filled, lights on a control panel aboard ship may signal that it is ready to be recalled.

Fish are easily herded. Curtains of bubbles rising from the bottom may be used to fence in schools of fish, just as a fence holds sheep. Like barking sheepdogs, small submarines can be sent down to herd the fish toward the bubble corral. They might use sonic waves or electronic goads. Once the fish are in a herd, gathering them in is readily accomplished.

There is, however, the possibility that harvesting the sea's living bounty may, in time, be harmful. Some of the most desired species of fish may become extinct. One way to avoid this is to stop being so choosy about the few species of fish we eat. We should quit selecting only such fish as halibut, mackerel, salmon, bass, tuna, and a few others. We should be less fussy over some of the shellfish and mollusks.

Fishermen are considering harvesting other types of sea life. Some will be found surprisingly tasty. Some, of course, will not. But the day may not be too far off when necessity, not taste, will govern the use of sea products.

Most types of seafood are equally

rich in food values. By a bit of imaginative processing and a little camouflaging, a trash fish may be made quite palatable. To some degree this is being done through the use of "fish flour." Having a no more fishy taste than ordinary wheat flour, it is rich in proteins and minerals. Not much is used now, because the public has not been educated to it. But fish flour holds great promise for the future.

Many things of the sea can be developed as tasty dishes. Increasing care is taken even today that no part of any fish is wasted. That which does not go into a package or can is ground into fish meal or fertilizer or is processed for its oil. Fish meal is used in poultry and cattle feeds. So the fish protein eventually gets to the meat-eating people.

Another way to assure a steady supply of sea products is by "ocean farming," or aquaculture. There is really nothing new about this idea. The Orientals have been raising oysters, shrimp, and prawns for years. They also have fish ranches where bass, halibut, and other species are raised under controlled conditions.

Although the United States lags in the area of aquaculture, it is seeding oyster beds, stocking streams and lakes, and improving sea harvest.

Much attention is being devoted to the study of the living habits of various species of sea life. Fish tagging is a method of checking the migrations of some species. Knowing the travel habits of these fish is of great importance to the seafood industry.

Today there is a tiny electronic fish tag that can be attached to, say, a salmon's fin. It gives off a sonic signal that can be tracked for about half a mile. Through the use of this instrument, scientists can study the behavior of a salmon as it cavorts around dams and fish ladders. Under development are larger sonic fish tags. Someday scientists may sit and track a whale's every move as it migrates from the Bering Sea all the way to its calving grounds off the coast of Baja California.

All in all, a steadily increasing interest is being directed toward the harvesting of the foodstuffs of the sea. The attention is well placed, for the world ocean contains enough to feed nations for countless years to come.

The Honey Boat

Polly Burroughs

People have many uses for the harbors of the sea. Find out what the main character in the following story thinks about some of those uses.

The harbor was quiet and still. Mist rose from the water in little wisps of smoke like steam from the spout of a teakettle, and the rising sun shone bright and clear.

A large figure loomed into view around the corner of the gray-shingled fish shed. Tattered bits of clothing streamed out behind as it stepped along the pier with a firm, sure stride, carrying a bundle of burlap bags. It was Ellie. Slowly, but majestically, she moved down the dock to her waiting skiff.

The little waves slapped softly against the sides of her rowboat when she pulled on the oars with short, firm strokes. Tying her dinghy to the mooring, she threw the bags into the cockpit of her catboat, *Dauntless*, and climbed aboard.

A sea gull squawked good-morning as he wheeled overhead and then glided down slowly, perching on the mast stub. He shrugged his wings and tucked them up neatly, waiting for breakfast. He was the same gull who had ridden with Ellie every summer for five years. She was sure, because the tip of one toe on his webbed foot was missing. Ellie always wondered whether it had been caught in a clam's shell, or perhaps some careless children had injured him. She would never know what had happened. But the gull never missed a day, rain or shine, and Ellie always gave him the best breakfast she could find.

She sat down in the cockpit and looked over her boat with pride—the kind of pride a skipper has who's devoted years of slow, careful work to keep his ship in tip-top condition. Every spring Ellie tuned the engine, scraped down the hull, puttied the seams, and gave *Dauntless* a fresh coat of paint. Sturdily built and nearly as wide as she was long, *Dauntless*'s mast was only a stub, but years ago she had been used as a pleasure boat to take summer vacationers sailing. She was a workboat now, and her ancient engine pushed her along at a slow but steady five knots.

Ellie looked back at the row of white whaling captains' houses, sedate and proud with their widow's walks, which lined the harbor front and sparkled in the morning sun. Turning east, she watched the little Chappaquiddick ferryboat, the *On Time,* crossing the harbor with its full load of two cars. The ferry was always on time because it had no time schedule.

Edgartown Harbor is formed by Chappaquiddick Island, a small island with several long, low sandspits and a few high hills covered with short, bushy pine trees, their growth stunted by the prevailing southwest winds. The island protects Edgartown Harbor from the Atlantic Ocean and provides a quiet place for boats to anchor.

She listened to the dull pa-thud-put, pa-thud-put, pa-thud-put of a fishing boat and watched the pie-shaped wake bubbling astern as the boat slowly motored out past the lighthouse to the fishing grounds offshore.

The chiming of eight bells from the church tower was suddenly interrupted by a roar from the cannon on the yacht club pier, which echoed across the harbor while the launchman raised the American flag. That was the signal Ellie waited for, and she fired up her engine, cast off the mooring, and started out.

Ellie had a very unusual job to do. No one else in all of Edgartown spent their mornings the way she did. Her job—and it was also her big interest in life—was to visit each boat in the harbor and pick up the garbage and trash from the day before, put it in her burlap bags, and cart it off to the dump. It was a messy but very necessary job. The town paid Ellie a small, a very small, sum of money every two weeks for her work. She didn't really mind the low wages so much—she liked to have things in the harbor clean and shipshape. In fact, she couldn't stand it if they weren't. Many a visiting skipper found this out the hard way.

She set about coiling her lines and piling up the burlap bags while *Dauntless* put-put-putted along. Overhead the gulls were screeching, arguing and scolding. They seemed to know Ellie was going to take it all—all that juicy garbage!

She pulled up alongside the port side of a lovely blue and white yawl. She put the engine out of gear, leaned over to grab the boat's rail, knocked on the deck with her free hand, and called out, "Garbage boat!"

The captain came up from below with three bags of trash.

"Don't just stand there. Take my line!" Ellie shouted impatiently to the man.

The captain put down his refuse and made the line fast on a cleat. Smiling good-morning, he handed his garbage down to Ellie and she put it in the burlap bag, which was placed in a trash can for support.

Ellie's next stop was the *White Mist,* a large schooner where she knew Cindy would be waiting. The little girl was a real tomboy—barefoot and dressed in blue jeans and a boy's shirt. Her long blond hair and bangs were the only girlish thing about her. The Palmer family lived aboard *White Mist* all summer, and Ellie took Cindy on the garbage route every day unless the weather was particularly severe. The little girl loved it and was overjoyed when Ellie taught her how to handle the lines, steer *Dauntless,* and pile up the garbage bags neatly. Ellie always paid her twenty cents at the end of the week for her help.

Cindy caught the line Ellie tossed and took a half hitch on the cleat, just as she had been taught. Then she helped pass the bags of garbage down to Ellie and climbed aboard.

"There's a heap of boats in today," Ellie explained, "and we'll be on our beam-ends if we don't load her careful-like."

"Can I skipper?" Cindy asked.

" 'Course you can, Cindy. It'll be calm for a spell—'spect

it'll blow up nor'east later. Keep her steady as she goes. That's a girl."

A bugeye, a large sloop, and a ketch all had their garbage ready when they motored up to the side Ellie called the back door. The skipper of one boat, who didn't want to be awakened so early in the morning, had carefully tied up his trash the night before and put it out in his dinghy.

This boat always had the best garbage in the harbor—clean and expensive. Ellie sifted it out until she found some muffins and lettuce leaves. She took the tiller while Cindy fed the gull, which was her favorite job aboard *Dauntless*.

The bird gobbled it down quickly and squawked for more.

"Hush up! You'll bust a boiler with all that squawkin'! That gull's a glutton!" Ellie shouted impatiently.

"Oh, please," Cindy begged, "he looks sad. Just give him one more piece of lettuce."

"Well—OK—just one more piece. If he don't quiet down now, I'll skin him for shark bait."

Cindy was delighted to see the gull preen himself and settle down. She wasn't sure whether or not Ellie was serious.

They were approaching a large yacht when Ellie spotted several bags of garbage floating down through the harbor. She told Cindy to speed up the engine, and they quickly caught up with the debris, which Ellie scooped up. She was furious! She had always wondered about this fancy yacht. Too many gulls hanging around the stern! She took the tiller from Cindy, spun the *Dauntless* around, and headed over.

"Garbage boat!" she called out.

"We don't have any," the skipper replied, coming up from below.

"You mean you don't eat? No trash at all?" Ellie asked.

"No, no. Nothing today," the skipper replied, and took refuge down below.

"He's a tonguey one, he is. City folk, you can be sure," Ellie muttered to Cindy. And with that she took the three bags of garbage and threw them on deck.

The skipper heard the splattering thud as the bags landed and burst open, the soaking mess sliding across his clean decks. He rushed topsides.

"What do you think you're doing?" he screamed at Ellie, shaking his fist.

"Go chase yourself! What do you think YOU'RE doin'? Next time you don't have any trash, I'll be tellin' the harbor master. Some folks'll say anything but their prayers. Go dump your own dirty garbage!" Ellie called back at him as *Dauntless* whirled about and headed for a large sloop.

"What're you so quiet for today? Sumpin' wrong?" Ellie asked Cindy.

"Oh, it's nothin'," Cindy replied, hanging her head.

"Well, it IS sumpin'! Come on now—out with it," Ellie said in a firm voice. "You'll bust a boiler yourself."

"It's just that my mother won't let me go fishin' alone! Says I'm too small. She wants me to play dolls with some friends. I HATE dolls!" Cindy blurted out, stamping her foot.

"Calm down. Hold on. Things like this can work out. Leastwise you can skipper a boat. And you're some smart—know that? You'll be able to go fishin' alone in no time. Can't do everythin' at once. Besides, it's good to play with someone your own age once in a while."

"I guess so," said Cindy.

"Look out where you step. Don't slip on the sour cream," Ellie cautioned as Cindy moved back to take the tiller. "Enough to ruin a good garbage bag. Makes you wonder about some folks—can't ever put a top back."

Ellie had given Cindy the tiller again, and *Dauntless* eased up beside the next boat.

"Garbage boat!" Ellie called out.

"How much does it cost?" asked the captain.

"If I want your money I'll say so. And it don't come in smelly paper bags. Are you goin' to hand her over or stand there? I got a heap of work to do."

"Money! Humph! More fancy trimmin' on that boat than a Sunday bonnet and he don't know nothin' 'bout keepin' a harbor clean. That figgers," Ellie grumbled, while the skipper went below and returned with several bags. He seemed embarrassed and didn't say a word.

It was noon before they finished. They had visited every

boat in the harbor and *Dauntless* was loaded to the gunwales.

"Well, Cindy, we're all finished for today," Ellie said as they pulled up to *White Mist* and Cindy scrambled aboard.

"Hey, skipper, ain't you forgot sumpin'?" Ellie called. "Not havin' you aboard is like chowder without clams. Here's your twenty cents."

"Gee, thanks, Ellie. See you tomorrow." Cindy waved from the schooner's deck.

"Shucks, ain't nuthin'," Ellie called back, spinning *Dauntless* around.

Ellie was put-put-putting along slowly toward the town pier when suddenly, out of nowhere, three boys zoomed by in an outboard, just missing *Dauntless* by inches!

"Pew! Pew! Pew! Look at the fat old lady in the funny honey boat! Pew! Pew! Do you stink!" they yelled at Ellie.

"Get outa here—keep away!" she cried, jumping up just as the wake hit the boat and threw Ellie across the cockpit in a heap on the floor. She scrambled up to grab the tiller.

"Drive it or milk it!" the boys shouted and swung in again, and then raced up harbor. Another large wave struck *Dauntless*, and Ellie lunged forward at the same time, struggling to keep the garbage bags from rolling off the foredeck. The side of her foot caught on the floorboard, and her ankle buckled under, sending a sharp pain up through her leg. The gull was jolted off the mast stub. Screeching and flapping, he finally regained his balance and sat down.

"You just wait till the harbor master hears about this! I'll get ya yet!" she shouted after the boys.

The burning pain in her ankle became worse, and her whole foot began to throb so much she had to sit down. Slowly she headed for the town dock again.

"What's the matter with you?" one of the fishermen standing alongside the fish shed called as Ellie pulled *Dauntless* alongside the pier.

"Shucks, ain't nothin'," Ellie replied. "Could be a dum sight worse. Can't have the peace of mind of a dog with them kids out there. Say, gimme a hand, will ya?"

The fisherman helped Ellie load her bags of trash into the back of the jeep. She motored back to the mooring and tied *Dauntless* up for the night. The pain made it very difficult for her to get into her skiff and row back to the pier. She hobbled into her jeep and drove off to the town dump. There was a huge flock of whining, screeching gulls waiting for her, and Ellie usually had some harsh words for them, but tonight her swollen ankle hurt so much she hardly noticed they were there. After she had finished, she went home and fell into bed.

Cindy waited all the next morning for Ellie, but she never came. Day after day the little girl got up bright and early to look for her friend. It was always the same. The empty boat lay still, tied to its mooring, and the gull sat patiently on the mast stub just as though he expected Ellie to arrive any minute. Cindy couldn't imagine what had happened to her friend.

And no one came to collect the garbage from the boats. The boatmen became very sloppy and lazy. First one threw his trash overboard, then another, and another. Each felt that if the others were doing it, then he too could throw his garbage in the harbor.

Old newspapers, beer cans, milk cartons, orange and grapefruit peels, oil cans, and soda bottles floated in messy patches of debris in the harbor and littered the once clean, white beaches.

Still there was no Ellie. Cindy finally couldn't stand it any longer and asked her mother if she could go find out what had happened to her friend.

She took the launch in to the pier, and the launchman pointed out Ellie's house up over the hill.

Cindy ran up the road as fast as she could to the little, gray, ramshackle house and, very softly, knocked on the door.

"Come in," a voice called, and Cindy slowly opened the door. She was shocked! There, in a simple iron bed, lay Ellie. She had one table, a little coal stove, and two wooden chairs. The room was cluttered with dirty dishes, glasses, and old magazines.

"What's the matter?" Cindy asked.

"Oh, nuthin'. Nuthin' at all," Ellie replied.

"But you haven't been out to *Dauntless* in more than a week! And you're in bed. There is something wrong!" Cindy insisted.

"Been just a bit tuckered, but shucks, ain't nothin' now, Cindy. Sprained my ankle—that's all."

"You shouldn't be here alone, Ellie. Please come back to our boat—there's plenty of room."

"Now don't go frettin'. The doctor come, and he says I'll be up in no time. Jest that I need to rest a bit—that's all. Now git on back to the schooner—hurry up—scat! I'll be aboard *Dauntless* in no time."

Cindy fought to hold back the tears as she walked slowly down the road to the launch. When she got to the schooner, her mother assured her Ellie would be all right.

That evening Cindy and her parents had dinner at the Seaside Inn instead of on their boat. While they were having

dessert, a man two tables away suddenly started to groan. His face was white, and after a moment he put his head down on the table. His dinner companions helped him up, and the restaurant owner quickly called the town ambulance, which came and took him to the hospital.

This was the first Cindy and her family saw of the mysterious sickness that was suddenly striking the people of Edgartown. The next day Cindy's father showed them an item in the *Vineyard Gazette*. The man at the inn was only one of a number of people who had suddenly been taken ill and were flat on their backs at home or lying in the town hospital. The town's two doctors rushed about answering emergency calls, and they became increasingly worried and exhausted as the number of sick people grew. And, worst of all, they had no idea what was making everyone sick.

The health officer and the two doctors were very puzzled. It didn't seem to be one of the contagious diseases. And it wasn't like anything they were used to. The symptoms were fever, headache, diarrhea, and vomiting. Some people were sicker than others; some had only one or two of the symptoms. The doctors decided to ask each patient a number of questions and then study the answers. Maybe this way they could get some clue.

But there was a big problem. The hotel guests came and went, the boats were in and out of the harbor, and it was only those in their own homes, or in the hospital, who could give them the detailed information they needed.

The health officer thought it might be something they were eating—in fact, he was almost sure the meat had gone bad. He took samples from all the grocery stores, hotels, and

restaurants in town and went back to his laboratory to test them. After studying for several days, he complained to the doctors and the Mayor, "There's nothing wrong here at all. And I was so certain. We must keep searching."

"If it's not a contagious disease, and they aren't eating bad meat, what could it be?" asked the Mayor, wrinkling his brow and shaking his head.

"We'll have to keep searching," replied the health officer. "That's all we can do."

Cindy hadn't become sick herself, but she had heard all the talk. Although Ellie had told her not to come back, the little girl felt she just had to go see how her friend was getting along. So she hurried back to the little house over the hill.

Cindy told Ellie how everyone in town seemed to be getting sick and no one knew what caused the Edgartown epidemic.

" 'Spect them doctors will find out what'sa matter, Cindy. Leastwise, that's their job," Ellie replied.

"Can you come back soon?" Cindy asked. "The harbor's awful dirty now without you collectin' the trash."

"You mean to say there ain't anybody collectin' the garbage? And they're throwin' it all in the harbor? Thunderation! Why, I'll bet even the fish wish they'd gone offshore in that mess. Cindy!"

Suddenly Ellie sat up, her eyes wide. "Cindy! Them folks might'a been eatin' bad fish. Now you run on back and tell your Pa to tell them experts to check the fish."

Cindy was very excited about having such important news, and hurried back to the schooner. The sun was setting behind the lavender and pink clouds which streaked the horizon, and the lighthouse was flickering like a firefly in the dusk when Mr.

and Mrs. Palmer came back to the boat from doing errands. When they heard Cindy's news, they immediately got in touch with the health officer.

Edgartown is on an island, out at sea, and for this reason it had never occurred to anyone that the beautiful, clean-looking water might be dirty. But just to be sure, the health officer took samples of fish from the local market and from the fishermen themselves to test in his laboratory.

He put bits of fish flesh in a blender and beat it up very fine. Then he put some of this mixture in a petri dish, which is a shallow, round glass dish with a cover, and he sealed it up tight. Then he waited.

After several days, the health officer went back to look at the smears of fish flesh under his microscope. He had learned to identify the many different-shaped cells the way people identify flowers. Some were octagonal, some round or fluted, some looked like little worms, and some were almost diamond shaped. If the fish were tainted, he would see cells of a certain definite shape.

He looked for a long time. He studied each sample carefully.

"There's nothing wrong with the fish at all," he assured the town authorities. "That's not our problem."

"Did you test the clams, too?" asked one of the doctors.

"Not much sense in that. If the fish are fine, certainly the clams will be too," replied the health officer. "But I guess we should try everything. Ten more were reported ill today. I'll make a test anyway."

He took some clams and seawater and ground them up fine in a blender, just as he had done with the fish. Then he put some samples in a petri dish and set them aside for a few days.

The doctors continued their search for more clues. Each day new cases of illness were reported, and there seemed to be no stopping this mysterious epidemic. The Mayor, the health officer, and the doctors had a meeting and decided they must call in extra help from one of the medical centers to work with them. While they were discussing this, the health officer was bent over his microscope, studying the clam culture.

"Mmmm—this is strange. Come look at those cells clustered together—little round disks. Look at those cell walls and the yellowish color. This isn't normal. We must do more tests."

The doctors gathered around. The health officer put different stains and dyes in the clam mixture and tried different temperatures to see what would happen. The men worked day and night studying the clams.

Finally, after a few days, the health officer had the answer. "Gentlemen, these clams are contaminated. It is dysentery which has made everyone who's been eating clams taken from the harbor sick. It seems impossible . . . but the harbor must be polluted. Let's go see for ourselves."

No one had thought before to take a careful look at the harbor. They were horrified. The water was littered with floating garbage!

"Why is it so dirty?" asked the Mayor.

"I've never seen such a dreadful mess!" exclaimed the health officer. "What happened? Where's Ellie?"

"She's in bed with a sprained ankle," replied a fisherman standing by. "Seems some boys went zooming by her in an outboard and she lost her footing."

"Oh, yes, I remember," said one of the doctors. "I strapped up her ankle. But I never thought to ask her about her garbage collection. How stupid of me!"

"I'll go see her immediately," replied the Mayor. He started off.

Word about the harbor spread quickly, and the townspeople swarmed down to the harbor front to see for themselves. Seizing the opportunity, the doctors put them right to work, cleaning up. Fishing boats, workboats, pleasure boats, visiting yachtsmen in their dinghies, and boys in rowboats all gathered to help pick up the debris. Scallopers used their drags to pull garbage off the bottom, and people on the beaches picked up papers, cans, and bottles. They piled it all on the town dock, where men were waiting in jeeps and trucks to haul it off to the dump to be burned. The harbor master went about arresting everyone who had thrown trash in the harbor.

The police cruised around town announcing on a loudspeaker that no one was to eat any clams or shellfish until further notice. Signs were posted everywhere, and restaurants were prohibited from serving shellfish. The town officials were glad they had caught it before things got any worse. If it had gone on much longer, the fish might have been affected.

The Mayor found Ellie in her shack, hobbling around the stove. He told her about the bad clams and how dirty the harbor had become.

"I better get down there," Ellie exclaimed. "Thunderation! People might'a kept things clean on their own!"

"You stay right here, Ellie. You're valuable property—this town is just beginning to realize how valuable! Rest up until your ankle is better."

"No—no! Shucks, my ankle ain't so bad now. I got to see for myself."

Ellie insisted, and she limped down to the harbor front with the Mayor to see the massive cleanup. She hobbled out on the town pier and began shouting orders to the men.

"Don't leave a paper, bottle, or bone!" she yelled at the men. "Look behind ya!" she shouted at one fisherman.

"Ah, come on, Ellie. Don't be so goldarn fussy!" the man yelled back at her.

"Get it all. You heard me! Ain't no use cleaning if you can't put it to right," Ellie called back.

The fisherman muttered to his helper: "She'd be a good one

to have on board in a calm. She never shuts up. You git her talkin' abaft the mains'l and you'd have a twenty-knot breeze in no time."

But Ellie heard him, and she was in no mood for such remarks.

"Garbage is my business and garbage it'll be. The only thing you ever stuck to was the day you set on the bench you'd just painted."

It took almost a week of good hard work before the harbor was finally clean. And it might take many weeks before the water purified itself and was no longer polluted. Every day the authorities went down to the harbor front and took fresh samples of water and shellfish to be tested in the laboratory.

The fishermen, who had often made fun of Ellie and her honey boat, began to see how very important her job had been. And the visiting yachtsmen realized that a small bit of garbage tossed overboard could be very serious. No one was likely to make fun of Ellie again.

The townspeople and the town officials decided they must somehow show their gratitude to Ellie for what she had been doing all this time. Everyone had been taking Ellie's work for granted for too long. So they declared the following Saturday "Ellie Day."

A large group gathered down on the town dock for the celebration. The man who owned the local shipyard spoke up and said he would refinish and paint Ellie's boat for nothing. Then the Mayor made a very fine speech, praising Ellie for her work. Afterward he read a letter of thanks from the town officials, stating that her salary would be doubled.

The audience cheered when Ellie limped up to the speaker's stand. She stood in front of the microphone to speak, but it bothered her. She brusquely pushed it aside, and in her best garbage-boat voice called out, "Shucks, it ain't nothin'. Things kind of average up in this world. Come on, Cindy—we got some work to do, and you can skipper today."

Everyone clapped and cheered again as Ellie hobbled down to the dock with the little girl trailing behind her.

"Good to be back on the job," Ellie said as she fired up *Dauntless*'s engine. "And there won't be a paper, bottle, or bone left in the harbor when we get finished, now will there?"

Monsters behind the Door

This is an adventure story about the sea. It is true. It begins over two thousand years ago. And it ends with five brave women who received the highest award the United States Department of the Interior gives, the Conservation Service Award.

"Humans are no better equipped to live under the water than fish are to live on dry land," an ancient Greek might have said. And for hundreds of years it was just that simple. People might sail on the surface of the sea. They might fish with nets or lines or spears. To most people, however, the surface of the sea was a closed door. And more than a few believed that behind the closed door lurked monsters. The ancient Greeks thought that the god Poseidon could beat the sea into a stormy rage with his trident. Viking stories tell of giant sea serpents that rose from the dark waters to snatch careless sailors.

But not everyone was worried about monsters and gods beneath the water. Some were trying to discover what really lay under the sea. There were problems, however. For that ancient Greek was right. Humans are not equipped to live underwater, and they cannot stay underwater for more than a few minutes without breathing. Air, then, is the first problem. How can a human breathe underwater?

Among the earliest recorded attempts to solve the problem was the diving bell. In fact, Alexander the Great is said to have used one over two thousand years ago. A diving bell is very simple. It works in the sea just as an upside-down glass works in a bucket of water. Of course, the diving bell is much larger because it must hold a person. Air trapped inside the bell (or upside-down glass) presses against the water and keeps it out.

But a diving bell has disadvantages. Unless air is pumped down from the surface, the air supply is limited. The person inside the bell soon uses up all the oxygen. Also, a diving bell cannot be easily moved from place to place underwater. So the diving bell was just a first step in undersea exploration.

In the early 1800's Augustus Siebe, a German living in England, made the first practical diving outfit. It had a strong glass window set in a metal helmet. This helmet was fastened to a watertight suit. Connected by a hose to an air pump mounted in a boat, the Siebe suit allowed divers to move around and to breathe underwater.

Like a dog on a rope, though, the diver was tied to the air hose and the safety line. Fish might swim swiftly by the glass window, but the diver could take only slow, heavy steps. The diving gear was weighted with lead to keep it from bobbing to the surface like a balloon. Humans were still outsiders clumsily tied to the air pump on the surface.

Moving gracefully through deep water like a fish was still a dream. And actually living under the water was a fantasy.

Then in the 1940's Jacques-Yves Cousteau and Émile Gagnan developed the Aqualung. The Aqualung consists of tanks of compressed air strapped to a diver's back. With this supply of air a diver can stay underwater without a long hose to the surface. Further, a diver wearing an Aqualung can swim, not stagger about with lead-weighted shoes. In a world filled with fish, the diver can move like a fish. So another problem was solved.

But the greatest adventure of all lay ahead. How much better if people could build a house underwater—an underwater laboratory. Divers with air tanks could swim out of the house to study underwater life and then return to refill their air tanks. Maybe at last humans could truly unlock the door to the mysteries of the sea.

Perhaps the best known underwater house is *Sealab*, built by the United States Navy in the late 1960's. Astronaut Scott Carpenter was one of the divers in the *Sealab* project. But to many people a more recent undersea project is the most exciting of all.

The project was named *Tektite II*. Its purpose was to study underwater life around a coral reef in the Caribbean Sea near the Virgin Islands. Five women, each a scientist or engineer, were chosen as aquanauts in the *Tektite II* project. All of the women were good divers. The leader of the team was Dr. Sylvia Earle Mead, a marine biologist.

For two weeks Dr. Mead and her team lived beneath the crystal water of the Caribbean. Their underwater home was a pair of upright metal cylinders 3.81 meters across and 5.64 meters high. In these two connected cylinders, Dr. Mead and her team slept, ate, and worked. Their windows looked out on a bright world of fish and coral and other sea life. Their door was an open hole in the

floor. As in the diving bell, air pressure kept the water out. After putting on their diving gear, they had only to slip through their door to enter the silent world deep beneath the Caribbean.

From inside the underwater house the team could communicate with scientists on the surface by means of closed-circuit television. But on their long swims to observe undersea life, they could not. The divers therefore always swam in pairs. In an emergency one diver could help her partner.

For two weeks Dr. Mead and her team explored the coral reef around their underwater house on the ocean floor. Some members of the team studied the tarpon, eels, lobsters, and other sea animals. Dr. Mead herself concentrated on the unusual plant life that grew around the coral reef. In effect, Dr. Mead and her team became a part of the undersea life around the reef.

After two weeks Dr. Mead and her team returned to the noisy world of the automobile and the airplane. What they learned in the silent world beneath the sea will help other scientists. For their accomplishments Dr. Mead and her four brave teammates received the Conservation Service Award.

After more than two thousand years, people can more freely explore the mysteries of the deep. Not only can they swim with the fish. They can also live beneath the sea. No one has yet found a sea serpent or the god Poseidon. But Dr. Mead and others like her have opened the door into the sea. And behind the door lurk not monsters, but answers to questions that began thousands of years ago.

Experiment

We do not think very much about the air we breathe. It is easy to forget that air is a mixture of gases (mostly oxygen and nitrogen). Gases can exert pressure, or force, just as a hand or a hammer or a foot can. In fact, it is this pressure that keeps water from filling a diving bell or an underwater house.

To prove this, stuff a piece of tissue paper or paper towel in the very bottom of a glass. Be sure that it fits tightly. Turn the glass upside down. Now carefully force the glass into a large container of water. Do not tilt the glass.

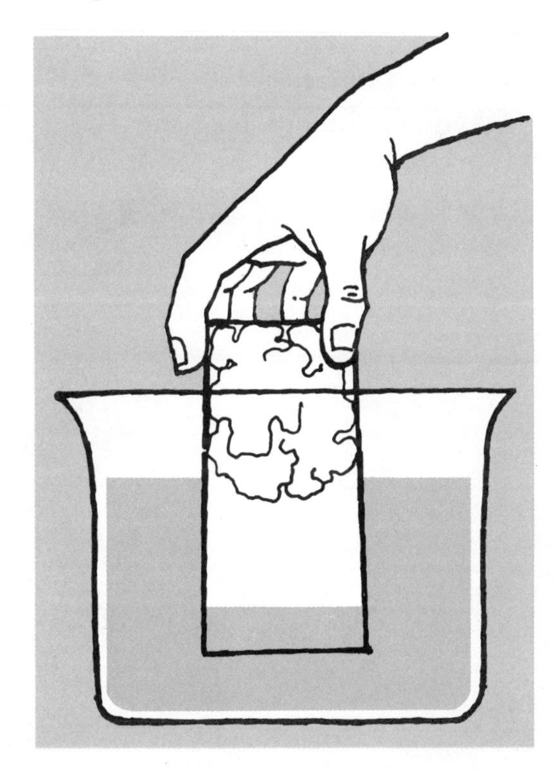

Observing and Thinking

1. Did the tissue get wet?
2. What happens if you tilt the glass? Why? Where does the air go?
3. What would happen if the glass had a hole in the bottom?

We rowed into fog,
  And out through fog . . .
  O how blue
How bright the wide sea!

Shiki

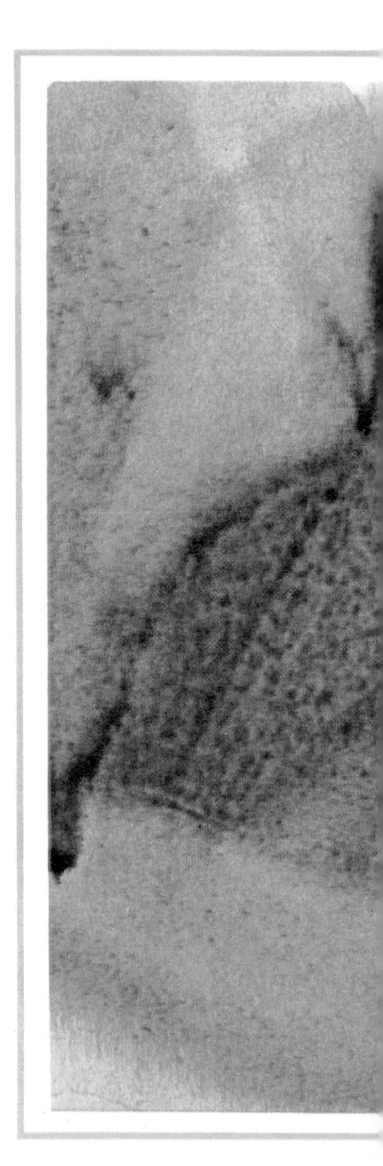

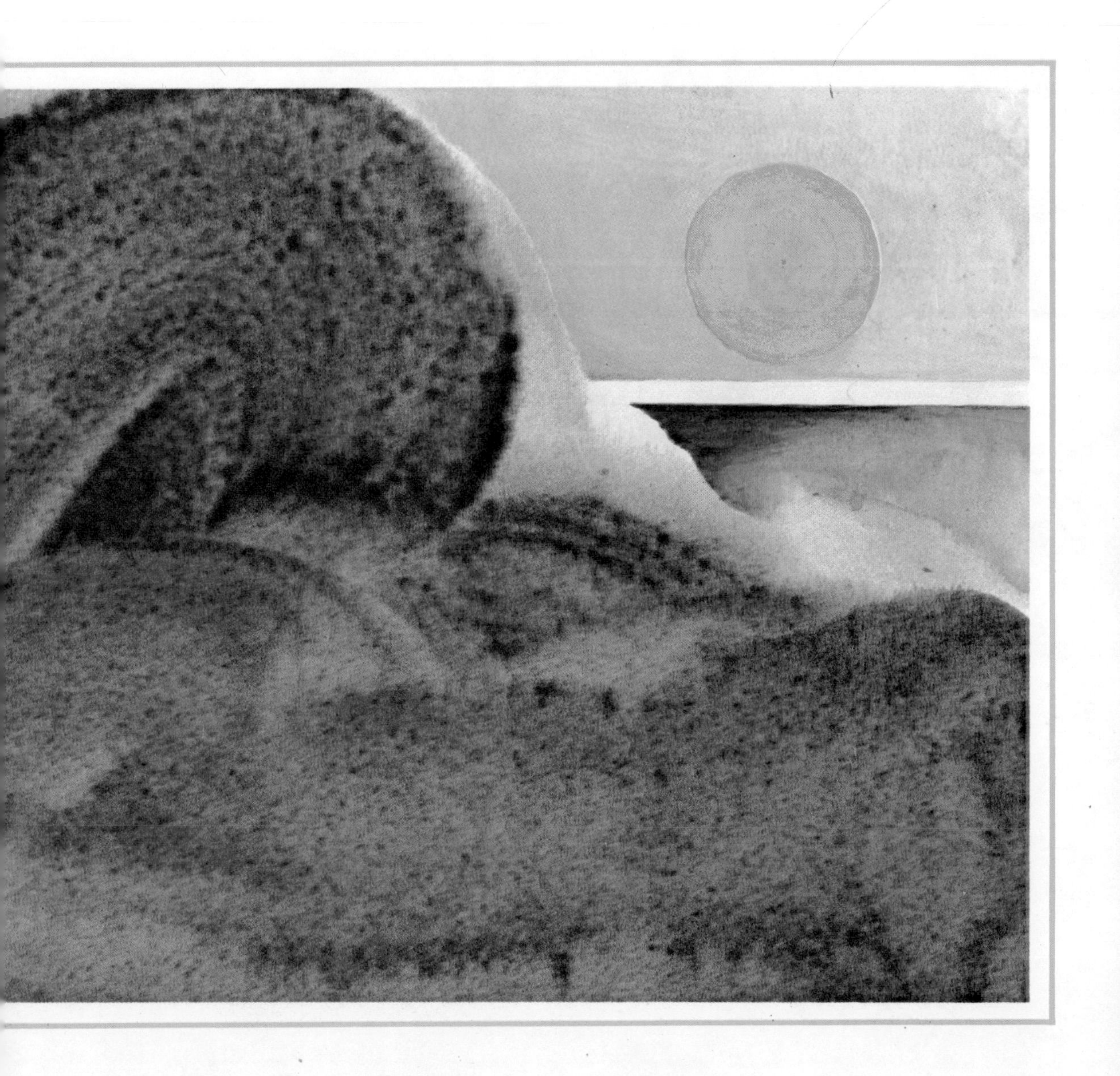

Americans at Work

"Men work together," I told him from the heart,
"Whether they work together or apart."

Robert Frost

Crafts Are a Family Thing

Bruce and Nancy Roberts

The section of the United States known as Appalachia is a beautiful mountainous area stretching from Pennsylvania to Alabama. Separated from each other and the rest of the country by steep rocky hills, the Appalachian people learned to make do with the materials at hand. Today they are building a new industry with hand skills learned from parents or grandparents.

"Turn down Brown Creek Road and keep going until the road gets narrower and you think it's going to end," says the man in the country store. "You'll find Wiley Blevins' house on the right."

Like Wiley Blevins, most mountain craftsmen of Appalachia live off the main highways. It takes real skill and daring to drive the dirt roads. Junked cars are a familiar sight, and the roads are one of the reasons. A car doesn't last long on rocky, rutted mountain roads.

But chairmaker Wiley Blevins does not worry about the road being rough on cars. This warm, friendly man has never owned one, for he is a deaf-mute. He is used to the long walk to the grocery store or doctor in all kinds of weather, although he sometimes rides home with a neighbor.

Each Sunday, on foot, he climbs steep, winding White Oak Creek Road to his church. Sometimes in the afternoon, after he is through working his vegetable patch, he sits on his front porch reading a large-print Bible. The Bible is one of his most prized possessions.

The rest of his time is spent working on the chairs that he makes by hand in the basement of his one-room home. He brought each stone himself from the creek and built the foundation. The little basement room is musty and damp but cool during the heat of the day. There Wiley Blevins sits weaving chair bottoms from reed splits. Only a few people weave these seats, for it takes time and patience.

Before he can work with the splits, he puts the bundles of reed into the icy mountain stream to soak. After a few hours they become flexible enough for him to begin weaving his chair seats. The rungs of the chair, untouched by power machinery, are still shaped by hand.

Mr. Blevins makes his chairs to order or sells them at a local fair, which is held once a year. The road to his house is traveled mostly by the families who live along it. So the thousands of tourists who drive by a few miles away on the main highway are not likely to learn about Wiley Blevins and his chairmaking.

Since quite a few of the mountain craftsmen live off the main roads, several of the mountain counties have formed a government-funded organization to help these people market their products. The organization has also encouraged many of the older men and women, no longer well enough to do heavy work, to take up crafts.

This help in selling their chairs, baskets, rugs, quilts, carvings, and toys has given many people a fresh interest in life and a sense of pride in their skill.

In some mountain families a skill has been handed down. In the Hicks family it is making and playing dulcimers.

Scarcely two months after he married Nettie Hicks, Ed Presnell made his first dulcimer, using her father's as a model. After he had made the first of these old-fashioned three-string instruments, he found such a demand for them that he kept right on. He carved them out of chestnut, sassafras, cherry, butternut, walnut, and maple, experimenting with all the different woods from the trees nearby. He would season the wood himself and polish it lovingly to bring out the grain.

For a while, Ed Presnell continued farming as he had done before he and Nettie Hicks married. In the evening he would sit carving out his dulcimers before the fire or on the porch. As the orders began to pile up, he turned entirely to dulcimer making. He made a special design for his instruments to give them good tone as well as beauty. By now he has lost count of the dulcimers he has made. But they number in the hundreds. This slight, full-bearded man is now known as the "king of the dulcimer makers." His son likes to carve animals, particularly ducks with a lively air. Mrs. Presnell gives the finishing touches such as sanding and polishing.

Not far from the Hicks family lives Mrs. Elsie Trivette. When she was a little girl, Mrs. Trivette watched her mother and learned how to spin. She went with her into the forest, where Elsie discovered which herbs and roots made the beautiful soft colors for dyeing wool.

The herbs are boiled outdoors in a huge black iron pot.

"I get my brown dyes from black walnut hulls. Some of that iron in my old pot blends in just right with the dye. Onion hulls will make yellow or orange. The sumac burs give deep red colors. And I use poke juice to mark off the design on burlap.

"My mother taught all of us to dye and hook rugs and knot bedspreads. We supported ourselves." The wool is hooked through a burlap bag, which forms the backing for her rugs.

There are many natural resources in Appalachia. This is one reason crafts have done well. There are stones for the jewelry maker, lumber for the wood-carver, clay for the potter, and cane for the basket-makers. Since the mountain people are not pressed for time, they can experiment with the materials around them.

But in the frontier days and for many years after, crafts were not a hobby. Skill with one's hands was very important to living in the wilderness. Men and women built their own houses. They made their own furniture, farm tools, and clothing. And they were proud of the work of their hands. The things they made gave comfort, dignity, beauty, and recreation to their lives.

There was a sense of satisfaction in making these tools and household objects. Years later when men and women no longer had to make things, they still took pleasure in doing so.

It is only natural that one of the greatest craft revivals in America is taking place in Appalachia, where craft skills were once needed in daily life.

Afterthought

1. Why was it necessary to form organizations to help the Appalachian people market their handcrafted products?
2. Why might other people want to buy these products?
3. Tell why you think the things the Appalachian people make by hand could or could not be made just as well by machine.

Construction

The giant mouth
chews
rocks
spews them
and is back for
more.

The giant arm
swings up
with a girder
for
the fourteenth floor.

Down there,
a tiny man
is
telling them
where
to put a skyscraper.

Lilian Moore

Food from the Past

Winifred G. Hammond

Farmers plant their grain, cultivate it, and then harvest it. But there is one grain we eat that no one plants or tends.

A Treasured Food

There is one grain food that you can buy in the grocery stores of the United States and Canada today that goes as far back in time as there have been people on this continent.

If you throw a handful of these grains into a pot of boiling water along with a few pieces of wild game, say duck or rabbit, you will taste the same flavors as did the people who lived thousands of years ago. The only difference is that their dinner was cooked in a basket with hot rocks instead of in a pan on a gas or electric stove.

This food is wild rice. It isn't a true rice, but the grains look something like stretched-out kernels of rice. It grows in water as true rice does.

Wherever wild rice grew, the Indians thought themselves fortunate. This was a treasured food, a food given them by the gods.

Today wild rice is the highest-priced cereal in the world. Even though it is boxed in a fancy box at a modern mill, it is still as wild and untamed as when it was first eaten by man. No scientist has changed it. Nor has it been crossed with any other grass.

An Ancient Harvest

Picture to yourself the ancient peoples that lived in the beautiful northern lake country of the United States and Canada. It is early fall. The manomini moon, the wild rice moon, shines white. From the distance comes the call of a loon. Closer is the splash of fish jumping in the shallows. Thousands of ducks are quacking their last sleepy talk to each other before quieting for the night. A warm wind, the manomini wind, soft as velvet, brings a rich scent of night and green things in water.

The people have come to the lake for the wild rice harvest. There are young men and women, old people, and children. Many are related. They have brought their few household possessions and have set up camp along the shores. There is noise and confusion, with dogs running and barking and getting in everyone's way. Aunts, uncles, and cousins greet each other and talk of everything that has happened since they were last together. The moon is so bright that nobody wants to go to bed. Everyone is excited and happy.

Tomorrow they will start the harvest. Soon there will be a meal of rice cooked with fish or duck. Or perhaps the duck will be roasted in the coals, and the rice will be cooked with dried blueberries. Many of the people have just come from the country of the blueberries. It will be a big feast. There will be plenty for all.

Gathering the Wild Rice. The next morning the sun shows the rice lake in all its beauty. As far as the eye can see, the rice stretches like a green island. Twice as tall as a man, the stalks stand with their roots in the shallow water. They bend gracefully back and forth in the light breeze. Along the top two feet of each stalk, the rice grains hang from their small stems, ready to drop off at the least shaking. Thousands of ducks and geese are already feasting. Clouds of blackbirds wheel overhead. Then they descend to the rice, bending it down and pecking the grains. The Indians know they must get their share before the birds and wind have stripped the stalks of the seeds.

Quickly the canoes are made ready, and the women push off. Only an occasional man or half-grown boy goes along, for this is woman's work. As long as the people can remember, it has been the women who have gone out each fall in the canoes to harvest the rice.

Two women go in each canoe. The rice stalks are so close together that it is impossible to paddle. So one woman pushes with a forked pole from the back seat of the canoe. The other woman knocks the rice off the stalks into the canoe. She holds two beater sticks. With one she reaches out and bends a bunch of stalks over the canoe. With the other she beats the rice heads to knock the grains into the canoe. Back and forth across the lake the women go in regular lines. Each path is next to the last so as much grain can be gathered as possible. When the canoe is low in the water, heavy with the grain, the women push to shore and unload.

Processing the Grain. The harvested rice is damp and slightly green. The women know that if they had waited until it was fully ripe, they would have reaped scarcely any. Most of it would have fallen into the water before they could have moved the boat into place. This damp rice must now be dried.

Some Indian tribes built low platforms of stout sticks and covered them with bark. The rice was laid on the bark. Then a fire was kept burning underneath. There was just enough fire to dry the rice but not enough to kindle the bark.

In other tribes the women stirred the rice and some hot coals in a basket. Indian women had to know just how many coals and how much rice to use, or both rice and basket would be spoiled. After the rice-gathering tribes met white people, the Indians traded for metal kettles. The rice could be put into a kettle over the fire and stirred with a paddle to dry it. This method was much easier. It took skill but not as much as the basket-and-coals method.

The roasting cracked the rice hulls and loosened them. The rice was then ready for the men's part of the work. This was the hulling and threshing.

Some tribes spread the rice on skins laid out on the ground and beat it with sticks. Others dug a shallow hole in the ground, covered the bottom with a clean skin, and put the rice into the hole. Then a man or youth would step into the hole and dance up and down, pounding the hulls off the rice with his moccasined feet. This dancing was often done to the rhythm of a chant.

When the hulls were loosened, it was the women's turn again. It was the women's job to separate the hulls from the kernels. The rice and hulls were put into wide shallow baskets or trays. As the women shook and jiggled the baskets, the hulls slipped off the edges as if by magic.

Preparing the Feast. The day was far gone by the time all this work was done. In the meantime men or boys had been out on the lake to catch ducks and fish. They had built fires ready for the cooks. Everyone was hungry. Now the women began the cooking. The good smells of food drifted along the shore and through the trees.

However, there was one thing more that had to be done. Before the feast could begin, there must be prayers to the Great Spirit. The Indians knew that the Great Spirit had given them this wonderful rice food.

A Legend

There are many legends that tell how the Great Spirit gave the rice to his people.

One of these tells of the boy Wenibozho, who lived with his grandmother. She loved her grandson so much that she did everything she could to make him happy. Perhaps she did too much for him. One day she realized that he was lazy and selfish. He hadn't learned the lessons of living in a hard world or the skills that were necessary in the Indian's life. She wondered what would happen to him when she was no longer there to care for him.

"My son," she said, "since you will not learn your lessons here at home with me, you must go away. You must take a long journey through unknown forests. You must become used to the hardships of life."

Wenibozho had no choice, so he went out into the dark forest. There were many animals in the forest. However, Wenibozho could not catch any of them to eat because he had never learned to shoot an arrow or throw a spear. He became very hungry. As he wandered along, some little bushes spoke to him.

"Sometimes they eat us," they said in low musical voices.

At first Wenibozho paid no attention to the bushes but went on through the woods. Soon he heard them again.

"Sometimes they eat us."

Wenibozho stooped and dug up one of the plants. He found that it had a long root that looked as if it would be good to eat. When he tasted it, he found that it was sweet and good. Since he was so hungry, he dug many of the plants and ate the roots. In fact, he ate so many that he became very sick. For three days he lay there in the woods, too sick to move.

At the end of the three days he felt better, so he wandered on. Many plants spoke to him, but he paid no attention to them. Finally he found himself at the edge of a lake. As he stood there, some of the grasses seemed to be waving at him. When he went closer, he could hear them murmuring.

"Sometimes they eat us," they said in soft musical whispers.

Wenibozho looked at a stalk of the grass and saw that its top was loaded with long seeds. He gathered some of the seeds and pulled off the hulls. He found that the kernels had a most pleasing taste.

"Oh, you are good," he said to the grass. "What are you called?"

"We are called manomin, or good berry," the grass told him.

Wenibozho ate and ate, enough to satisfy his hunger. The rice did not hurt him at all. When at last he went back to his grandmother, he took some of the manomin with him as a present for her. And ever after that, so the Indians say, they have had manomin to eat.

Early Explorers

The good berry has had many names besides the ones given it by the Indians. It was mentioned in reports by early explorers who called it wild rice, wild oats, squaw rice, water oats, and other names. Fur trappers and explorers often traded with the Indians for the grain. It became one of the main parts of their diet. A cupful was said to make a meal for two.

Manomin, the good berry, was taken back to Europe by plant explorers in the early days of the settlement of North America. An effort was made to get it started in the lakes of Sweden, but this was not successful.

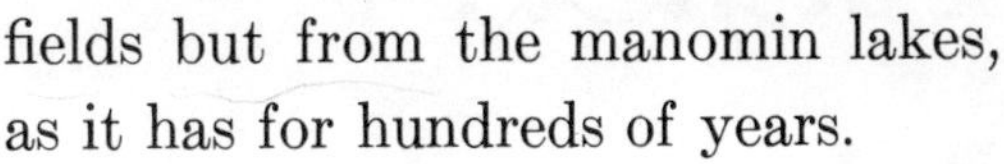

Wild Rice Today

Many efforts have since been made to plant the rice in other lakes and in other countries. Few of these have been successful. The manomin goes its own way and resists all efforts to make it into a tame plant. Its ways are those of wild plants. The wild rice that is sold in the markets today does not come from the farmer's fields but from the manomin lakes, as it has for hundreds of years.

Harvesting. Much of the wild rice is still harvested by Indians. Many Indian families still make a yearly trip to the rice lakes. There they camp, enjoying the beauty of the fall and the company of friends and relatives. A few still roast the grain in pots and dance the hulls off. However, most of the rice is sold to a buyer who will process it in a modern mill.

Processing. At the mill the drying is done in big drums turning over slow gas fires. The hulls are taken off by machine hullers instead of the dancing feet of men. Big shakers replace the jiggling bark trays of the women. And power fans give blasts of air to carry away the hulls.

No matter how it is gathered or processed, manomin, the good berry, is still a wild food. It is one link that unites us with the people of long ago.

Cabin Number Seven

Louisa R. Shotwell

Roosevelt Grady and his family pick fruits and vegetables. They travel from place to place, going wherever the crops are ripe. At the beginning of this story they are traveling to a workers' camp with their crew boss, Cap Jackson.

One day as they were going north, Cap Jackson let Roosevelt and Matthew and Sister ride alongside of him right up in the front of the truck. They begged him to tell them about Willowbrook.

"Willowbrook? It's a whale of a camp," he told them. "Room for half a dozen crews like ours. Maybe more. Must be twenty cabins all hitched together in a single row. And they have three rows like that. Fill up three sides of a square, they do. A great big hollow square, one row of cabins to each side. Right in the middle of the square there's a shack with cookstoves in it for folks that don't bring along their own stoves the way your mamma does. The cookshack has a juke box in it, too, and a loudspeaker so I can call my folks to come when it's time to cash in their bean tickets."

Roosevelt knew what that meant. So did Sister and Matthew. When you've picked your hamperful of beans, you drag it off to be weighed and then you get a ticket, and later on Papa trades in the ticket for money. Fifty cents, seventy-five cents, something like that, depending on how big the hamper is and what they are paying that day. Florida hampers weigh thirty-two pounds, sometimes, when they're full.

"How'll I know which cabin's ours?" asked Matthew. "If they're hitched together and they all look alike, how'll I know when I'm home?"

"You'll get to know. Each cabin has its own door with a number on it to tell you which one your family belongs in. Has its own window, too."

"A square has four sides. You told us about three of them. What's on the fourth side of the square?" Roosevelt wanted to know. "The empty side?"

"Guess," Cap ordered.

"Willow-brook. A brook. I guess a brook. And fish in it." That was Matthew.

"Wrong," said Cap.

"I guess a willow tree," said Sister. "Nice and droopy with lots of shade to play in."

"Wrong."

"A schoolhouse?" asked Roosevelt. He was quite sure this was not the right answer. He was only hoping.

"All wrong," said Cap. "No brook, and I don't recall seeing a willow tree anywhere around. The name of that camp's a fake. No school, either. There's a big brick school building five miles down the road for the resident children, but there isn't any school at Willowbrook."

"Then what does fill up the empty side of the hollow square?" asked Matthew. "Tell us, Cap. We give up."

"Beans," said Cap. "A bean field, right on the doorstep."

When they finally came to Willowbrook, sure enough there was the hollow square with the cookshack in the middle and on the square's empty side, the bean field. No brook. No willow tree. No schoolhouse. And no sign of Digger Burton's crew.

The way it worked at Willowbrook, your papa stood in line at the cookshack door and waited his turn for a man called Bucky to say which cabin his family could have. Bucky was the camp manager. His entire name was Bucky Bean, and he ran things at Willowbrook.

"Bucky Bean?" With his index finger, Matthew scoured out his right ear and then his left, making believe he hadn't heard right. "Is his name really and truly Bean? Mr. Bucky Bean?"

"Must be," Mamma answered. "That's what your papa said, and I don't know why he'd make it up."

"Ho—ho—ho," said Matthew. "Mr. Bean's in charge of

beans." He thumped on his chest with his fists and limped around in a circle, chanting:

Mister Bean
What I mean
Pick 'em clean
Or ol' man Bean
He'll get himself
A bean machine!

"Matthew!" Mamma spoke sharp. "Where'd you hear that?"

"No place. It just popped out of my mouth. Don't you like it? I do. Do you want some more? Bean—seen—green—queen—screen—"

Just then Papa came back from standing in line.

"Number Seven," he announced. "That's where we belong. See who can find it first."

On each cabin door there was painted in black a huge sprawly number. It should have been easy to find Cabin Number Seven, but it wasn't. There was something queer about those numbers.

Sister was the first to spot Number Seven and while Roosevelt was still puzzling in his head, she figured out what was the matter. Times were when Sister promised to grow up as smart as Mamma, and this was one of those times.

"There's ours," she cried, and she darted over to a door and pointed.

"That's no seven," said Roosevelt. He was tired and cross, and he guessed he knew what a seven ought to look like.

"Maybe it's not a seven," said Sister, "but the man who painted it thought it was. Look." And pointing, she counted out the cabins backwards to the beginning of the row: "Seven, Six, Five, Four, Three, Two, One. This one's Number Seven, all right."

The figures looked like this:

1234567

"That old Camp Manager Bucky Bean must have let a first-grader do his painting for him," said Roosevelt, crosser than ever because he hadn't located Number Seven ahead of Sister.

"Maybe," said Sister, "but whoever did it, he looks at things through a looking glass. Backwards!" She giggled, and so did everybody else, even Roosevelt. Once you knew what was the matter, the figures did look comical.

Roosevelt lugged his mother's metal suitcase into Cabin Number Seven and set it in the middle of the floor. Then he ran back outdoors to have a look around the camp. He walked along, counting cabins. Starting from the bean field, the three sides of the hollow square had twenty cabins to a side. Just what Cap said. Times three, that made sixty families. Suppose every family was like the Gradys and had six people to it; there would be six times sixty people living in that camp. Six times sixty: 360 folks. Could mean as many as seven or eight crews, nine or ten, even. Not that many now, because the whole far side of the square stood padlocked and empty.

But just suppose. Suppose you had ten crew leaders and each one picked out crews as different from each other as Cap Jackson and Digger Burton did. And suppose half the crew leaders didn't like the other half any better than Cap liked Digger. There'd sure enough be plenty of chance for quarrelings.

Cabin Number Eight had a fat lady living in it named Mrs. Clay. She was big enough to fill up the cabin with no help from anybody else, but besides herself there were her husband James, skinny and sour-looking, and a large collection of children, all girls.

The Gradys hadn't been one hour at Willowbrook before they found themselves acquainted with Pearly Ann Clay because Pearly Ann was seven years old and so was Sister and right away they started being girl friends. But nobody in the Grady family had the rest of the Clays sorted out until Matthew met Mrs. Clay.

It was the next day. Mrs. Clay had just finished her wash and was hanging out her clothes on a line stretched across from her cabin to the cookshack roof. Her clothespins were in a bucket on the ground, so she would put half a dozen of the pins in her mouth at once and pull them out one at a time as she needed them. She had a wide mouth to suit the rest of her. It accommodated six clothespins without stretching.

Mrs. Clay hadn't noticed Matthew at all, and when he said to her, "Mrs. Clay, how many children have you got?" she was so startled she blew the clothespins right out of her mouth and they flew every which way. Matthew limped around picking them up and when he brought them back, he said:

"How about if I hand these to you one at a time out of the bucket? That way we can have a satisfac-tory conversation."

Mrs. Clay gave Matthew a rather peculiar look, but:

"Let's try," she said. Matthew handed her a clothespin. "Now then. What did you ask me?"

"How many children have you got?"

"Well, let me see," said Mrs. Clay. "We'll start at the top. Two clothespins this time, please. There." She set the two pins firmly into a pair of blue jeans. "That's Marlene and Cherry. Twins."

Matthew handed her another pin.

"This is Lulubelle. Now two more, please. These are Sue Ellen and Tillie: twins again." Now it was diapers she was hanging up. She reached down her hand to Matthew for another pin. "And one for little Baby Bethalene. Six girls, and they're all mine.

"Now one for Wanda. She's the child of Clay's brother, and she's the size of my Marlene and Cherry. Wanda scraps with her own folks, so she mostly travels with us. That's seven."

"And Pearly Ann," said Matthew, handing up another clothespin.

"And Pearly Ann," said Mrs. Clay. "She makes eight. Eight girls. That's how many children I've got."

"Where'd Pearly Ann come from?" persisted Matthew.

"Pearly Ann?" Mrs. Clay hung up the last dress in her basket. Thin blue and white stripes it had, and she kind of smoothed it out with her hands as she talked. "When Pearly Ann was a mite of a baby, no longer than a shoe box, her mamma died. Down in South Carolina, in the strawberries, it was. Her papa, he was half crazy, he felt so bad to lose his wife, and he said to me, 'What am I going to do with Pearly Ann?' So I said, 'You give Pearly Ann to me and don't you fret. I'll look after her just as easy, right along with mine. One extra isn't going to be a speck more bother than what I've got already.' And that's the way it's been. Seven years now and Pearly Ann fits in with us so good, I declare I mostly dis-remember she didn't start out being my baby at all."

When Matthew felt like working his memory, there was nothing he couldn't recall. That night the Gradys heard every word of his talk with Mrs. Clay, exactly the way it happened.

The thought of those clothespins tickled Papa so hard he choked. He had to wipe his eyes before he could speak one word.

"There's one thing about you, Matthew," he said.

"What's one thing about me?" asked Matthew.

Papa picked him up and set him on his knee. Very gently he rubbed his feet, the good one and the bad one. Then he put a finger under Matthew's chin and tipped up his face.

"There's nothing wrong with your head," Papa told him. "Or your funny bone."

Mamma was struck to know about all those Clay children.

"Think of that," said Mamma. "Six girls of her own and two more that don't rightly belong to her, but she keeps them in the family just as if they did. I could be wrong, but that man of hers looks to me to be no help at all. And that poor South Carolina strawberry-picker who lost his wife, her telling him one more child wouldn't be a speck of bother. What's more, I do believe she meant it. I declare, I'm going to talk to that woman. Find out how she does it. I marvel at her."

"You have anything in mind?" asked Papa, in his teasing voice. Before Mamma could answer, he went to speaking serious. "Addie Grady, I do say this and I want you to hearken to it. You have no call to marvel at any other woman. How ever many extra children she adds on to her family, she can't beat you. You're the best."

"Henry Grady," said Mamma, tossing her head. "How you talk." But she did look pleased.

Beans were running good, and soon sweet corn began to come along. One day Papa brought home a big basket of runty ears, good to eat but so small the packing house wouldn't take them, so Bucky Bean told Papa he could carry them home.

"This is a sight more corn than we can eat," said Mamma. She took a good bit over half of the ears and gave them to Mrs. Clay. The two of them sat in their doorways and husked the corn. Roosevelt helped. He liked to pull off the long green jackets and then go after every bit of silk and grub it out.

Mrs. Clay told Mamma: "Fresh corn. This is a treat. We've had a rough season, me and Clay and the girls." She didn't call her husband James, or James Clay, or Mr. Clay; just Clay. "Willowbrook is the first place our crew has been in five weeks where there's anything like regular work."

"Is that a fact!" said Mamma. "And all those girls to feed."

"Clay eats aplenty, too. He may look small, but it takes a powerful quantity of victuals to keep his strength up. We didn't starve, though. Over in Lakeland County when the drouth burned up the beans, they fixed it for us to get food from the government. Surplus, they called it. Stuff nobody will buy and they save it for when folks get hungry. Dried milk and flour and rice and like that. Cheese, too. You could do a right tasty dish from it. Oh, yes, and peanut butter. That kept it from being tiresome. It's a caution what use you can make out of peanut butter."

"Did the dry spell kill all the beans in Lakeland County?" Mamma asked.

"Not all, no, but there was another thing. Machines."

"Machines," said Mamma. "I keep hearing and hearing, but I never saw one yet. Not to pick beans with, I didn't. Tell me."

"Oh, they have 'em all right. One place where we've gone for years—Mr. Simmons—we went there and he'd beat the drouth by irrigating so his beans were good, but over the winter he'd bought himself a bean-picking machine. He let us stay and do a field once over by hand, but then he turned in the machine and stripped it clean. That machine really finished up the crop. Once over and that's it."

"They must cost a pile of money, those machines."

"That's what Bucky Bean told Clay. 'We don't go for the machines,' he told him. Besides the cost, Bucky's boss figures to get more beans to the acre when people do the picking. He can plant the rows closer together when he uses people, and he can have three, four, even five pickings to a field. And the machine tears the beans, too. Handpicked beans bring in a good bit better price on the market."

"Still, the time will come," said Mamma.

"Sure the time will come." Mrs. Clay nodded her head. "But meanwhile I don't aim to worry. Not yet, I don't."

"What don't you aim to worry about, Mrs. Clay?" said Papa, who had sauntered up. He took the last ear of corn away from Mamma and began to husk it.

"Mechanical bean-pickers," Mrs. Clay answered. "That's what I don't figure to let trouble my sleep. Life is short enough if you take what comes without trying to foretell future events."

"But what's it going to do to us?" said Mamma. "When they get machines to harvest everything? Machines for carrots and onions and cucumbers and spinach and all like that?"

"And strawberries," said Roosevelt.

Mamma went on. "There won't be any jobs at all, not for folks like us, there won't. Folks who live on the season."

Papa finished husking his ear and tossed it into the basket.

"Strawberries," he said. "I should live to see the day they get a machine to pick strawberries. Addie, it looks as if Mrs. Clay and I are great believers in Providence. Plug along and rest easy and trust in Providence to come up with something when the time is right."

"Providence is well and good," said Mamma, snappy-like, "but sometimes it can use help from folks."

"Maybe it's that folks don't always see so plain what Providence throws their way," said Papa. "Anyway, Providence fixed it for us to have a nice mess of corn for dinner tonight, didn't it? When do we eat?"

America the Beautiful

O beautiful for spacious skies,
    For amber waves of grain,
For purple mountain majesties
    Above the fruited plain!
        America! America!
    God shed His grace on thee,
And crown thy good with brotherhood
    From sea to shining sea!

Katharine Lee Bates

Bahama Adventure

Eugenie Clark

Eugenie Clark, a Japanese-American marine biologist, has a rare gift, the ability to communicate her enthusiasm for her lifework. Sometimes, though, her work involves the unusual, such as riding—of all things—a giant loggerhead turtle deep beneath the sea.

Because of my studies in the behavior of sharks and the data I was accumulating on other large sea animals, I was invited to attend a number of meetings and conferences sponsored by the Office of Naval Research. One of these was held near Philadelphia. . . . It gave me a chance to visit the newly opened Aquarama, where Curator Don Wilkie invited me to bring my children to ride the porpoises.

Niki, our youngest, was now four years old. He had exceptional breath control and complete lack of fear. He took the longest ride, hanging on to the dorsal fin of Star, a remarkable porpoise that seemed to know exactly when to bring Niki to the surface for air. Niki learned to dive off a high diving board and swim underwater to the side of a pool soon after he could walk. He would frighten people. When he noticed he had an audience, he would dive off the board and, instead of swimming directly to the side, would swim to the bottom and hold on to the drain until people started diving in after him. Then he would let go and laugh bubbles all the way up to the surface.

. . . .

My days with the children were sometimes exasperating. On one such day, I stumbled on a marvelous cure for a headache. I had just come back

from a long day of driving to what turned out to be a poor spot for diving with children. After rinsing off and drying four squirming, screaming kids, I felt a migraine headache coming on. I was tired and chilled and decided to soak in a hot tub. Diving equipment, water toys, wet towels, and bathing suits were lying all around the bathroom. The place looked so messy, the children were arguing and fighting about some minor matter, my head started throbbing, and I suddenly wished I had the peace and quiet I've known at the bottom of the sea. The tub was filled near the brim. I reached for the nearest snorkel, stuck it in my mouth, and sank my head to the bottom of the tub. In a few minutes, my headache cleared miraculously and I could face the noisy tribe again.

. . . .

In July, 1960, I took the four children and their lovable nursemaid, Geri Hinton, on Sid Anderson's Bahama Adventure cruise. Sid had asked me to teach a course in marine biology to the diving teachers, nurses, doctors, and students. Geri assured me that I wouldn't have to worry about taking care of the children while I was diving and teaching. The children learned to dive among beautiful coral reefs on that trip, and we all took turns caring for a very

seasick Geri, who hardly ever came out of her room unless we pulled into a port and she could debark.

Hera saw her first shark underwater on this trip. We were scuba diving together with Stan Waterman, who was taking movies of a large green moray eel. Hera started swimming after a gorgeous colored queen triggerfish. I saw a shark about five feet long swim by her. She looked up and I thought she saw it, but then she went back to following the triggerfish. When we surfaced, I told her about the shark. "Oh, I saw it, but it was so small compared to the ones we dissect at the Lab. But, Mommy, did you ever see such a beautiful triggerfish!" I had to admit we had none that colorful on the central west coast of Florida.

On this Bahama Adventure trip, I had a unique experience. I can get so absorbed in catching small fish in glass jars that I temporarily forget about the rest of the world. I often stay down more than an hour playing this rewarding game and making a collection in my net bag. Other divers, especially my children, get bored with my staying in one small area for so long, matching my wits with little gobies. So I would tie a string to my weight belt and put a cork float at the end. Then the children could snorkel-dive and come

pull the cork when they wanted to go back to the ship.

One day after we came back to the ship, which was anchored near a staghorn coral reef for the day, others were still diving around the ship and I still had lots of air left. I sent the children aboard to check Geri, who was suffering as usual in her bunk. Soon I was absorbed in collecting fishes again. No one else was scuba diving now, but many were snorkeling and making an occasional dive to the bottom, about 30 feet. I had been down for some time when suddenly I felt a light tap on my back. I figured it was someone from the surface and looked up. There were a number of divers watching me intently. Three had movie cameras and were taking movies of me simultaneously, but I wasn't doing anything in particular and thought they were wasting a lot of film.

Then I felt another tap, and I turned and looked over my shoulder. An enormous brown eye, more than twice the size of mine, looked into my face mask. It was so close I had to back away from it to see what creature it belonged to. I moved very slowly as the eye kept watching me, and a flipper tapped me again. It was a huge old loggerhead turtle. Its carapace was encrusted with barnacles and one flipper was half

missing, perhaps bitten off by a shark long ago.

The turtle came close to me again, and I realized he was looking at my glass jar as if he were hypnotized by it. I swam away very slowly, almost crawling along the bottom, holding one hand out and using the glass jar as a lure. The turtle kept following it.

I remembered diving with a native in the Palau Islands who hopped a ride on a turtle whenever he could. I had never been this close to one in the sea before and decided to try it. I let the jar fall into the sand, and while the turtle looked at it I swam gently over his back, then quickly grabbed the front of his big shell with my arms, flattened my body onto him, and hung on tightly.

He took off, but not whiplike, as did the large nurse shark I once tried to ride. I was surprised at how easy it was to hold on and steer him. I rode him to the surface, then back to the bottom, up again and held him as the children went wild with joy and even got Geri to the railing to watch me ride the turtle. I rode him around the coral reefs, and in a few minutes I could bank and turn him through narrow passages.

. . . .

Star Island

Louise Dickinson Rich

As an orphan, a State Kid, Larry had lived in one foster home after another. Now he was going to live on a small island off the coast of Maine. Larry felt sure he would not like his new foster home with the Chandlers.

The house was like the others, trim and white. A low ell extended from one side. Like the others, the house was surrounded by flowers. A tortoiseshell cat slept in the sun on the stone doorstep, and a big black dog came bounding around the corner as they approached.

"I suppose I ought to take you in the front door, the first time," Mrs. Chandler remarked cheerfully, "but we're not very fierce for front doors on Star, except for company. You're not company. You're family, so we'll start the way we're going on and use the kitchen door."

She led the way to the door of the ell, stooping to stroke the cat. "This is Boots," she told Larry. "The smartest cat in Maine, if I do say so." She snapped her fingers, and the dog came to attention on the path below them. "And this is Mate. Mate, shake hands with Larry."

The big dog obediently lifted a paw. Larry, feeling a little foolish, shook it. He had never lived with anybody who owned a dog. Mate searched Larry's face with enormous brown eyes. Then he whined softly and laid his head against Larry's knee.

"Look at that!" Mrs. Chandler exclaimed. "He's taken to

you right off. You're going to be great friends, I can see that."

She opened the door. "Nobody locks their doors around here. For one thing, we don't have anything worth stealing, and for another, nobody'd steal it anyhow. Half of us are first cousins, and you don't steal from relatives. Well, come in, come in."

Larry started to follow her. Then he turned back. Mate was looking at him with a question in his eyes. What did you do when a dog looked at you like that? Larry didn't know. His hand went out almost by itself and rested on Mate's huge head. The plume of a tail began to wag, slowly at first and then with frantic joy. Suddenly Larry felt good. Maybe Mrs. Chandler was right. Maybe he and Mate were going to be friends.

Mrs. Chandler had called the room that they entered "the kitchen." It didn't look like any kitchen Larry had ever seen. Windows filled three sides of it. The blank end was occupied by a big black iron cookstove with a huge woodbox beside it. There was an iron sink with a hand pump under the windows overlooking the village and harbor. Wherever Larry had lived before, cooking had been done by gas or electricity, and water had come out of faucets. Still, he recognized the stove and the sink as belonging in a kitchen.

An oval table covered with a red-and-white-checked tablecloth occupied the middle of the room. On it were salt and pepper shakers, a sugar bowl, and a heavy glass jar full of knives, forks, and spoons. The Chandlers must use this as a dining room, too.

And as a living room. In a corner between two windows was a comfortable armchair. A table heaped with magazines and books stood beside it. A rocking chair with a basket of mending on the floor next to it faced another window. A rather battered desk, stacked with papers, filled one wall space. One windowsill held a transistor radio. The TV set must be in another room, Larry decided.

Mrs. Chandler seemed to read Larry's thoughts. "Out here, folks just about live in their kitchens," she said, "except for sleeping. We've all got dining rooms and parlors, but we don't use them much, except for weddings and funerals. A kitchen seems more natural-like, somehow."

Larry wondered if Miss Carr knew about this. When you'd been a State Kid all your life, you learned a few things. One thing Larry had learned was that caseworkers were fussy about the homes in which they placed children. Even the Whites, who had been quite poor, hadn't lived in the kitchen. Maybe when Miss Carr found out, she'd take him away from this awful island.

Outside, Mate barked once.

"Land!" Mrs. Chandler exclaimed. "Here's Pa now. I meant to show you your room—" She bustled around, putting a stick of wood in the stove and opening the drafts so that the fire roared. "Usually he stays around the store gabbing with the other men until dear knows when. But I guess there wasn't much gabbing today. Too much excitement at home, with all you children coming."

Mr. Chandler came in, moving quietly for all his size. "Well, young feller," he said, "it's good to have you aboard. You probably feel like a cat in a strange garret now, but you'll shake down in no time. If anything puzzles you, don't be afraid to ask questions. We'll do the same. The sooner we understand each other, the better. First question I want to

ask you, do you like lobster stew? Because I surmise that's what we're having for supper."

Larry couldn't help laughing. It wasn't the sort of question foster parents usually asked. Usually they wanted to know things like where you had lived last, or how old you were, or even what happened to your parents. Things that they knew the answers to already, or that were none of their business.

"I don't know, Mr. Chandler," he said. "I never ate lobster."

"Never ate lobster?" Mr. Chandler seemed shocked. "Then we'd better start making up for lost time. You've sure got a treat in store for you." He sat down in the armchair and pulled off his boots. "Another thing. This 'Mr. Chandler.' Makes me want to look behind me to see who you're talking to. I don't suppose you want to call us Ma and Pa first off. How's Uncle Joe and Aunt Emma for a starter?"

Foster parents often wanted to be called "uncle" and "aunt." Larry guessed he had more fake aunts and uncles than anybody in the world. Habit made it easy for him to say, "All right, Uncle Joe. That'll be fine."

"Now we've got that settled, how about handing me my

slippers there by the woodbox, Larry? Thank you. I'll talk to you about that woodbox tomorrow. It's going to be your job to keep it filled. I've been doing it since our youngest went over to the main, and I'll be some old happy to be shut of that chore."

Now, Larry thought, I'll see whether he meant what he said about questions. Youngest, he'd said. That meant there were more than one. "How many children do you and Aunt Emma have?" Larry asked carefully.

"Two—a boy and a girl. Good young ones, too, if I do say it."

"What happened— Where—?" Larry didn't quite know how to ask.

"What happened to them?" Uncle Joe was cheerful about it. "That's something maybe you can explain to me, after you've been here for a while. Same thing that happened to all the young people on Star and on lots of other islands, too. They went over to the main to high school. After they saw how folks live there, there was no holding them. They got used to television and movies and steam-heated houses and hot running water and all, and the way we live here seemed pretty slow to them. Slow and hard. So they cleared out as soon as they could. There are only three left on Star, and I surmise they'll leave as soon as they're old enough."

"Now, Pa," Aunt Emma objected, "that ain't quite fair. You're making it sound like the only thing the young ones were interested in was skylarking around having a high old time. Our own have worked hard and done well for themselves. You're as proud of them as I am. You think they're the white hen's chickens."

"Yup," Uncle Joe agreed roundly. "Martha's married to a mainlander and lives out west," he explained to Larry, "and Carl is in Texas working for the government. I'm proud of them, I don't deny it. Only it seems a shame—"

"You see, Larry," Aunt Emma interrupted, "we've got a good life here on Star Island. We'd like to know that it will keep on the same after we're gone. It won't—not with the young folks all going over to the main as soon's they've shed their milk teeth. They claim that the world moves on and they want to move with it. Maybe they're right. But I can see the day"—she gazed out the window at the village below—"the day when every house down there, instead of just four or five, will be empty, and there'll be nothing living on Star except gulls and fish crows."

There was a knock at the door, and Miss Carr's voice asked, "May I come in? Lon Cole is waiting to take me and Miss Bridges back to Stillport, but I wanted to check—"

"Everything's fine," Aunt Emma assured her. "Come in and set a minute."

Miss Carr seated herself in the rocking chair and glanced around the room. She used what Larry privately called "the caseworker look." It observed everything, even things behind closed doors, he almost believed. To his surprise, she seemed completely satisfied with what she saw.

"Well, Larry," she said, "we've known each other for a long time, so I don't have to make my little speech to you."

Larry grinned. He couldn't help it. He knew that speech by heart. It was full of words like "adjust" and "cooperate," "helpful" and "obedient."

"I'll tell you this instead, although probably I shouldn't," Miss Carr went on. "I haven't always been entirely happy about some of the foster homes in which I've left you. This time I am happy. I really envy you, as I said before. You're going to have a wonderful life here in Starhaven."

Sure, Larry thought. So wonderful that the kids who were born and brought up here couldn't stand it. Who did Miss Carr think she was kidding?

Larry relaxed a little over supper. The lobster stew was delicious, faintly pink and dotted with freckles of butter. The Chandlers didn't act as though he were either company or a curiosity. They talked easily about events of the day, interrupting each other occasionally to explain something to him. Best of all, Mate of his own accord lay down as close as he could get to Larry's chair. All through the meal, his eyes remained fixed on Larry's face. When Larry, pretending to scratch his own leg, scratched instead the big dog's ears, Mate's tail wagged enthusiastically. There was no doubt about it; Mate really did like him.

Dessert was deep-dish apple pie, warm from the oven. Larry scraped his plate and said, "I guess that was the best supper I ever ate, Aunt Emma." He meant it, too. Aunt Emma smiled, but before she could answer, the door burst open noisily.

It was Matt Cole, acting—Larry thought resentfully—as if he owned the place. He glanced at Larry and said breezily, "Hi, Aunt Em. Got a piece of that pie for me? Ah, Mate, old-boy-old-boy-o! What's the good word?"

Mate scrambled up from beside Larry. He was wagging all over and pretending to growl. Matt roughhoused the dog briefly and said, "That's enough. Lie down and behave."

Mate flopped down, rolled over on his back, and waved his front paws in an idiotic manner. He looked so silly and so pleased with himself that everybody except Larry laughed.

Larry didn't join in. He knew that he was being a sorehead, but he couldn't help it. Everything had been going so well, and then Matt had to come in and spoil it. In one minute flat he had made Mate forget all about Larry and had caused Aunt Emma to bustle around getting milk and pie for Matt as though he were the king of England. Who did he think he was anyhow, calling her Aunt Em? Why didn't he go home where he belonged and eat his own mother's pie?

Matt finished his milk, set the glass down with a thump, and for the first time addressed Larry directly. "Aunt Em said—"

There it was again. Aunt Em! Matt must have heard Larry call Mrs. Chandler Aunt Emma and was making fun of him. Larry had met that sort before—kids who delighted in picking on a new boy.

Matt went on smoothly, "—she was giving you Carl's room. It's neat, huh?"

"Larry hasn't seen it yet," Aunt Emma explained. "I meant to— But with one thing and another—"

"Hey, come on, then!" Matt jumped up. "These your things? I'll help you carry them up and unpack them."

Oh, no, you don't, Larry thought. You're not going to paw

my stuff over and tell everyone I've got only two sets of underwear.

Aloud he said, "No, thanks. I'll do it myself later."

His tone must have been even more surly than he had intended, because everyone looked at him in surprise. Aunt Emma started to say something, but changed her mind when Uncle Joe cleared his throat loudly. Matt looked as though he had been slapped. It would do him good, Larry thought with satisfaction. It was time someone took him down a peg.

After a little silence, Matt said, "Well, I guess I'll be going home. Come on, Mate. Walk me down the hill." He went out with the dog at his heels.

Three hours later, lying in bed, Larry couldn't go to sleep. The windows under the eaves were still pale rectangles. There had been no television to watch. There wasn't a set on the whole island. Aunt Emma had said that on Star they went to bed before it was dark under the table. Uncle Joe had added that they pried the sun up in the morning. Larry supposed that meant that they all got up before sunrise. He wasn't used to such early hours.

That wasn't what was keeping him awake, though. It wasn't the strange surroundings, either. Larry couldn't remember a more comfortable bed. It was soft and wide, and covered with a bright patchwork quilt. The room was all right, too. The ceiling sloped on the sides, so that it was almost like a cozy cave looking out over the village and the sea. Anywhere else, Larry decided, he would have liked the room.

If only it weren't so quiet! That was what was keeping him awake—the almost frightening stillness. There were no sounds of cars stopping or starting, no footsteps going along a pavement, no voices next door, talking and laughing. Strain his ears as he might, all he could hear was the faint sighing of the wind and the deep, steady rumbling of the surf on the outer reefs.

His thoughts turned to the other people sleeping under this roof. Aunt Emma and Uncle Joe hadn't said anything about his rudeness to Matt, but he could tell that they hadn't liked it. Matt had managed to put him in the wrong all the way round. He had won the Chandlers' sympathy and topped that off by walking away with Mate. One of these days, Larry promised himself, he'd get even with Matt Cole. He'd show him! Somewhat comforted by this unfriendly thought, he closed his eyes resolutely.

But still sleep would not come. Larry got out of bed quietly and went to the window. There wasn't a light in the village—not a streetlight or a single glowing window. All he could see was the dark loom of the land against a dull-silver ocean. The sky was full of stars—brighter, closer stars than Larry had ever known. By their dim light he could make out a smudged band on the horizon. That was the mainland, so terribly far away. As he crept back to bed, he wished with all his heart that he were there.

He was almost asleep when something cold touched his cheek. He stiffened, holding his breath. A ghost? A bear that had somehow sneaked into the house? Or something too horrible to imagine?

Then he heard a soft whine and the thump of a strong tail beating the floor. The bed shook as Mate jumped onto it, turned around and around, then curled up beside him.

Larry let out his breath. "Oh, Mate!" he whispered, and threw his arms around the big dog. "Oh, Mate—Mate—"

Then suddenly they were both fast asleep.

Larry was wakened by Mate's rough tongue licking his face. It must be very early, he thought drowsily. The room was barely light. Still, he could hear the rattle of pots and pans from downstairs, and Mate plainly thought it was time to get up. Larry rolled out of bed and dressed quickly.

In the kitchen he found Aunt Emma at the stove, turning blueberry pancakes. Uncle Joe was seated at the table, eating them. If they had been upset by Larry's conduct last night, they had forgotten it this morning. They both started talking at once.

Aunt Emma said, "If you want hot water to wash with, there's plenty in the teakettle." Larry had found out the night before that the kitchen served as a washroom in addition to everything else.

"Before you pull up to the table," Uncle Joe requested, "let Boots in, will you, Larry?" Then he saw Mate. "I thought you were out chasing rabbits. Slept on your bed, I suppose?" he asked Larry.

Larry, splashing icy pump water on his face, nodded. He hoped he wasn't getting Mate into trouble. Maybe there was a rule against his sleeping on beds.

There didn't seem to be.

"He always slept there when Carl was home. He hasn't been upstairs once since Carl left." Aunt Emma rubbed the dog's shaggy head roughly. "Seems good to have a boy in the house again, don't it, old feller?"

"The time to start making a lobsterman out of you is right this very morning," Uncle Joe said. "I thought I'd take you out hauling with me."

"There's no law that says you have to go," Aunt Emma assured Larry. "Maybe you'd rather explore the island today."

Larry tasted a pancake dripping with butter and maple syrup. It was as good as the lobster stew had been last night.

"I'd like to go," he heard himself saying.

Then he remembered, a little too late, that yesterday he had decided not to adjust and cooperate anymore. Maybe getting up so early had dimmed his wits. Well, being agreeable just once probably wouldn't hurt.

When Larry and Uncle Joe arrived at the harbor, the rosy dawn was full of the sound of powerful motors warming up. Larry was wearing Carl's outgrown hip boots and oilskins. Mate was close at his heels.

"Does everybody here go to work before sunrise?" Larry asked.

"The wind comes up with the sun," Uncle Joe explained. "By noon, it's apt to be pretty choppy outside. We aim to be back home before then." He led the way to a small rowboat drawn up on the shore. "Get in and sit down, Larry. Not you, Mate. You're staying ashore today."

Uncle Joe shoved the skiff into the water, took up the oars, and began rowing with short, strong strokes. Mate barked frantically, then seemed to shrug his shoulders as he started back up the road. He had disappeared by the time Larry and Uncle Joe reached the *Petrel*, Uncle Joe's lobster boat.

"Climb aboard," Uncle Joe directed. He tied the skiff to a floating buoy and clambered into the *Petrel*. "Now stand by and I'll show you how to start this tub."

Larry could tell by Uncle Joe's tone that he was proud of his boat, even if he did call her a tub. He watched carefully as Uncle Joe adjusted knobs and levers and finally stepped on the starter. The motor purred into instant life.

"Cast off the line," Uncle Joe ordered, and then smiled at Larry's puzzled expression. "I mean, untie that rope up front.

You'll learn sea lingo in no time. You're going to be a big help to me."

Once they were on their way out of the harbor, Larry had time to examine the boat. A glass shield and a small roof protected the steersman from wind and spray, but the rest of the boat was open to sky and sea. Wooden tubs stood about the deck. Some were empty, and some contained an evil-smelling hash of decayed fish that must be the lobster bait Miss Bridges had spoken of yesterday. The engine was under a wooden box in the center of the craft. Beside it was a spoollike drum. There was a pulley built on an arm projecting from the side of the wheelhouse. At the stern, a short mast supported a furled sail. It all looked simple and businesslike, but Larry hadn't the least idea how anything worked. He'd find out, he supposed.

The deck underfoot began to rise and fall, and Larry saw that they had left the harbor behind. A boy waved from a nearby boat. It was Tom, looking unfamiliar in oilskins. He seemed happier than he had yesterday. Larry waved back. Then the two boats veered apart.

"I've got a gang of traps over by Roaring Bull Ledge," Uncle Joe shouted over the noise of the motor. "We'll start there. My buoys are red and white. See how quick you can spot one."

Larry strained his eyes. The whole sea was as many-colored as a rainbow, reflecting the sunrise. There were no buoys that he could see, though. Then the sun burst over the horizon, and the sea turned green. Sharp and clear against the glittering water was a speck of red and white. Larry shouted and pointed.

"Good boy!" Uncle Joe exclaimed. "You saw her soon as

I did, and I knew where to look. You've got regular seaman's eyes."

He was not being polite. He meant what he said. Larry had a sudden conviction that Uncle Joe always meant what he said. It was a good thing to know.

The *Petrel* slowed and drew alongside the buoy. Uncle Joe picked up a boathook—a long pole with a hook on the end—and caught the line attached to the buoy. Quickly he hitched the line to the pulley and spool and moved a lever. The spool turned, and the line tightened and began reeling in.

"Man and boy, I've been lobstering for fifty years, Larry," Uncle Joe remarked thoughtfully, "and I still get excited every time I haul a trap—wondering what's in it. Might be almost anything—a new kind of sea creature that nobody's ever heard of, for instance, or a diamond necklace someone dropped overboard from an ocean liner. Or it might be nothing at all. I guess the suspense is what keeps us lobstermen going. That and being our own bosses. Don't know what else it could be. Oh, the money's good. But lobstering is a hard, dangerous life. Most of us could earn more ashore, and easier and safer, taking orders from someone else— Whoops, here she comes!"

The cagelike trap swam up out of the green depths into the light. Uncle Joe swung it aboard with a splashing of seawater. Without Carl's slicker and boots, Larry would have been soaked to the skin.

Examining the trap at close quarters, Larry saw that the ends held funnel-shaped nets. Between them, in the center of the trap, was a bag of coarse mesh. Uncle Joe explained that this was a bait bag, and that the funnels were called trap heads.

"Lobsters aren't very smart, Larry. They scent the bait and crawl in the big ends of the funnels to get it. No reason why they can't crawl out the same way, except that they ain't got the sense to figure that out."

He reached into the trap and took out a large green lobster. The shells from the stew last night had been red. Lobsters were naturally green, Uncle Joe explained. Cooking them turned them red.

"If they're too small, the law says we have to throw them back," he went on, taking a metal measure out of his pocket. "You measure from the eye to the end of the body. This one's a keeper."

He wedged one of the claws with a small wooden plug. "That's the business claw. We plug 'em so they won't take a nip out of us." Then he tossed the lobster into one of the empty tubs and reached into the trap again. This time he pulled out a big starfish, which he tossed overboard in disgust. Larry had thought it rather pretty, but he didn't say so. It might sound silly.

"If you want to make yourself useful," Uncle Joe said, "you can fill bait bags." He handed Larry the bag that he had removed from the trap. Larry looked at it helplessly. "Here, I'll show you." Uncle Joe scooped up a handful of bait and stuffed it into the bag. "Go ahead. It don't smell like the perfumes of Araby, but it won't hurt you."

Larry dipped his hand into the bait tub carefully. The odor was terrible. For a moment he thought he was going to be sick. Then he filled his lungs with clean, salt air and felt better. Uncle Joe was looking at him with approval, but all he said was, "You'll do." He put the bag back into the trap, tossed the trap overboard, and started the *Petrel* again.

All morning long, they cruised from buoy to buoy. The sun rose higher into the sky. The sea turned from green to blue and purple. Whitecaps began to appear on the crests of the waves. Once they were near enough to the mainland so that Larry could make out the houses of Stillport, like toy houses in a toy town. Once they were almost out of sight of land, except for the back of Star Island. It looked wild and deserted. They could have thought themselves the only persons left in the world, if it hadn't been for the sight of other, distant lobster boats going about their business.

At some time during the morning, Larry discovered that he didn't mind the smell of the bait anymore. He didn't even notice it. At about the same time, he found himself getting excited, as Uncle Joe did, each time they pulled a trap aboard. This was fun! There were all sorts of odd things in the traps—fish, prickly little sea urchins, big crabs, and peculiar creatures called sea cucumbers. And of course, lobsters.

"One thing I'll say," Uncle Joe told him. "You're no Jonah. This is about the best haul I've had all summer." Larry felt pleased and proud. "We'll pick up the string at Old Maid's Reef, and then we're done." Uncle Joe sounded well satisfied.

The sun was straight overhead now, and the sea was rough. Star Island looked like a paper cutout pasted against the sky. Uncle Joe turned the bow of the *Petrel* toward it.

"She's breezing up a mite," he said. "I'll hoist the riding sail. A boat handles better in a breeze with a sail. Here, you take the wheel."

Larry looked at him in astonishment.

"Nothing to it, really," Uncle Joe informed him. "See that highest point of the island? Just you keep the bow headed straight at it. You don't have to pull and haul on the wheel. Easy does it." He walked back to the stern.

Larry knew an instant's panic. What if the engine stopped, or a ledge suddenly appeared before him? What would he do?

Then his nervousness left him. The motor was beating like a strong and steady heart, and Uncle Joe would have told him about any ledges. He moved the wheel slightly. The bow of the *Petrel* swung obediently. This wasn't so hard. All he had to do was keep her headed straight for that highest peak.

Larry's eyes were watering when Uncle Joe came forward to stand beside him. He'd hardly dared to blink for fear of wandering off course.

"You're doing fine," Uncle Joe said. "Keep her steady as she goes. I'll take over when we go into the harbor. The channel's a mite tricky till you know it. Right now I'll start cleaning up this mess."

He dipped a pail of water from over the side and began to swab down the deck with an old broom.

As they drew closer to the island, other boats joined them. Everyone was on the way home. Larry saw Tom. He was throwing old bait overboard to the congregation of gulls that had appeared out of nowhere. Larry didn't dare take a hand from the wheel to attract his attention. He contented himself with hoping hard that Tom would notice him.

Yesterday—only yesterday—both he and Tom had been pretty much impressed to see Matt Cole handling a boat.

Well, today he, Larry Scott, was handling a boat himself.

Afterthought

1. What disadvantages might there be in living on an island like Star Island? What advantages might there be?
2. Why would the people living on Star Island need to get along well with each other?
3. What signs are there that Larry's home with the Chandlers may turn out to be a happy one?

I hear America singing, the varied carols I hear,
Those of mechanics, each one singing his as it should be
blithe and strong,
The carpenter singing his as he measures his plank
or beam,
The mason singing his as he makes ready for work,
or leaves off work,
The boatman singing what belongs to him in his boat,
the deckhand singing on the steamboat deck,
The shoemaker singing as he sits on his bench,
the hatter singing as he stands,
The woodcutter's song, the plowboy's on his way in the
morning, or at noon intermission or at sundown,
The delicious singing of the mother, or of the young wife
at work, or of the girl sewing or washing,
Each singing what belongs to him or her and to none else,
The day what belongs to the day—at night the party
of young fellows, robust, friendly,
Singing with open mouths their strong melodious songs.

Walt Whitman

When Carlos Closed the Street

Peggy Mann

This long selection is for you to read alone—for your own pleasure. If you enjoy it, you may want to read the whole book.

Sometimes people are separated by more than distance, even when they live only a block apart. In this story a wall of misunderstanding and hostility has grown up between two neighborhoods. And Carlos has an opportunity to tear the wall down—but not without real danger to himself.

A fire hydrant divided the block. To the east of the hydrant, the territory belonged to the Young Kings. To the west, the block belonged to the Spanish Angels.

The rules, of course, did not apply to the grownups. They could walk where they wanted. But, as it happened, most of the Puerto Rican families lived in the brownstone rooming houses to the west of the fire hydrant. And most of the Negroes lived to the east. So even the grownups seemed to stick pretty much to the hydrant rule.

The few social workers who came into the street talked in big words about the damage the split was doing to the Spirit of the Street.

But Carlos couldn't see it that way. He liked the Spirit of the Street just fine. It was exciting, never knowing when a fight would break out between the Kings and the Angels.

It worked out well. Except when they played stickball on the street. The trouble was that the ball would often get socked down to the Other Territory. Then you had to look around quick. Dash into Their Side. And try to escape back again, before you were caught. Otherwise, if one of Them grabbed your ball that was the last you'd see of it.

But the real danger was getting caught yourself. Then you could get beaten up pretty bad.

That happened to Carlos one Saturday afternoon.

He was fielding a fly ball which Juan Rodriquez had batted out. Carlos jumped high for the ball. But he missed. He often missed. He wasn't too good at stickball.

His team stood watching, disgusted, as the ball landed and bounced down *Their* part of the block.

"*Caramba!*" said Juan Rodriquez. "Now we'll never get it back! There's too many of Them out today."

It was true. This was the first sunny Saturday of early spring and everyone it seemed had come out to sit on the brownstone stoops in the sunshine.

A rickety card table was set up right on the other side of the hydrant. Four men were playing cards. And one of the men, Carlos knew, was the father of Big Charles and Jimmy. Big Charles Williams was the leader of the Young Kings. And Big Charles *was* big. And mean. Carlos didn't ever want to mess with him. Or with anyone from his family!

"Well," little Luis said, "I guess that's the end of *that* ball! Right, man?" But the way he was looking up at Carlos meant that he expected his brother to *do* something about the ball. Even though Luis' words had said just the opposite.

"Listen!" Carlos scowled. "That ball isn't lost. I'm going *in* there!"

"You *are!*" Luis said. But it wasn't a question. He said it as though he had known all the time that Carlos would go.

Carlos took a deep breath. And he looked at Their Territory. Big Charles wasn't there. In fact, none of the Young Kings seemed to be hanging around. Maybe they were busy messing up some other block. They did that sometimes.

He couldn't even see Jimmy, or any of the Princes—the kids who were too young to make it yet with the Kings. Of course, they might be hanging around in the doorways. They often seemed to run out from nowhere if they spotted you in Their Territory.

"I think the ball went right over there," little Luis said, pointing to some garbage cans. And before Carlos half realized what he was doing, he found himself dashing past the fire hydrant. Past the four men at the bridge table. Past a bunch of kids beating out time on an empty oil drum. Past some women on camp chairs doing their sewing.

He looked around. But he couldn't even see that dumb ball.

No one over here seemed to be paying much attention to him. But he *felt* they were. He felt that everyone knew he had come over. That they were all watching him. And waiting.

Two little girls were wheeling a doll carriage down the sidewalk. They looked harmless enough. "You didn't see a ball come bouncing around here?" Carlos asked them, in what he hoped was a friendly manner.

Then it happened.

A tall boy came running out of one of the doorways. "Hey! Whose sister you bothering there?" And he jumped Carlos, throwing him flat to the sidewalk.

Three other boys joined in, sitting on Carlos, beating on him, shouting at him, and laughing in a terrible kind of way.

Carlos struggled. He tried to fight back. He bit into somebody's ankle. There was a scream of pain.

Then, suddenly, as fast as it had started, it was over. Someone was saying, "Git offa him!"

And they got.

Carlos scrambled to his feet.

Jimmy was standing there. Jimmy, the kid brother of Big Charles!

Jimmy was the same age as Carlos. But he was a lot bigger. Maybe he'd said, "Git offa him!" so he could beat up Carlos all by himself.

Carlos glanced back. His own boys were lined up on their own side of the fire hydrant, watching. It sure didn't look like they were about to come over and rescue him.

Carlos cleared his throat. "I was just—" The words came out squeaky. He started again. "I was only looking for our ball."

"This it?" Jimmy took a ball from his pocket.

Carlos nodded. What? Was this guy going to make him jump for the ball, or something? Or beg for it, like a dog?

"It went behind the garbage pails," Jimmy said. And handed him the ball.

Carlos took it, put it in his pocket, too surprised to say anything at all. He glanced back toward his own boys. They seemed very far down the street. Maybe Jimmy would jump him if he started to run back home. Jimmy, and all of his gang.

"I been wanting to talk to you," Jimmy said.

"Yeah?" Carlos cleared his throat again. "About what?" He tried to sound tough, even though he felt as soft as marshmallows inside.

"We was thinking," Jimmy said, "our gang might challenge yours to a game."

"*My* gang?" Carlos tried to sound important. Actually, he had no gang, just a bunch of kids he hung around with all the time. "What kind of game was you thinking of, man?" he said.

"Stickball."

Carlos nodded, as though he were thinking it over. Was this some trick, or something? Was Jimmy keeping him here, talking—so the Princes could all get down here on the street and jump him?

He had just decided to make a run for it, when Jimmy said, "We figgered that way we'd all get the whole street to play in. 'Stead of half a block. We wouldn't have so many lost balls."

NO

Carlos shrugged one shoulder. "Sure," he said. "Sounds okay to me. I'll have to talk it over with my—my *gang*."

Slowly he sauntered off toward the fire hydrant. The back of his neck began prickling. But nobody jumped him.

When he got back to his own side everyone crowded around him as though he was some kind of hero or something.

"What happened? What was you talking about?" little Luis wanted to know.

Carlos threw the ball up a little way in the air, and caught it. "Well," he said, in a careless way, "we was discussing things. Jimmy and me."

"What kind of things?" Juan demanded.

Carlos said the words very slowly to give them more importance. "Jimmy and I was saying it might be a good idea if we had a stickball game against each other one afternoon. His gang against—mine."

"Whaddaya mean, *your* gang?" said Pepe Andino. "Who says *you* got a gang?" Pepe was the brother of Angel Andino, chief of the Spanish Angels. After his narrow escape with the Princes, Carlos didn't want to go getting the Angels on his neck! "I didn't mean my *gang!*" he explained hastily to Pepe. "I meant the Princes against—us."

Pepe nodded. "Well," he said. "Why not? The Princes are mostly bigger than us. But we hit good. And we can run fast."

"Besides, *we* got Juan Rodriquez!" Fernando said. Juan Rodriquez was probably the best long-distance hitter on the whole street.

"Well," said Carlos, "I'll go back then and tell the Princes we agree. Right?" Even though he had no gang, he wanted Jimmy to keep on *thinking* that he was in charge over here.

And before anyone could say anything else, he hurried back to the hydrant and signaled.

Jimmy walked over, some of his boys behind him now. "Well," he said, "how about it?"

"All set," Carlos said. "My gang agrees. We challenge the Princes to a stickball game next Saturday afternoon at three o'clock."

"You're on, man!" said Jimmy. And, to settle the matter, the two boys shook hands.

It was the talk of the street all that week. At least, it was among Carlos' kids. Then Pepe told his brother about it. And Angel Andino himself got interested. He even volunteered to be umpire. "After all," he told Carlos, "as head of the Spanish Angels I got to see to it that our side comes out on top!"

Then it turned out that Big Charles had the same idea. *He* wanted to umpire the ball game!

Carlos and Jimmy talked it over at the hydrant. "Listen," said Jimmy, "once *they* get into the act, it won't be any stickball game. It'll be a rumble."

"How about letting the Spinster Lady be umpire?" said Carlos. The Spinster Lady was neither Spanish nor black. She was Greek. So she could walk anywhere she liked on the street. On either side of the hydrant. The trouble was, however, that she hardly ever walked anywhere. Because she very rarely came out of the house.

"She probably doesn't even know the *rules* of a stickball game," Jimmy said.

And Carlos agreed that the Spinster Lady *was* a dumb idea.

They finally decided that Angel Andino should umpire one inning, and Big Charles the next. It was a little risky. It would mean the two street gangs—the *real* gangs—would all be out in full force that afternoon. But so what, even if it did turn out to be a free-for-all street fight, that would be even more exciting than a stickball game.

Yet, as he walked away, Carlos found himself hoping hard that the gangs wouldn't get into the act and mess up the game.

On Thursday morning, in the middle of Social Studies, Carlos was hit by a great idea. They'd sell tickets to the ball game! They'd turn the front steps of the houses into bleachers. A reserved space on the steps would cost a penny. And they'd collect boxes and oranges crates from Morales' Grocery Store down the street. These would be Box Seats, set out by the curb. A Box Seat would cost a nickel.

He could hardly wait for school to be over that day. The idea kept exploding around inside him.

When he finally got back to his block and told the other boys about it, they were just as excited as he had been.

Carlos appointed six helpers and they all started out right away to sell tickets.

Some people seemed put out at the idea of buying space to sit on their own front stoop. "What do you think we pay rent for!" Mrs. Rodriquez demanded. "Supposing I want to sit on my own steps and I don't *want* to watch your stickball game! Me, I am sick to death of stickball games. One time my baby got hit in the head with a ball from your game."

But most people didn't seem to mind paying to sit on their steps. After all, the price wasn't high. And they wanted to be on hand to cheer their team.

The ticket sellers even managed to collect $1.35 for the special Box Seats, before they had so much as collected the boxes from the grocery store.

On Friday after school Carlos and his helpers made the tickets. They looked like this.

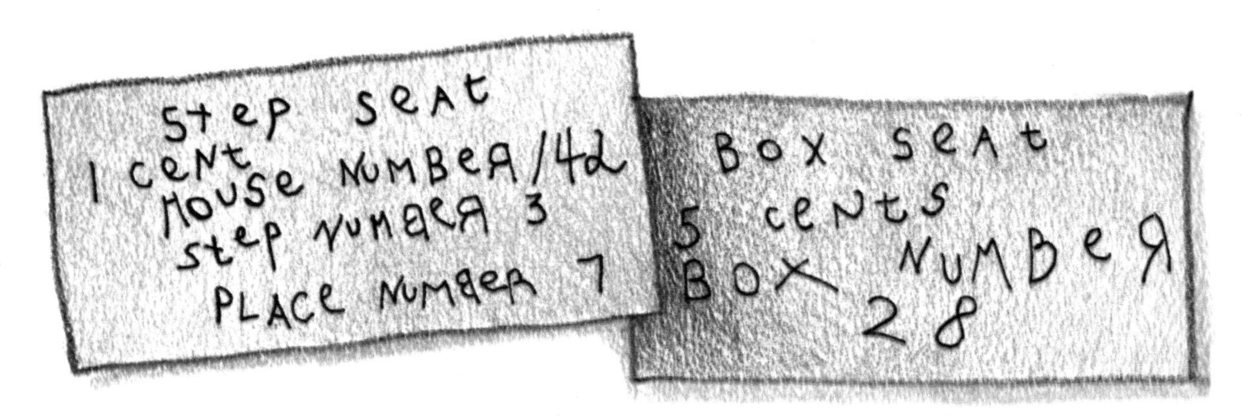

They gave Mr. Morales eight free tickets for himself, his wife, and his children, because he had gone to a lot of trouble collecting enough wooden boxes to set out along both sides of the curb.

On Saturday morning when Jimmy noticed all the wooden crates and boxes being piled up in the areaways he signaled to Carlos.

"Yeah? What is it?" Carlos said, coming to the hydrant which he and Jimmy had begun to think of as their office.

"Whatchu doin' with all those boxes, man?" Jimmy wanted to know. "You goin' to build a barricade for a rumble after the game?"

"No," Carlos told him. "Nothing like that." And he explained about his ticket-selling idea.

"Hey!" Jimmy exclaimed. "You got something there! I think we'll sell tickets for our steps too. You mind if we use your idea?"

Carlos shrugged. "Sure," he said then, with a grand gesture. "Why not?"

Around noontime Carlos began to feel worried.

Here they were, making such a big deal about this ball game, selling tickets, turning everyone on. And what would happen? Every few minutes the game would have to be called because of some dumb car coming down the street. For an ordinary game this was okay. They were used to it. But for *this*—practically a World Series of 94th Street!

He decided to talk the problem over with Jimmy.

"Yeah," Jimmy agreed, sitting himself on the hydrant as though it were his office chair. "Matter of fact, man, I been thinking about the same problem myself. It's going to be some crummy game if every minute we got to stop for traffic."

That word—*traffic*—reminded Carlos of something. But he couldn't quite think what. He stood there frowning, chewing at the inside of his lip. *Traffic!* If he could only remember what it was he was trying to think about. He was certain it was something which would solve the problem.

Then he *did* remember! It was *two* words. *Traffic tie-up.* Two words he had heard often on the radio. *There's a traffic tie-up on the West Side Highway. A traffic tie-up on the Henry Hudson Parkway. We advise cars to take an alternate route.*

That's what they'd do! They'd have their own traffic tie-up on 94th Street! And cars would have to take an alternate route.

He explained the idea to Jimmy, who agreed. "Man," he said, "you really got something there!"

Then both boys went running home to collect some clotheslines.

They decided not to start the tie-up until the game began. No sense messing up the traffic until it was really time.

They waited until everyone who had bought tickets was sitting in the bleachers, or on their Box Seat by the curb. Carlos had stationed one of his boys at each of the brownstone steps to collect the tickets and direct the people to their proper places.

He himself took charge of the Box Seats. (He didn't want anyone else to know that he had also given free tickets to Angel Andino's mother and grandmother and aunt. After all, it didn't hurt to get in extra good with an important person like Angel!)

People who didn't have tickets were at the windows. And, Carlos noticed when he glanced up, some—like the Spinster Lady—who had back apartments had been invited in by neighbors with street-front windows. It seemed as though the whole block was lined up to watch this ball game!

Mr. Moriority, who had bought a Box Seat, said to Carlos, "Sure if I'd of known you'd have this kind of a turnout, lad, I'd have brought along some soda pop to sell."

"It's not too late," Carlos told him. "We still got some important business to attend to. You have plenty of time to get the soda pop up here before the game begins."

So Mr. Moriority hurried back to his candy store on Columbus Avenue. He returned shortly wheeling two crates of soda pop in an old baby carriage.

While Moriority was selling refreshments, the traffic tie-up began.

Carlos, little Luis, Fernando Diaz, and Pepe Andino tied ten long pieces of clothesline to the banister of a house at the end of the block. Then they carried the lines across the street and tied them securely to a banister on the opposite side.

"That's pretty good!" Pepe said, surveying their work. "Any car tries to get through all *that* clothesline and they'll get tied up swell!"

Angel Andino blew his whistle.

Farther down the street, Big Charles blew *his* whistle.

The game was about to begin. The boys on the teams ran out, took their places. Juan Rodriquez was the first at bat.

Carlos noticed that for all her objections about paying a penny to sit on her own steps, Mrs. Rodriquez was right there on the top step cheering on her son in an excited stream of Spanish words.

Juan Rodriquez socked the ball far out into Their End of the street. A cheer went up from the Spanish bleachers. Mr. Diaz—who had once been to a bullfight in Mexico City—loudly called out, *"Olé!"*

And Juan raced off and made first base before the ball was returned to the pitcher, Jimmy Williams.

Then Carlos stopped watching the game. A taxi had come across Columbus Avenue. It had driven straight into the clotheslines, and it was honking.

Carlos ran down and tried to wave the taxi away.

The driver got out. "What do you think you're doing here?" he demanded.

"The street's closed," Carlos told him.

"What do you mean, closed? This ain't no play street!"

"It is today," Carlos told him. "We got a big game going. Can't you see?" He waved toward all the spectators lining the curb, the steps, hanging out windows, cheering.

There was a lady inside the cab. She put her head out the window and said, "Driver, take another street. I'm in a hurry!"

The driver gave Carlos a dirty look, climbed into the cab, slammed the door, backed off. And the taxi turned down Columbus Avenue.

But there was another car coming now.

Carlos quickly decided he'd be more use directing traffic than playing in the game, since he wasn't too good at stickball. Only a few times in his life had he ever managed to hit the ball past the first sewer on the street.

So he stood in front of the clotheslines, motioning to the oncoming cars, and pointing in the direction the taxicab had taken. Surprisingly, every driver obeyed him.

It was fun standing there, waving his arms, making all those big cars do what he wanted. Maybe he'd be a traffic cop instead of an airline pilot.

Then a big red truck came charging, it seemed—straight at the clotheslines. Carlos had never felt so little in his life. He wanted to run, but he just stood there frozen, like a rabbit he had once read about in a storybook. A rabbit caught in the headlights of an oncoming car. Too terrified to move.

With a great tearing sound of brakes, the truck stopped suddenly. The driver leaned out of the window, saw the mesh of clotheslines, and swore loudly. Since Carlos was the only

one standing there, all the swearing was shouted straight at him. Carlos had thought he knew all the swearwords there were—but the driver said some new ones.

Then the truck driver looked back—and swore some more. Other cars were waiting in line behind him. It was impossible now to back out and go down Columbus Avenue. And *then* all the cars blocking the street began honking!

Carlos promptly switched back to his first ambition: airline pilot. This traffic-directing business wasn't so easy as it seemed.

Within a few minutes a double line of honking cars stretched straight across Columbus Avenue. And *they* blocked all the cars and trucks which were coming down the avenue. It was a *two-way* traffic tie-up! A terrible one!

Some of the drivers got out of their cars and started shouting at other drivers in front of them. There was so much traffic that no one could see the clotheslines which were causing all the trouble. No one but the truck driver, who was busy now swearing back at all the people who were swearing at *him*. Everyone thought the huge red truck had caused the tie-up. The driver was trying to tell them that it wasn't his fault at all. But he was so furious by now that it didn't even sound like English he was talking. Anyway, no one seemed to understand a word he said.

But then came a sound everyone understood. The swearing and shouting stopped as if by magic. So did the honking.

Carlos turned around. A police car was coming slowly down 94th Street, its siren wailing.

This was a one-way street, of course. But that didn't matter to the police. They could drive anywhere they liked. Even the wrong way down a one-way street. The ballplayers on both sides of the hydrant had made way for the police car. They stood by the curbs, watching to see what would happen.

Carlos felt cornered. The traffic tie-up on one side of him. The police car coming toward him on the other side. There was nowhere at all to run.

So he just stood there.

This had turned out to be some game, he thought dismally. He wondered whether they'd have to give back all the money they had collected.

The police car stopped, right in front of him. There were two cops inside. One of them got out, walked over to Carlos. "What's going on here?" he said.

Carlos felt that his insides were dropping right out of him. But he tried to make his voice sound low and brave. "I—" he said. "We—" That, however, was all he could say. He was too scared to make any more words come out.

Grandmother Gomez had taught him to stay clear of the cops. And he'd obeyed her—until today. He had never said a single word to a policeman. When one even came in sight on the street, Carlos always hid in a doorway or ran down the block.

And here he was with a big tall cop looking down at him, talking to him. With everyone on the block watching. Including Grandmother Gomez.

Then the cop looked at the clotheslines and, surprisingly, he laughed. "Some cabbie phoned in, talking about a tie-up on this street. I didn't figure he meant *this* kind of tie-up!"

He took a knife out of his pocket and cut the clotheslines. Then, with a hand firm on Carlos' shoulder, the cop walked him over to the police car, opened the door. "Have a seat in here for a minute, son," he said.

Since the other cop was sitting right behind the wheel, there was nothing else that Carlos could do. He was trapped

between them. He climbed in, and sat on the very edge of the seat.

The first cop slammed the car door. The red truck had already moved on down the block. But the cop went to the middle of Columbus Avenue where the traffic was still all in a jumble. He waved one hand; held up the other. And it was like magic. In less than a minute the traffic started moving again.

"Whose bright idea *was* all this?" the cop behind the steering wheel said to Carlos.

Because he could think of nothing else to answer, Carlos told the truth. "Mine," he squeaked out, in a voice which didn't sound like his at all.

"And who are you, the Traffic Commissioner? You decide which streets are to be closed to cars?"

"Well—" Carlos said feebly, "we got this game going—this important game."

"What game?" the cop said, looking out the car window. "I don't see any game."

Carlos looked out the window. It was true. No one was playing anymore. The teams were still standing on the curb. And they were all staring at the police car—with him inside it! No one, he knew with certainty, would even lift a finger to help him. They would all just stand there watching while he was driven off to jail. And when he finally got out, Grandmother Gomez would be waiting—with a strap.

He felt too scared and too miserable even to cry.

Then, because no one else would help him, he decided he'd better try helping himself. "There *was* a game," he said desperately. "The most important game of the season. A no-fire-hydrant game!"

ITY CAB

"And what," said the cop, "might that be?"

The man sounded friendly enough. But Carlos wasn't fooled by that. On TV the cops usually sounded friendly like this, when they were doing the Questioning. That part always came before the Arrest.

On TV the Bad Guy often said at the Questioning that he wouldn't talk till he saw his lawyer. But Carlos had no lawyer. Besides, he didn't feel like the Bad Guy. So he decided to answer the cop.

"A no-fire-hydrant game means we were using the whole street to play in. For the first time in history. Both teams could spread out down the whole street. We even sold tickets! That's how important a game it was. That's why we couldn't have cars honking through here every minute."

"You should've come to the precinct house," the cop said.

"For what?" Carlos said. "There's nothing illegal about stickball!" He was proud of himself for using this big word to the cop. *Illegal.* Maybe he'd do okay as his own lawyer.

"What I meant," the cop said, "you should have come to ask us to help."

Carlos said nothing. But he snorted to himself inside. He could just picture himself walking into the police station of his own free will! He never even went near 100th Street, the block where the station house was. He had known that much since the age of two years old! A station house was a place to stay away from. Not to walk into! Not unless you were brought there in handcuffs.

The other tall policeman came back and climbed into the car. Carlos sat small and very scared between them. Now they would drive him away to the Twenty-fourth Precinct

Station House. He wondered how many days or weeks or months it would be before he got back home again. Would they send him Up State, to the place Angel Andino talked about sometimes?

The steering wheel cop told the other one about the reason for the traffic tie-up. Then he said, "You know, Billy, there are no garages on this block. No commercial buildings."

The cop called Billy nodded. "And there sure are plenty of kids on the street," he said. "It should qualify. We could give it a try, anyway." He looked down at Carlos. "There aren't too many play streets in this area. Would you like us to see what we can do about getting this street closed off—officially?"

Carlos was staring down at his wrists, wondering whether they'd use handcuffs. He heard the words that the cop had said. But he wasn't paying too much attention. Maybe they were trying to trick him. He decided not to answer.

"Hey, kid—" the steering wheel cop said.

Still Carlos didn't say anything.

"What's your name?"

This time Carlos decided to talk. "I want to see my lawyer," he said.

Both cops laughed loudly. "Lawyer!" the one called Billy exclaimed. "We're talking play streets, and he's talking lawyers!" He put one hand on Carlos' knee. "You watch too much TV, son," he said. "Come on, now. What's your name?"

"Carlos." After a long pause he added, "Gomez."

"Well, listen, Carlos," the cop said. "You can't tie up traffic anymore. Not your way. But we might be able to get this street closed officially. Now, what I want to know is

—would you like to call off your big game for today? Postpone it till the block is turned into a play street? Or do you want to have the game today, with the traffic as usual?"

What was going on here? Were they asking what *he* wanted to do? Him? Carlos Gomez? Were two big cops waiting to hear what *he* had to say?

There was silence in the car. It seemed like they were waiting.

"Well—" Carlos said slowly, to test things out, "if you want to know what I think—"

There was a long pause. The cops still said nothing.

"I think we should call the game off for today." He didn't much care whether the game went on today or not. All he cared about was that these two cops cared what he had to say!

"Would you like me to make an announcement about it?" the cop named Billy asked.

Carlos nodded.

"Maybe you'd like to come with me, son?"

The cop named Billy took a large bullhorn from the back seat of the car. Then he opened the door and got out. "Come on, Carlos." His voice sounded friendly enough. Carlos climbed out after him. It seemed he'd been in that car for hours, being grilled by the two policemen. But after all, it had probably only been a few minutes. Everyone was still sitting on the stoops, or on their box seats, or hanging out the windows. The street had never been so quiet. They were all watching the police car.

The cop named Billy held the bullhorn up to his mouth. His voice came out thundering-loud. But still somehow it sounded polite.

"Ladies and gentlemen, boys and girls. Because of the official request put to the department by Carlos Gomez, we will return to the station house and ask the Captain to make an official request to the Department of Traffic. If the request is approved, this street will be designated as a play street. It will be closed to traffic every afternoon from three until sunset. And all day Saturday and Sunday."

A cheer went up from the street. A cheer louder than the one which had come for Juan Rodriquez' three-sewer hit. This cheer came from all the people on *both* sides of the fire hydrant.

"Ladies and gentlemen," the bullhorn voice boomed on, "it would help to get the request approved, if you'd all write letters. Address them to the Captain, Twenty-fourth Precinct. Tell him why you feel you need the street closed. You can give your letters to Carlos Gomez. He'll bring them to the station house."

The cop lowered his bullhorn and looked down at Carlos. "Okay with you, son?"

Carlos nodded. He felt staggered with surprise. They weren't going to arrest him at all! They weren't even going to take him in! Then something even more amazing happened. The cop named Billy handed the bullhorn to him. "Here, Carlos," the cop said, "I think *you'd* better tell them about the game being called off today. Or ask their opinion about it. If it comes from me, some people might call it police interference."

So Carlos found himself holding the bullhorn up to his mouth. And then to his own huge surprise, he heard his voice booming out, "Hey, everybody. For today, the game's called off. Let's all go home and write some letters. We'll have our Big Game the day we get this street officially closed."

He handed the bullhorn back to the cop named Billy. He felt that he might explode with pride. He was proud of the way his voice had hollered through the bullhorn. Proud the way people were starting to get up from their seats, as though they were going to obey him. And proud most of all because he had used the same special-sounding word that Billy the Cop had used. *Officially*. The day we get this street *officially* closed.

Glossary

Key to Pronunciation

Listed below are diacritical symbols and key words. The boldface letters in the key words represent the sounds indicated by the symbols.

/ā/	cake	/h/	home	/ō/	rope	/th/	thin
/a/	hat	/(h)w/	white	/o/	top	/th/	this
/ä/	father	/ī/	pie	/ô/	saw	/u/	nut
/är/	car	/i/	pig	/oi/	oil	/ûr/	fur
/âr/	care	/ir/	dear	/o͞o/	moon	/v/	vine
/b/	boy	/j/	jump	/o͝o/	book	/w/	will
/ch/	church	/k/	kite	/ôr/	fork	/y/	yes
/d/	duck	/ks/	box	/ou/	out	/yo͞o/	use
/ē/	bean	/kw/	quit	/p/	pet	/z/	zoo
/e/	pet	/l/	look	/r/	run	/zh/	azure
/f/	fun	/m/	man	/s/	see	/ə/	above
/g/	go	/n/	not	/sh/	ship		circus
/gz/	exact	/ng/	sing	/t/	top	/ər/	butter

Abbreviations Used for Parts of Speech

adj.—adjective
adv.—adverb
conj.—conjunction
interj.—interjection
n.—noun
pl.—plural
prep.—preposition
pron.—pronoun
v.—verb

Aa

a·baft [ə·baft′] *prep.* Behind; farther aft than: *abaft* the mainmast.

a·bash [ə·bash′] *v.* To confuse or embarrass; shame: The astronaut was *abashed* by the applause.

aber natürlich. A German expression meaning "but of course."

a·brupt [ə·brupt′] *adj.* Sudden; hasty.

ab·sent·ly [ab′sənt·lē] *adv.* Showing a lack of attention: The prisoner stared *absently* out the window.

ab·sorb [ab·sôrb′ *or* ab·zôrb′] *v.* 1. To take in and hold; suck in: Towels *absorb* water. 2. To take the full attention of; occupy fully: The listeners were *absorbed* in the music.

a·byss [ə·bis′] *n.* A bottomless space, as a crack in the earth; chasm.

ac·co·lade [ak′ə·lād] *n.* Any great honor or praise: Their pottery brought them well-deserved *accolades.*

ac·com·mo·date [ə·kom′ə·dāt] *v.* To hold comfortably; be suitable for: The cage *accommodates* two birds.

ac·cu·mu·late [ə·kyōōm′yə·lāt] *v.* To heap or pile up; gather together; collect: Ms. Frye is *accumulating* facts about sea plants.

ac·cus·tom [ə·kus′təm] *v.* To make familiar or adapted by habit: The bus driver was *accustomed* to driving in heavy traffic.

ad·dled [ad′(ə)ld] *adj.* Confused or muddled.

af·fect [ə·fekt′] *v.* To act on; have an effect on: Fear *affects* the mind just as disease *affects* the body.

al·ter·nate [ôl′tər·nit] *adj.* 1. Existing, happening, or following by turns; every other: We opened *alternate* windows. 2. Substitute: We took the *alternate* exit.

alto ahí. A Spanish phrase meaning "stop there; halt."

am·bi·tion [am·bish′ən] *n.* 1. An eager desire to succeed. 2. The object of such a desire: Her *ambition* was to be a doctor.

a·mends [ə·mendz′] *n.pl.* Something done or given to make up for a wrong, a loss, injury, etc.: The motorist made *amends* for backing into the parked car.

am·ple [am′pəl] *adj.* 1. More than enough; abundant; liberal. 2. Sufficient; adequate.

an·tiq·ui·ty [an·tik′wə·tē] *n.* 1. Ancient times, especially before the Middle Ages. 2. A relic of ancient times.

a·poth·e·car·y [ə·poth′ə·ker′ē] *n.* A druggist or pharmacist.

ap·par·ent [ə·par′ənt] *adj.* That only appears to be; seeming: The bully's *apparent* courage is only a bluff.

ap·prove [ə·prōōv′] *v.* 1. To have a good opinion: I *approve* of your idea. 2. To accept as good; think well of: The inspector *approved* the work. 3. To consent to; authorize: The mayor *approved* the plan.

ap·prox·i·mate·ly [ə·prok′sə·mit·lē] *adv.* About; around; coming close to, as in quantity: The storm brought *approximately* one inch of rain.

apt [apt] *adj.* Having a natural tendency; likely.

ar·e·a·way [âr′ē·ə·wā′] *n.* A sunken court or passage that gives access, air, and light to a basement.

ar·roy·o [ə·roi′ō] *n.* Especially in the southwestern United States, a small ditch cut out by a creek, usually dry.

as·cent [ə·sent′] *n.* The act of rising or climbing.

ash·cake [ash′kāk′] *n.* A cornmeal cake baked in hot ashes.

as·sur·ance [ə·shōōr′əns] *n.* 1. Self-confidence. 2. Certainty; guarantee.

a·stern [ə·stûrn′] *adv.* 1. Behind a ship. 2. In or toward its rear end.

au·gust [ô·gust′] *adj.* 1. Inspiring awe, admiration, etc.; majestic; imposing. 2. Of high birth or rank; eminent.

a·venge [ə·venj′] *v.* To get revenge by inflicting punishment, injury, etc., in return for a wrong received: The fighter *avenged* his opponent's insults.

av·er·age [av′rij]. 1. *adj.* Of or like the ordinary or usual type; medium. 2. *n.* The sum of the elements in a set of numbers divided by the number of elements in the set: The *average* of 4, 6, and 5 is 5.

Az·tec [az′tek] *n.* One of a nation of highly civilized Mexican Indians conquered by the Spanish in 1519.

Bb

bal·let [bal′ā *or* ba·lā′] *n.* 1. A dance with formal steps and movements performed by costumed dancers. 2. A group that performs ballets.

ban·is·ter [ban′is·tər] *n.* A post that supports a railing, as along a staircase.

ban·shee [ban′shē] *n.* In certain myths, a spirit whose wailing was supposed to warn that someone was going to die.

bar·na·cle [bär′nə·kəl] *n.* A sea shellfish that attaches itself to rocks, ship bottoms, etc.

bar·ren [bar′ən] *adj.* 1. Not yielding fruit or crops. 2. Not producing: Soil erosion has created thousands of acres of *barren* land.

bar·ri·cade [bar′ə·kād′ *or* bar′ə·kād] *n.* An obstruction hastily built to bar passage or for defense; barrier.

bath·y·sphere [bath′ə·sfir] *n.* A hollow, spherical steel structure with windows, used in underwater diving for deep-sea observation.

bay [bā] *n.* 1. A reddish-brown horse. 2. A body of water partly enclosed by land; an inlet of the sea or of a lake. 3. A deep, prolonged bark or cry, as of dogs in hunting.

ba·zaar [bə·zär′] *n.* 1. An Oriental marketplace or street of shops. 2. A store for the sale of many kinds of goods.

bel·lig·er·ent [bə·lij′ər·ənt] *adj.* Inclined to fight; warlike: The saleslady's *belligerent* attitude sent customers away.

bends [bendz] *n.pl.* A sometimes fatal blood disorder caused by too rapid a change from a high to a normal air pressure, often affecting divers.

ber·serk [bûr′sûrk *or* bər·sûrk′] *adj.* In a frenzy of wild rage.

bill of fare. A list of the dishes provided at a meal; menu.

bleach·ers [blē′chərz] *n.pl.* A section of seats for spectators at outdoor sports events.

boast [bōst] *v.* To talk in a vain or bragging manner; brag: The players *boasted* about their victory.

born [bôrn] *adj.* 1. Brought forth or into being. 2. Resulting from: The lumberjack's hands are rough with callouses *born* of his work at felling trees.

bounty hunter. A person who gets paid to capture or kill predatory animals.

brack·et [brak′it] *n.* A support, often a wooden triangle or a metal right angle, for a shelf or other fixture sticking out from a wall.

brack·ish [brak′ish] *adj.* 1. Somewhat salty. 2. Tasting unpleasant.

bred [bred] *v.* A form of the word BREED. Produced young; propagated.

breech·es [brich′iz] *n.pl.* 1. Short trousers that fasten below the knees. 2. Any trousers.

brown·stone [broun′stōn′] *n.* A reddish-brown sandstone; a dwelling faced with brownstone.

buck·le [buk′əl] *v.* To bend under pressure; crumple; warp: The dam *buckled,* then collapsed.

buck·skins [buk′skins′] *n.pl.* Clothing made of soft, strong, grayish-yellow leather from skins of deer or sheep.

bull·horn [bo͝ol′hôrn′] *n.* A hand-held electric-powered instrument for amplifying the voice.

buoy [boi *or* bo͞o′ē] *n.* A floating object, held in place by an anchor, used to mark a channel or dangerous spot in the water.

Buoy

bur·row [bûr′ō] *n.* A hole made in the ground by certain animals.

Cc

cab·bie [kab′ē] *n.* A taxicab driver.

ca·ble [kā′bəl] *n.* A heavy rope, now usually made of steel wire.

cal·cu·late [kal′kyə·lāt] *v.* To figure by using mathematics.

caramba. A Spanish exclamation expressing surprise, shock, etc.

car·a·pace [kar′ə·pās] *n.* The hard, bony covering of certain animals, as the turtle or lobster.

catch [kach] *n.* A hidden trick or difficulty: There is a *catch* in this arithmetic problem.

cav·i·ty [kav′ə·tē] *n.* 1. A sunken place; hole. 2. A hollow place in a tooth caused by decay.

ca·vort [kə·vôrt′] *v.* To prance about; caper.

cen·tu·ry [sen′chə·rē] *n.* 1. A period of 100 years, counting from some particular time, such as the birth of Christ. From A.D. 1 to 100 was the first century; from 1901 to 2000 is the twentieth. 2. Any period of 100 years.

chan·cel·lor [chan′s(ə)lər] *n.* In some European countries, a chief minister of state.

chant [chant]. 1. *n.* A very simple melody in which many words or syllables are sung on each note. Chants are used in the services of some churches. 2. *v.* To sing a chant. 3. *n.* Any monotonous singing or shouting of words.

chant·y [shan′tē *or* chan′tē] *n.* A rhythmical song for sailors working together.

chis·eled [chiz′(ə)ld] *adj.* As though cut or chipped with a chisel, a tool with a sharp, sloping, flat edge used to cut or chip wood, stone, or metal.

chron·ic [kron′ik] *adj.* Lasting or coming back again and again: I have *chronic* bad luck.

cleat [klēt] *n.* A wood or metal fixture with arms to which a rope may be fastened.

coarse [kôrs] *adj.* 1. Composed of rough particles; not fine. 2. Rough.

com·mer·cial [kə·mûr′shəl] *adj.* 1. Of or having to do with the buying and selling of goods. 2. Created or made to be sold, with profit as the object.

com·plex [kəm·pleks′ *or* kom′pleks] *adj.* 1. Complicated; intricate; not simple. 2. Made up of a number of parts.

con·cen·trate [kon′sən·trāt] *v.* To gather or focus one's entire attention: The student *concentrated* on each test question before answering it.

con·fide [kən·fīd′] *v.* 1. To tell in trust or confidence: I *confided* my secret to my mother. 2. To have trust; place confidence: I *confided* in her.

con·fi·dence [kon′fə·dəns] *n.* Faith in oneself; self-reliance.

con·scious [kon′shəs] *adj.* Aware of some object, fact, or feeling: The patient was *conscious* of pain in his left leg.

con·sole [kən·sōl′] *v.* To comfort in sorrow or disappointment; cheer.

con·stit·u·ent [kən·stich′ōō·ənt] *n.* A voter represented by an elected representative: Mary's *constituents* elected her president of their class.

con·sump·tion [kən·sump′shən] *n.* The amount of something used up: The cold weather caused a rise in the *consumption* of fuel.

con·ta·gious [kən·tā′jəs] *adj.* Easily spread from person to person, as by contact; catching: *contagious* laughter.

con·tam·i·nate [kən·tam′ə·nāt] *v.* To make impure or spoil by mixing with or getting into: Smoke *contaminates* city air.

con·vert [kən·vûrt′] *v.* To change, turn, or transform: We *converted* our garage into a bedroom.

con·vic·tion [kən·vik′shən] *n.* A strong, firm belief.

coun·te·nance [koun′tə·nəns] *n.* 1. The expression of the face: The clown had a sad *countenance*. 2. A face.

cow·er [kou′ər] *v.* To crouch, as in fear or shame; tremble.

craft [kraft] *n.* 1. Skill, especially in work done with the hands. 2. An occupation or trade requiring skillful or artistic work: Making pottery is a *craft*.

crag·gy [krag′ē] *adj.* 1. Full of crags, rough masses of rock jutting out from a cliff. 2. Like a crag; jutting: My uncle has *craggy* eyebrows.

cre·a·tion [krē·ā′shən] *n.* The world or the universe, including all living things.

crest·fall·en [krest′fô′lən] *adj.* Low in spirits; downcast; dejected.

crit·ter [krit′ər] *n.* A creature, usually an animal.

cross [krôs] *n.* A breeding together of related kinds of animals or plants, or the result of such breeding: A mule is a *cross* between a donkey and a horse.

cul·ture [kul′chər] *n.* A colony or growth of bacteria, viruses, etc., in a prepared medium, as for study.

cy·cle [sī′kəl] *n.* 1. A series of events that always happen in the same order and return to the original position, as the waxing and waning of the moon. 2. A series of predictable stages in the growth of a plant or animal or the completion of a process, as the erosion of a river valley.

cyl·in·der [sil′in·dər] *n.* A geometric figure bounded by two circles in parallel planes and the parallel lines joining them. The lines may or may not be perpendicular to the planes.

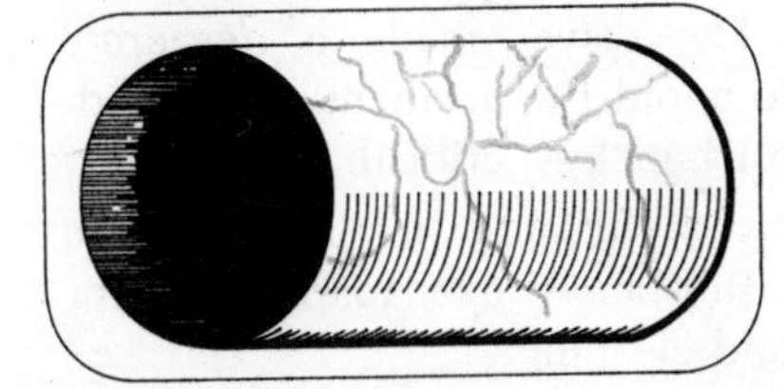

Cylinder

Dd

dearth [dûrth] *n.* A great scarcity; lack.

de·bark [di·bärk′] *v.* To go or put ashore from a ship; land; disembark.

de·ceiv·ing [di·sēv′ing] *adj.* Giving a false impression.

deft [deft] *adj.* Quick and skillful: Jane has a *deft* swimming stroke.

del·i·ca·cy [del′ə·kə·sē] *n.* A choice food: Fried frog legs are a *delicacy.*

del·ta [del′tə] *n.* A piece of low land shaped like a fan, formed at the mouths of some rivers by deposits of soil or sand.

delusions of grandeur. A mental state involving one's beliefs, usually false, about oneself.

de·pose [di·pōz′] *v.* To remove from high office.

de·scend [di·send′] *v.* 1. To go or move from a higher to a lower point; go down. 2. To come or derive by birth from a certain source: He is *descended* from a duke. 3. To make a sudden attack; swoop.

de·scent [di·sent′] *n.* 1. The action of going or coming down to a lower point. 2. Family origin; ancestry.

des·ig·nate [dez′ig·nāt] *v.* 1. To choose or appoint for a definite duty or purpose. 2. To point out; represent.

de·spair [di·spâr′] *n.* The heavy feeling that comes when all hope is lost or given up.

des·per·ate [des′pər·it] *adj.* 1. Very great; extreme: The driver made a *desperate* attempt to avoid the accident. 2. Considered almost hopeless; critical.

de·ter·gent [di·tûr′jənt] *n.* A synthetic cleansing substance, like soap, used for washing and cleaning.

di·a·ry [dī′(ə)rē] *n.* A personal record kept day by day of what happens or what one thinks about each day.

di·et [dī′ət] *n.* 1. The food and drink that a person or animal is used to; daily fare: The *diet* of most Americans includes meat at least once a day. 2. Food and drink specially selected for someone's health, appearance, etc.

dig·ni·ty [dig′nə·tē] *n.* Proper pride in one's worth or position: No matter how loudly the crowd hissed and hooted, the speaker retained his *dignity* throughout his speech.

di·min·ish [di·min′ish] *v.* 1. To make smaller or less; decrease: The jelly sandwich *diminished* his hunger. 2. To grow smaller or weaker; lessen; dwindle: The winds *diminished.*

dis·as·ter [di·zas′tər] *n.* An event causing great distress or ruin, as fires, floods, etc.

dis·pute [dis·pyōōt′] *v.* To argue or challenge in debate; quarrel.

dis·tinct [dis·tingkt′] *adj.* Easy to perceive or understand; sharp and clear.

dole·ful [dōl′fəl] *adj.* Sorrowful; mournful.

don·ga [dong′gə] *n.* A steep and narrow ravine formed by water erosion.

dor·sal fin [dôr′səl fin] *n.* A vertical fanlike or winglike part along the back of a fish or other sea animal having a backbone or spinal column.

dredge [drej]. 1. *n.* A large machine used to scoop out or suck up mud, sand, etc., from the bottom of a body of water. 2. *n.* Something like a net that is used to gather shellfish, etc., from under the water. 3. *v.* To clear, widen, or remove with a dredge.

drought [drout] *n.* A lack of rain for a long period; severe dry spell. Also **drouth** [drouth].

du·bi·ous [d(y)ōō′bē·əs] *adj.* Not sure or certain; doubtful: She was *dubious* about leaving without permission.

dul·ci·mer [dul′sə·mər] *n.* 1. A stringed folk instrument similar to a violin. The pitch of the melody string is usually controlled by a sliding stick. 2. A musical instrument having wire strings that are struck with two padded hammers held in the hands.

dye [dī]. 1. *v.* To give lasting color to by soaking in liquid coloring matter. 2. *n.* A colored preparation, often dissolved in a liquid, used for dyeing. 3. *v.* To color or stain.

Ee

ef·fect [i·fekt′] *n.* 1. Something brought about by some action or cause; result. 2. The ability or power to produce some result: Punishment had little *effect* on her.

e·go·tism [ē′gə·tiz′əm] *n.* The habit of talking or writing about oneself, often boastfully; conceit.

e·lat·ed [i·lā′tid] *adj.* Filled with joy or pride, as over success or good fortune.

el·e·gant [el′ə·gənt] *adj.* 1. Graceful and refined in style, manners, or taste. 2. Tasteful, luxurious, and beautiful.

e·lim·i·nate [i·lim′ə·nāt] *v.* 1. To get rid of: Sunglasses *eliminated* the glare. 2. To remove from competition, as by defeating.

ell [el] *n.* An extension or room that forms right angles to the main part of a house.

em·bold·en [im·bōl′dən] *v.* To make bold or bolder; encourage: The response of the audience *emboldened* the young musicians.

em·boss [im·bôs′] *v.* To form or decorate with raised designs: Jean's gold bracelet was *embossed* with birds and butterflies.

e·mer·gen·cy [i·mûr′jən·sē] *n.* A sudden and unexpected turn of events, calling for immediate action.

en·cour·age [in·kûr′ij] *v.* 1. To give courage or hope to; inspire with confidence or the wish to do well. 2. To be favorable for; help or foster: Watering *encourages* plant growth.

en·dan·ger [in·dān′jər] *v.* To expose to danger.

en·dur·ance [in·d(y)ŏŏr′əns] *n.* The ability or power to bear up or last under continued effort, hardship, or strain.

en·dure [in·d(y)ŏŏr′] *v.* To bear up under; stand firm against.

en·thu·si·asm [in·thōō′zē·az′əm] *n.* Keen interest or liking.

en·thu·si·as·tic [in·thōō′zē·as′tik] *adj.* Expressing eager interest or approval.

ep·i·dem·ic [ep′ə·dem′ik] *n.* The sudden spread of a disease among many people.

es·ti·mate [es′tə·māt] *v.* To make a close guess about (size, number, cost, etc.): He *estimates* the cost to be twenty dollars.

e·vap·o·rate [i·vap′ə·rāt] *v.* To turn into vapor: Boiling *evaporates* water.

ex·ceed [ik·sēd′] *v.* 1. To be greater or better than: Crops *exceeded* estimates. 2. To go beyond the limits of: The task *exceeds* his abilities.

ex·cerpt [ek′sûrpt] *n.* A passage or section taken from a piece of writing.

ex·tend [ik·stend′] *v.* To stretch or reach out.

ex·tinc·tion [ik·stingk′shən] *n.* The condition of no longer existing.

ex·tract [ik·strakt′] *v.* To take out, as by pulling, squeezing, etc.: The dentist *extracted* a decaying tooth.

Ff

fash·ion·a·ble [fash′ən·ə·bəl] *adj.* 1. In style; stylish. 2. Of or attracting socially prominent people: The actress lived in a *fashionable* neighborhood.

fate [fāt] *n.* Final outcome; end: The jury will decide the robber's *fate.*

fath·om [fath′əm] *n.* A measure of length equal to six feet, used mainly in measuring the depth of water.

fea·ture [fē′chər] *n.* A prominent characteristic or quality.

feis·ty [fīs′tē] *adj.* 1. Stirred up, troubled, disturbed. 2. Spirited.

felices Pascuas. A Spanish phrase meaning "a happy Christmas."

fer·tile [fûr′təl] *adj.* 1. Producing or able to produce abundant crops or vegetation.

2. Capable of producing seeds, fruit, young, etc.

fer·vent [fûr′vənt] *adj.* Very eager and earnest; ardent.

fleet [flēt] *n.* A group of ships, aircraft, motor vehicles, etc., used together or belonging to one company.

flour·ish [flûr′ish] *v.* 1. To grow or fare well or prosperously; thrive: Bees *flourish* in honeysuckle. 2. To wave about or brandish: The lawyer *flourished* the photograph before the jury.

flu·ted [flo͞ot′əd] *adj.* Grooved along the edge: The antique dishes have *fluted* rims.

for·mal [fôr′məl] *adj.* Prim; ceremonial.

for·mu·la [fôr′myə·lə] *n.* A mixture prepared by prescription or recipe.

frus·tra·tion [frus·trā′shən] *n.* 1. The state of being kept from doing or achieving something. 2. A state of dissatisfaction arising from problems that are unresolved.

fun·gi [fun′jī] *n.pl.* A form of the word FUNGUS, a plant with no chlorophyll, flowers, or leaves, as a mold, mushroom, etc.

furl [fûrl] *v.* To roll up and fasten: He *furled* his umbrella when the rain stopped.

Gg

gal·ley [gal′ē] *n.* In ancient and medieval times, a long, narrow ship with sails and oars, usually rowed by prisoners or slaves.

gar·ret [gar′it] *n.* A small room or set of rooms in an attic, under a sloping roof.

gaunt [gônt] *adj.* Gloomy and barren; desolate: A high, *gaunt* wall surrounded the prison.

ghost town. A deserted town, especially an abandoned mining town in the West.

great·coat [grāt′kōt′] *n.* A heavy overcoat.

grill [gril] *v.* An informal expression meaning "to question hard and thoroughly."

grub [grub]. 1. *n.* A slang term for FOOD. 2. *v.* To dig or dig up. 3. *n.* A fat, wormlike larva of an insect.

gun·wale [gun′əl] *n.* The upper edge of the side of a ship or boat.

guy [gī] *v.* To ridicule or tease: Maria's brothers *guyed* her about her boyfriend.

Hh

hab·i·ta·tion [hab′ə·tā′shən] *n.* 1. A dwelling place. 2. The act or state of inhabiting or living in.

half hitch. A knot that can be unfastened easily.

halt·ing [hôlt′ing] *adj.* Uncertain; hesitant.

han·ker [hang′kər] *v.* To have a strong desire; wish: The mail clerk was *hankering* for a cup of hot coffee.

heark·en [här′kən] *v.* To listen or pay attention: *Hearken* to my words.

heed [hēd] *v.* To pay close attention to.

Hit·ler [hit′lər], 1889–1945, leader of Nazi Germany, 1933–1945.

hoist [hoist] *v.* To raise or lift, especially by mechanical means.

host·ess [hōs′tis] *n.* A living female animal, as a whale, on or in which a parasite lives.

hy·drant [hī′drənt] *n.* A large upright pipe coming from a water main, from which water may be drawn for fighting fires or washing streets.

hy·rax [hī′raks] *n.* Any of various small rodentlike animals of Africa.

hys·ter·i·cal [his·ter′ə·kəl] *adj.* Showing or caused by uncontrolled excitement or emotion.

Ii

i·den·ti·fy [ī·den′tə·fī] *v.* To recognize,

claim, or prove to be a certain person or thing: The judges *identified* the prize-winning artist.

ig·no·rance [ig′nər·əns] *n.* The condition of being ignorant, not informed, unaware, etc.; lack of knowledge.

il·lu·mi·nate [i·lo͞o′mə·nāt] *v.* To light up; brighten.

im·press [im·pres′] *v.* 1. To affect the mind or feelings of: The politician's campaign speech *impressed* the voters. 2. To fix firmly in the mind, as ideas, beliefs, etc.: The tidal wave was forever *impressed* on the memory of the seamen.

in·di·cate [in′də·kāt] *v.* To point out; show: The traffic officer *indicated* the school-zone sign Mother had failed to see.

in·hos·pi·ta·ble [in·hos′pi·tə·bəl *or* in′-hos·pit′ə·bəl] *adj.* Providing no shelter or comfort: Antarctica has an *inhospitable* climate.

in·tent [in·tent′] *adj.* Directing all one's efforts or attention: The teacher was so *intent* on making his point that he failed to hear the alarm.

in·trep·id [in·trep′id] *adj.* Very brave; fearless.

ir·ri·gate [ir′ə·gāt] *v.* To furnish (land) with water, by using pipes, ditches, or canals: The fruit growers of the West *irrigate* their crops.

Kk

keen·ly [kēn′lē] *adv.* In a sensitive way; with perception: The weather observers studied the gathering clouds *keenly*.

kin·dle [kin′dəl] *v.* To set fire to; light.

knot [not] *n.* A speed equal to one nautical mile (6,076.1 feet) per hour.

kop·je [kop′ē] *n.* A small African hill, often covered with scrubby growth.

Ll

la·goon [lə·go͞on′] *n.* A body of shallow water, as a point or inlet, usually connecting with a river, a larger lake, or the sea.

lapse [laps] *v.* To pass gradually; slip: The girl *lapsed* into a daydream.

laugh·ing·stock [laf′ing·stok′] *n.* One who provokes laughter and ridicule.

law-a·bid·ing [lô′ə·bī′ding] *adj.* Obedient to the law.

Le·o·nar·do da Vin·ci [lē′ə·när′dō də vin′chē], 1452–1519 Italian painter, sculptor, and architect. He was also a pioneer in biology, geology, engineering, and military science.

li·a·ble [lī′ə·bəl] *adj.* Likely; apt: It is *liable* to rain.

lin·go [ling′gō] *n.* A language or talk that seems outlandish or is not understood.

lin·sey [lin′zē] *n.* A coarse cloth woven of linen and wool or cotton and wool.

loon [lo͞on] *n.* A web-footed diving bird resembling a duck, but with a pointed bill and a weird, laughing cry.

Loon

lum·ber [lum′bər] *v.* To move along clumsily and heavily: The elephant *lumbered* through the jungle.

lu·na·tic [lo͞o′nə·tik] *n.* A mentally ill person.

Mm

ma·chet·e [mə·shet′ē *or* mə·shet′] *n.* A heavy knife used as a tool and as a weapon, especially in South America and the West Indies.

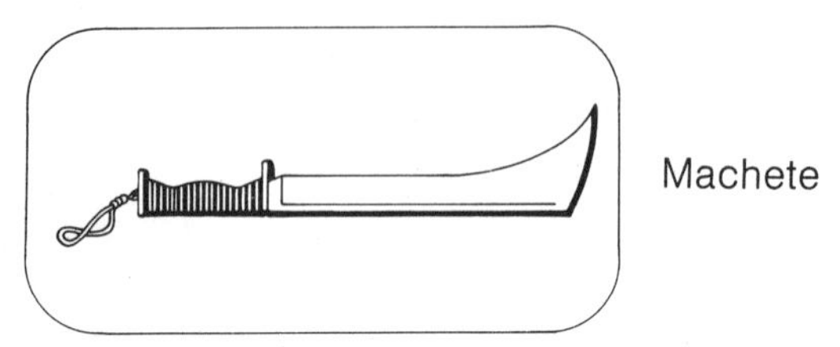

Machete

main·s'l [mān′səl] *n.* Contraction of MAINSAIL. The principal sail on a mainmast.

man·go [mang′gō] *n.* 1. A juicy tropical fruit having a slightly acid taste. 2. The tree it grows on.

Man·hat·tan [man·hat′ən] *n.* An island in the Hudson River. It is a part of New York City.

mar·i·ner [mar′ə·nər] *n.* A sailor; seaman.

mar·quis [mär′kwis *or* mär·kē′] *n.* The title of a nobleman next in rank below a duke.

marsh [märsh] *n.* An area of low, wet land; swamp; bog.

men·ace [men′is]. 1. *n.* A threat; a danger. 2. *v.* To threaten with danger.

mere [mir] *adj.* Being nothing more or less than; being nothing but: A bus ride used to cost a *mere* five cents.

me·ter [mē′tər] *n.* The standard unit of length in the metric system, equal to 39.37 inches.

mi·grant [mī′grənt]. 1. *n.* A person, animal, bird, etc., that migrates. 2. *adj.* Moving regularly from place to place: *Migrant* workers travel from region to region of the United States to harvest the crops.

min·i·a·ture [min′(ē)·ə·chər]. 1. *n.* Something made or represented on a small scale: The zoo director displayed a *miniature* of the proposed zoo nursery. 2. *n.* A tiny painting, most often a portrait. 3. *adj.* Very small; tiny.

mon·arch [mon′ərk] *n.* A ruler, as a king, queen, etc.

mo·nop·o·ly [mə·nop′ə·lē] *n.* Exclusive control or possession of a product or service by a single person or group.

moor·ing [mo͝or′ing] *n.* 1. A place where a thing is moored. 2. The line, cable, anchor, etc., that holds something in place: Our boat had slipped its *moorings* during the night.

mute [myo͞ot] *adj.* 1. Lacking the power of speech. 2. Not making noise or speaking; silent.

muz·zle [muz′(ə)l] *n.* The front end of a firearm.

myth [mith] *n.* A story or legend that explains certain practices or beliefs of a people: Greek and Roman *myths* are often about gods and heroes.

Nn

naiye-paise. A unit of money related to the rupee. One hundred naiye-paise equal one rupee.

neu·rot·ic [n(y)o͝o·rot′ik] *adj.* Of, resulting from, or suffering from a mental or emotional disturbance marked by unusual anxiety, depression, fear, etc., usually not very serious.

non·cha·lant [non′shə·länt′] *adj.* Showing a jaunty coolness; not excited or concerned: She accepted the prize with a *nonchalant* air.

nu·tri·ent [n(y)o͞o′trē·ənt] *n.* A nourishing substance; food.

Oo

oc·ca·sion·al [ə·kā′zhən·əl] *adj.* Occurring or appearing now and then.

o·ce·lot [ō′sə·lət *or* os′ə·lot] *n.* A wildcat of Central and South America, having a spotted, yellowish coat.

oc·tag·o·nal [ok·tag′ə·nəl] *adj.* Having eight sides.

olé. A Spanish word meaning "bravo; well done."

os·cil·late [os′ə·lāt] *v.* To move back and forth in a regular way, as a pendulum.

o·val [ō′vəl] *adj.* Having the shape of an egg or an ellipse.

o·ver·se·er [ō′vər·sē′ər] *n.* A person who supervises laborers at their work.

Pp

pace [pās] *n.* 1. A step in walking. 2. The length of the average step in walking, about three feet.

pal·at·a·ble [pal′it·ə·bəl] *adj.* Pleasant to the taste; savory.

pa·thet·ic [pə·thet′ik] *adj.* Arousing, expressing, or deserving pity or sympathy; pitiful: The trapped fox gave a *pathetic* wail.

pee·vish [pē′vish] *adj.* Easily annoyed or irritated; childishly cross.

pen·e·trate [pen′ə·trāt] *v.* 1. To enter into or through; pierce. 2. To see through.

pen·in·su·la [pə·nin′s(y)ə·lə] *n.* A piece of land nearly surrounded by water, often joined to the mainland by a narrow strip of land.

per·ceive [pər·sēv′] *v.* 1. To become aware of by means of one of the senses; see, hear, feel, smell, or taste. 2. To come to understand. 3. To observe; notice.

per·il·ous [per′əl·əs] *adj.* Full of peril; risky; dangerous.

per·sist [pər·sist′] *v.* To continue firmly or stubbornly in spite of opposition, warning, difficulty, etc.

pe·ti·tion [pə·tish′ən] *n.* 1. A formal, written request, often with many signatures, sent to a person or group in authority. 2. An appeal.

phys·i·cal [fiz′i·kəl] *adj.* 1. Of or having to do with matter, material things, or the laws of nature. 2. Involving size, shape, density, etc.

plan·tain [plan′tin] *n.* 1. A tropical herb sometimes growing to a height of thirty feet. 2. Its bananalike fruit, edible when cooked.

point of view. The position from which a person looks at or considers an object, situation, etc.: Each contestant wrote from a different *point of view.*

poke juice. A dark-red liquid taken from the berries of pokeweed that may be used as an ink or stain.

po·lar [pō′lər] *adj.* Having to do with, coming from, or found near the North or South Pole.

pool·ing [po͞ol′ing] *v.* Combining (money, things, efforts, etc.) for common benefit.

pre·cinct [prē′singkt] *n.* An area of a city or town marked off as a district for voting or for police supervision.

pre·cip·i·tate [pri·sip′ə·tit] *adj.* Moving or acting with or showing reckless speed; rash.

pred·a·tor [pred′i·tər] *n.* A person or animal that lives by preying upon others.

pre·dic·a·ment [pri·dik′ə·mənt] *n.* A situation that is trying, dangerous, or embarrassing.

preen [prēn] *v.* To clean and arrange (feathers, etc.) with the beak, as a bird.

pre·his·tor·ic [prē′his·tôr′ik] *adj.* Of or belonging to the period before the start of written history.

pre·serve [pri·zûrv′]. 1. *v.* To keep from danger or harm; watch over; protect. 2. *n.* An area set apart for the protection of wildlife, forests, etc.

pro·ce·dure [prə·sē′jər] *n.* A way of proceeding; method of doing something.

proc·ess [pros′es]. 1. *n.* A series of operations or a method for producing something: The United States government has a well-planned *process* for minting coins. 2. *v.* To prepare or treat by a special method: Cotton is *processed* at textile factories.

prom·on·to·ry [prom′ən·tôr′ē] *n.* A high point of land sticking out into the sea; headland.

pro·vi·sion [prə·vizh′ən] *n.* Something, as a supply of food, provided or prepared against future needs: The mountaineers stored *provisions* long before the winter storms arrived.

pug·na·cious [pug·nā′shəs] *adj.* Fond of fighting; quarrelsome.

pul·ley [po͝ol′ē] *n.* A small wheel with a grooved rim over which is passed a rope or chain that moves freely with the turning of the wheel.

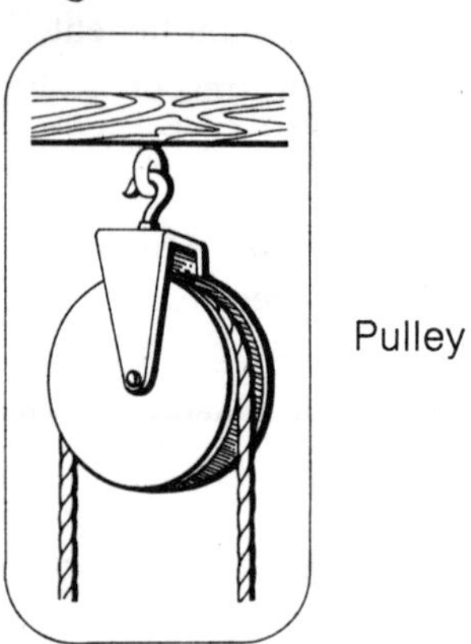

Pulley

pur·pose·ly [pûr′pəs·lē] *adv.* For a purpose; intentionally; on purpose.

Qq

quak·ing [kwāk′ing] *adj.* Shaking or trembling, often with great force.

quar·ry [kwôr′ē] *n.* 1. An animal being hunted by man or another animal. 2. Anything that is hunted or eagerly pursued.

quer·u·lous [kwer′(y)ə·ləs] *adj.* 1. Tending to complain or find fault. 2. Whining: The mother ignored her *querulous* child.

Rr

rancho. In the United States, a Spanish word that means "cattle ranch."

reap [rēp] *v.* 1. To cut down or gather in (grain); harvest (a crop). 2. To take a grain crop from, as a field.

rea·son·ing [rē′zən·ing] *n.* The process of drawing a conclusion from a set of facts or premises.

re·bel [ri·bel′] *v.* 1. To resist actively, opposing authority: The American colonies *rebelled* against England. 2. To be filled with dislike or opposition.

re·ced·ing [ri·sēd′ing] *v.* Moving back; withdrawing, as floodwaters do.

re·cit·al [ri·sīt′(ə)l] *n.* 1. The act of reciting or telling in great detail. 2. A detailed statement.

re·coil [ri·koil′ *or* rē′koil] *n.* A leaping or shrinking; a springing back, as of a gun that has just been fired.

re·ferred [ri·fûrd′] *v.* Thought of or regarded as; spoken of: Cats that roam the streets are *referred* to as "alley cats."

ref·uge [ref′yo͞oj] *n.* 1. Shelter or protection from danger or distress. 2. A safe place.

ref·use [ref′yo͞os] *n.* Worthless things; trash.

re·gret [ri·gret′] *v.* To recall or look back at something with disappointment; to feel sorry that something happened.

reg·u·late [reg′yə·lāt] *v.* To control according to certain rules: A police officer *regulates* traffic.

re·lent [ri·lent′] *v.* To become gentler or more compassionate: Mother *relented* and forgave us for being late to breakfast.

re·luc·tant [ri·luk′tənt] *adj.* Unwilling; not eager: My little brother is always *reluctant* to go to bed.

remote control. Operation from a distance, as by radio waves: The model airplane was flown by *remote control.*

re·plen·ish [ri·plen′ish] *v.* To provide with a new supply; fill up again: The truck driver stopped to *replenish* the gas tank.

rep·re·sent [rep′ri·zent′] *v.* To be an agent of; act and speak for: Two senators *represent* each state.

re·proach [ri·prōch′]. 1. *v.* To blame for some wrong. 2. *n.* Blame.

re·sent·ful [ri·zent′fəl] *adj.* Feeling or showing anger and ill will based on real or imagined wrong or injury.

res·i·dent [rez′ə·dənt] *adj.* Living in a place, especially at one's place of work: The hotel has a *resident* physician.

re·sist [ri·zist′] *v.* 1. To work or strive against; oppose. 2. To keep from: Joe can't *resist* teasing his brother.

res·o·lute [rez′ə·lo͞ot′] *adj.* Determined or bold.

re·stric·tion [ri·strik′shən] *n.* The condition of being limited; confined; kept within bounds: Bad weather places *restrictions* on boating.

re·trace [ri·trās′] *v.* To go back over: The woman *retraced* her path and found her purse.

re·vi·val [ri·vī′vəl] *n.* A renewal of interest in something long neglected or forgotten.

rev·o·lu·tion [rev′ə·lo͞o′shən] *n.* The overthrow of an established government by those formerly under its authority.

rile [rīl] *v.* To annoy or irritate.

rue. A French word meaning "road; street."

rum·ble [rum′bəl] *n.* A street fight, usually between gangs of teen-agers.

ru·pee [ro͞o·pē′] *n.* The basic unit of money in certain countries, as India and Pakistan.

Ss

sa·fa·ri [sə·fä′rē] *n.* An expedition or journey, as for hunting, especially in eastern Africa.

schol·ar [skol′ər] *n.* A person who has learned a great deal through serious study; one who shows advanced knowledge.

scu·ba [sk(y)o͞o′bə] *n.* A device used for breathing underwater (*s*elf-*c*ontained *u*nderwater *b*reathing *a*pparatus).

sea·son [sē′zən]. 1. *n.* One of the four divisions of the year as determined by the earth's position with respect to the sun. The seasons are spring, summer, autumn, and winter. 2. *v.* To make fit for use by aging or drying, as wood.

sea·wall [sē′wôl′] *n.* A wall built to keep waves from striking the shore and washing it away, or to serve as a breakwater.

se·date [si·dāt′] *adj.* Calm and serious.

seed·ing [sēd′ing] *v.* 1. Spawning. 2. Collecting together for purposes of raising, as young oysters.

sew·age [so͞o′ij] *n.* The waste matter that is carried off in sewers.

sheathe [shēth] *v.* To put into a cover or case for a blade, as a sword.

shift·less [shift′lis] *adj.* Showing a lack of energy or ambition; lazy.

shoal [shōl] *n.* 1. A shallow place in any body of water. 2. A sandbar or bank underwater that makes such a shallow place. 3. A school of fish.

sieve [siv] *n.* A utensil with holes in the bottom, used to separate solids too large to pass through from fine pieces or a liquid.

silt [silt] *n.* Fine particles carried in or deposited by water.

skit·tish [skit′ish] *adj.* Easily frightened; likely to shy, as a horse.

slack·en [slak′ən] *v.* To make or become slower, less active, or less forceful.

slick·er [slik′ər] *n.* A waterproof overcoat, as of oilskin or plastic.

so·nar [sō′när] *n.* A device that locates underwater objects by sending high-frequency sound waves and picking up their echoes with a microphone.

soo·gan [so͞o′gən] *n.* A coarse blanket.

sor·cer·er [sôr′sər·ər] *n.* A wizard, conjurer, or magician.

Spanish moss. A trailing, grayish-green plant that gets its nutrients from the air and rain and lives on trees and other plants.

spe·cial·ize [spesh′əl·īz] *v.* To make or become fit for a particular use, environment, etc.: The doctor *specialized* in the treatment of nose and throat diseases.

spe·cies [spē′shēz *or* spē′sēz] *n.* 1. A group of living things that are more or less alike: Leopards and lions are of different *species.* 2. Kind; sort; type.

spig·ot [spig′ət] *n.* A faucet.

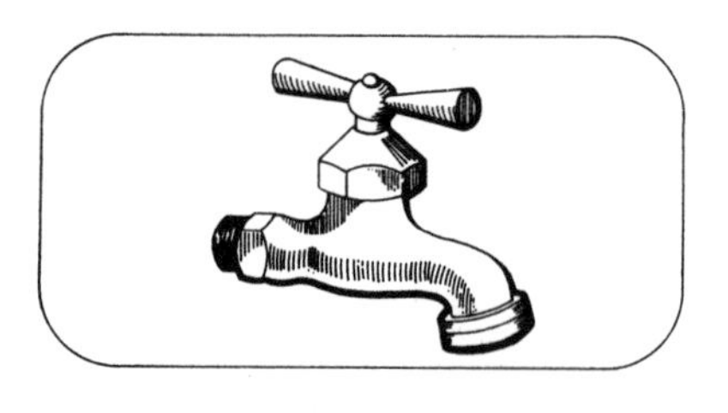

Spigot

spin·ster [spin′stər] *n.* A woman who has never married, especially one no longer young.

splint [splint] *n.* A piece of metal or wood for holding the parts of a fractured bone in position.

staghorn coral. A large branching coral that looks somewhat like antlers, found especially in waters off Florida.

steed [stēd] *n.* A horse, especially a spirited one.

stick·ball [stik′bôl′] *n.* A baseball-like game played with a broomstick and lightweight ball, usually in streets or small areas.

sti·fle [stī′fəl] *v.* To keep back; suppress; repress.

stoop [sto͞op] *n.* A small porch or platform at the entrance of a house.

strand [strand] *v.* To leave behind or in a helpless position: The airline passengers were *stranded* in the desert.

stunt [stunt] *v.* To stop the natural growth or development of: Lack of proper feed *stunted* the cattle.

suf·fuse [sə·fyo͞oz′] *v.* To overspread, as with a fluid or color: The faces about the campfire were *suffused* with firelight.

sum·mon [sum′ən] *v.* To send for or order to come; to call into action.

sup·ple [sup′əl] *adj.* Bending easily; flexible or limber.

sur·plus [sûr′plus] *n.* An amount above what is needed or used; something left over; excess.

symp·tom [sim′təm] *n.* A sign or indication of the existence of something, especially an indication of some bodily disease or disorder.

sys·tem [sis′təm] *n.* 1. A group of parts or things that are so related or that act together in such a way that they are considered as a whole. 2. Any group of facts, concepts, or beliefs that are organized into an orderly plan: Louis Braille developed a *system* of writing that can be read by touch.

Tt

tank·er [tangk′ər] *n.* A cargo ship built to carry liquids, especially oil.

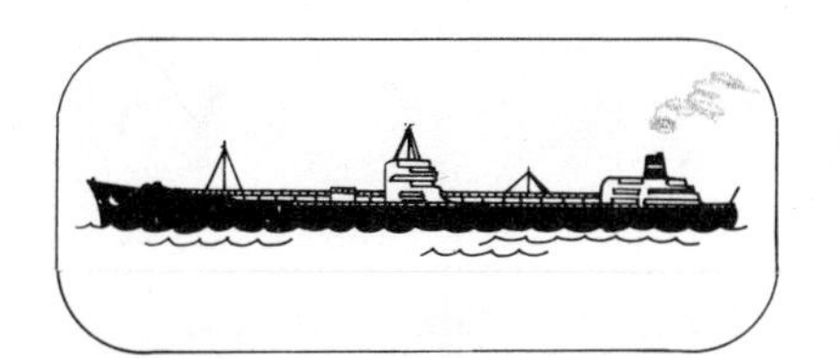

Tanker

ten·sion [ten′shən] *n.* 1. Mental strain; nervous anxiety. 2. The act of stretching or the condition of being stretched.

ten·ta·cle [ten′tə·kəl] *n.* A long, flexible outgrowth from the main body of an animal, as an octopus, squid, etc., used for moving, seizing prey, etc.

terms [tûrmz] *n.pl.* Conditions or stipulations, as of a sale, contract, etc.: The *terms* of the house sale did not include painting the inside.

teth·er [teth′ər]. 1. *n.* A rope or chain used to tie an animal so that it can range only so far. 2. *v.* To fasten or confine by a tether.

tex·ture [teks′chər] *n.* The look or feel of the surface of any substance: The artist selected paper with a grainy *texture.*

the·o·ry [thē′ə·rē *or* thir′ē] *n.* 1. The basic principles of a branch of science or the arts. 2. Knowledge, as distinguished from its practical use: In *theory,* you are correct. 3. An unsupported opinion.

thong [thông] *n.* A narrow strip of leather, used as a whiplash or more often for tying or fastening.

tin [tin] *n.* A container or box made of tin.

tri·dent [trīd′(ə)nt] *n.* A three-pronged spear, as the one carried by the mythical god of the sea.

tri·fle [trī′fəl] *n.* Anything of very little value or importance: The storm did not do a *trifle* of harm.

tur·quoise [tûr′k(w)oiz]. 1. *n.* A sky-blue to greenish-blue mineral, some varieties of which, when highly polished, are used as gems. 2. *adj.* Light greenish blue.

Uu

un·bid·den [un·bid′(ə)n] *adj.* Without having been asked, called, or invited: an *unbidden* guest.

un·der·growth [un′dər·grōth′] *n.* Small trees and shrubs growing under forest trees; underbrush.

un·du·late [un′d(y)ə·lāt] *v.* To move or cause to move like a wave or in waves: The wheat *undulates* in the wind.

un·sea·son·al [un·sē′zən·əl] *adj.* Unseasonable; not coming at the right time; not suited to the season.

ur·gent [ûr′jənt] *adj.* Needing or demanding prompt action or attention; pressing: There is an *urgent* need for trained nurses.

Vv

ve·ran·da [və·ran′də] *n.* A long, open, outdoor porch, usually roofed, along the outside of a building.

vict·uals [vit′(ə)lz] *n.pl.* Food.

vir·gin [vûr′jin] *adj.* Not yet or not previously touched, used, etc.: Pioneers founded settlements in America's *virgin* wilderness.

vow [vou] *n.* Any solemn promise or pledge.

Ww

wa·ger [wā′jər] *v.* To bet.

wean [wēn] *v.* To cause (someone) gradually to give up a habit, dependence, etc.: Chewing gum sometimes helps *wean* smokers away from cigarettes.

widow's walk. A railed platform on the roof of a coastal house used as a lookout. The term comes from the practice of the seaman's wife who used such a lookout to watch for her husband.

wirklich. A German word meaning "truly, really."

wist·ful [wist′fəl] *adj.* Wishful; longing.

wood·en·head [wo͝od′(ə)n·hed′] *n.* A person who is dull or stupid.

wunderbar. A German word meaning "wonderful, miraculous."

Yy

yarn [yärn] *n.* An adventure story, especially one that is made up.

yawl [yôl] *n.* A sailboat with a mainmast near the bow and a shorter mast very near the stern.